TOWN&
AUCTIONS
IN·BRITAIN

✦THE BARGAIN HUNTER'S HANDBOOK✦

✦ Eric Geen ✦

Produced by the Publishing Division of The Automobile Association

Written by Eric Geen

Edited by Antonia Hebbert and Edwina Johnson

Designed by Peter C Gibbons

Head of Advertisement Sales:
Christopher Heard, tel: (0256) 20123 Ext 21544

Advertisement Production:
Karen Weeks, tel: (0256) 20123 Ext 21545

Printed and bound in Great Britain by Unwin Brothers
Ltd., Gresham Press, Old Woking, Surrey

Produced by the Publishing Division of The Automobile
Association

First published 1991
Second edition 1992
Third edition 1993

Published by The Automobile Association, Fanum
House, Basing View, Basingstoke RG21 2EA

ISBN: 0 7495 0686 5 (Third edition)

A CIP catalogue record for this book is available from
the British Library.

· CONTENTS ·

AUCTIONS IN BRITAIN

This book is about auctions. It lists over 400 salerooms holding regular auctions that will be of interest to the casual browser, interested amateur, bargain hunter, serious collector, or professional dealer. Some of the auctions are specialist sales, devoted to an area of particular interest to collectors. Most are general sales, though, and include a mixture of household goods and antiques. You can find all sorts of things at these auctions – a Victorian pewter teapot perhaps, or a box of old crockery; a Regency sideboard or a pre-war butcher's delivery bicycle. The best auctions are those at which everything and anything can turn up, from the essential to the ridiculous.

Any auction-goer will know the excitement of arriving at an auction, never being sure what they are going to find, discovering perhaps an old photograph album or a piece of well-crafted furniture, and enjoying the constant surprises and changes that an auction offers. There can be few better ways of passing a morning than browsing around an auction and listening to an entertaining auctioneer. Most towns have at least one auction house that holds regular sales, and there are regular auctions in many villages, too. Auctions take place every day of the week, and wherever you happen to be in Britain, you will never be more than a few miles away from a saleroom.

Venues

The traditional country auction is held out in the open, perhaps in the market square of a country town. Following the custom of generations, vendors set out their goods on the ground, and the auctioneer walks along the rows, taking bids for each lot as he comes to it. Cash changes hands on completion of each successful bid.

Such auctions are a delight, but they are not the whole story. Auction venues vary, so a wide range is included in this book — open air, cattle pens and sheds, purpose-built salerooms or specially rented halls, and some grand settings like Sotheby's Summers Place – a magnificent mansion with 37 acres of gardens and fields in Billingshurst, West Sussex. Whatever your choice, you will find something to interest you on the following pages. Remember, though, that it is always worth checking sales days and times with the organisers before setting out on a journey, as they may be subject to change at short notice.

Recently I spent a very pleasant weekend on an 'auction trip', visiting sales in East Anglia and making the attractive town of Bury St Edmunds my headquarters. On my way there, on Friday, I visited Thos Wm Gaze & Son's auction at Diss in Norfolk. The next day I got up early to attend Lacy Scott's Saturday morning sale in Bury, and then on Sunday I spent a very enjoyable day at Lynford Hall, Mundford, where Tyrone R Roberts holds six-weekly sales. When an American friend of mine told me she wanted an extra dimension added to her holiday in England, I suggested she follow a special 'auction itinerary', which I prepared for her. This included a visit to a different auction on each of the six days she spent travelling from Cornwall to London.

Viewing

Viewing times are often quite generous. The viewing gives potential bidders an opportunity to examine goods closely, so they can decide how much to bid. I prefer to view just before a sale begins, because I particularly enjoy the spontaneity of finding something and deciding how much it is worth on the spot. However, many people prefer to examine a piece well before a sale, and then to go away and think about it. Making a successful bid for something never seems such a matter of life or death after a good night's sleep.

How high to bid

Deciding your maximum bidding price is the most skilful part of buying at auction. The value of anything is only what someone is prepared to pay for it. If you have your eye on something special, though, look at prices for comparable items in shops. An increase in value is not inevitable, so don't buy purely to make an investment.

Once you've decided your price, stick to it and don't bid higher. It is easy to get carried away. Remember, too, that you should take account of the buyer's premium, which will be added on to the successful bidding ('hammer') price by the auctioneers after the sale. This varies from nothing at all to 10 per cent or more, depending on which auction house you are at. Many auctioneers will also charge VAT on the buyer's premium, so it is important to check this when deciding how high to bid.

Bidding and paying

Concern about proper behaviour and protocol is often a deterrent to potential auction-goers. One thing is for sure: the auctioneer won't think you're bidding if you inadvertently twitch your nose or scratch your ear. If auctioneers are in any doubt about whether or not a bid is being made, they will ask, and if there is any confusion, the lot will be offered for sale again. No auctioneer is going to sell to someone who doesn't want to buy.

It is always wise to register and have a 'paddle' number, even if you don't intend to bid. Registering costs nothing and does not oblige you to bid or buy, and you may regret not having registered if something catches your eye during the sale. Now that many salerooms are computerised, the 'paddle' system is supposed to speed up the process of paying, although the wait for paperwork to be completed after a successful bid rarely takes longer than 10 minutes at any sale.

I like the old system in which you hear the successful bidder's name — it helps to focus irritation if you know who is outbidding you. Shouting names across the saleroom can cause confusion, however. I remember one Norfolk auction where the auctioneer was constantly trying to increase the bids by shouting what sounded like 'Five pounds Shirley!' or 'Twenty pounds Shirley!' It wasn't until I'd visited the auction a few times and become used to the Norfolk accent that I realised what he was shouting was 'Five pounds, surely!'

Bidding is something that worries people, but it shouldn't. It is fun and exciting. Once you have got over the initial embarrassment of waving your hand at the auctioneer, it becomes second nature. The problem then is to stop yourself from bidding for everything in sight!

Bidding increments are the stages by which bidding advances. Auctioneers always announce them at the start of the sale. If you don't know them, you may find yourself paying much more than you expected. Typical increments would be 50p for bids up to £5 and £1 for bids up to £20. After this, bidding may advance in increments of £2 or £3 — for example £22, £25, £27, £30. Bids from £30 to £100 are usually increased in £5 increments, and thereafter by £10 increments. Bids over £1,000 are usually increased by £50 each time.

To **start and stop** bidding, you must make clear gestures. Once you have raised your arm to let the auctioneer know you're interested, he will invite you to bid again. If you want to stop bidding, shake your head firmly. If your bid is successful and the auctioneer doesn't know your name, shout it to him across the saleroom.

Paddle bidding is used in all the main auctions and is becoming increasingly common in smaller ones. It entails registering your name and address on arrival at the saleroom, and receiving in return a plastic card or plastic 'paddle', with a number written on it. The auctioneer asks for this to be shown at the completion of every successful bid.

Payment at traditional open-air sales is often made in cash, on the spot. Even at indoor salerooms, the auctioneers may want cash rather than cheques from people they don't know. Find out what is acceptable — unless you're happy to brazen it out.

Prices

One of the great benefits of buying goods at auction is that with every purchase, old-fashioned virtues of thrift are combined with the more fashionable virtues of environmental awareness and recycling. However, this does not automatically mean that goods will necessarily be cheaper at an auction than elsewhere. In the auction business the rules, such as they are, change all the time.

If you are looking for bargains, your hunting will be influenced by social trends as much as anything. Fifty years ago anyone who did not buy brand-new goods did so because he or she could not afford them. Although collecting fine antiques was a recognised pastime, buying second-hand goods (which were seen as other people's rejects) was totally looked down on. Today many items which for years were regarded as

having little or no real value, such as gramophones, cigarette cards, fountain pens and even butcher's bicycles, are now much sought after in their own right. Auctions have played a part in bringing about this change.

Prices for similar lots can vary greatly, even at the same sale. You would normally expect to pay more for antiques than for modern items. Even in the best auctions, there are usually lots which sell for only a few pounds. It is the very flukiness of prices at auctions which makes them so fascinating to attend.

Practicalities

You should check what the auctioneers' policy is on storage, transportation and shipping before bidding – although most auctioneers do not insist that goods are moved immediately after a sale. The storage, transportation and shipping details given with each entry in this book show whether the auctioneer is willing to *advise* you of suitable companies.

Selling at auction

This book is mostly about buying, but auctions can be an excellent way to sell something, too. At an auction, the whole of the sale price goes to the vendor (except a percentage which the vendor must pay the auctioneer in commission, and VAT).

If you are considering selling in this way, be careful. If you choose the wrong auction your valuable goods may be sold for a fraction of their true worth, because no one has realised their value. One way of safeguarding yourself is to put a 'reserve' price on a lot, below which it may not be sold. The disadvantage to this method is that even if your item is not sold, you still have to pay the auctioneer commission.

It is wise to have your goods valued before you sell them. Most auctioneers carry out valuations free of charge, although they may charge expenses if they have to travel to your home, etc.

Auctions on the Continent

For generations, British auctions have provided fodder for a highly active shipping trade to the Continent, but with the opening of a free European market the situation is reversing. British buyers are becoming increasingly aware of the bargains to be found on the other side of the Channel, just a short trip away from home.

Price factors

Prices at Continental auctions compare favourably with those in Britain, and bargains may be found in certain categories, such as china and quality furniture. It is possible, for example, to find decoratively carved oak headboards, which are now becoming increasingly fashionable in Britain, for reasonable prices in France, Holland and Belgium. Longcase or grandfather clocks are now hard to find in good condition at sales in Britain, whereas in Holland you can find well-preserved examples without much difficulty. They often sell for less than the comparable British auction price.

When deciding how much you can afford to bid, be cautious; if you are looking for a bargain, do some homework before you set off on your journey, and be sure to find out how much it will cost to bring your purchase home. If you are in any doubt about the financial viability of a purchase, consult reputable dealers and auctioneers in your area to find out how much a similar piece would be likely to fetch at auction in Britain.

Viewing and bidding

If you are intending to buy something at a Continental auction, it is essential to make full use of the viewing. It is also advisable to make any bid in writing before an auction begins, so that there can be no mistake during the proceedings, even if you feel reasonably confident speaking another language. Remember that on top of the hammer price there will be an additional charge, representing the buyer's premium and tax. In Holland this is 25 per cent. At sales at the Hotel Drouot in Paris it is 9 per cent, and in other countries it ranges from 10 per cent to 17 per cent.

Transporting your goods

Salerooms are usually happy to give advice on how to get your purchase home, and will often be able to put you in touch with reputable transportation and shipping companies in the area. If you are not in too much of a hurry, you can always wait for your purchase to be taken as part of a container load, which is comparatively inexpensive. However, it is amazing how much can be packed into a car, even if it is laden with holiday luggage — it is worth suffering some discomfort if a bargain is good enough. Thanks to the free European market, goods can now be moved freely from one European country to another without export documents (although there are a few rare exceptions to this rule).

Remember ...

Continental auctioneers are usually experienced at welcoming bidders from other countries, and many of them have an excellent command of English. Even if you do not buy anything, you will find that a visit to an auction abroad is a wonderful opportunity to soak up local atmosphere, and to gain understanding of that country's language, culture and people.

Auctions in Amsterdam

Sotheby's and Christie's conduct all their Amsterdam sales in English, and catalogues are also printed in English. Both establishments lack the élitist reputation of their British counterparts. Although they hold sales of the highest quality goods, they also try to cater for the interests of the general public; a visit to Christie's Amsterdam saleroom is all part of an everyday shopping trip for many local people.

Amsterdam has five excellent auction houses, all within easy walking distance of one another. Sales are conducted in a friendly, light-hearted manner. Peter Trommelen, the proprietor of De Eland's, actually hands out free bottles of wine to bidders during sales. If a bidder makes a small bid, a high bid or a joke, he or she is handed one of the free bottles. Some salerooms conduct auctions in Dutch, but the auctioneers will often speak in English and German, too, when they realise they have bidders in the room from these countries.

L Gijselman is another example of an auction house with excellent sales. Their regular auctions of furniture, paintings, jewellery, silver, complete dinner services, antiques and so on usually comprise over 3,000 lots. Some will sell for as little as the eqivalent of five pounds, whereas others could fetch tens of thousands. The saleroom is a bright, modern building, with sales on four floors. I found the best bargains in the rear ground-floor saleroom. They were catalogued without estimates, because they were not considered of high enough quality to merit them. Among them I discovered a marble-topped washstand, some pine country furniture from East Germany, and a good selection of beautifully carved dressers and sideboards. The lots came from all over Europe, but some of the most interesting

finds that I made were in the boxes of bric-à-brac. They contained good quality china, glass and other household goods, all for the equivalent of a few pounds.

Auction houses

Christie's Amsterdam Cornelis Schuytstraat 57. *Tel:* (020) 575 5255
De Zwaan Keizersgracht 474. *Tel:* (020) 622 0447
L Gijselman Overtoom 197. *Tel:* (020) 616 8586
Sotheby's Amsterdam Rokin 102.
Tel: (020) 627 5656
Veilinghuis de Eland Elandsgracht 68.
Tel: (020) 623 0343

Auctions in Paris and France

There are some excellent auctions in France, many within easy reach of day-trippers and holiday-makers. The centre, of course, is Paris, where nearly all auctions take place under one roof — that of the Hôtel Drouot. This large, modern building at 9 rue Drouot has no less than 18 separate salerooms. These are used by independent Parisian auctioneers. There are sales every weekday (and sometimes on Saturdays and Sundays, too), and it is possible to buy all manner of things: lace, ornamental and domestic china, paintings, furniture, antiques — anything, in fact, from Portobello Road-style bric-à-brac to high-quality goods. Some of the auctioneers specialise in certain fields and it is possible to find auctions that are entirely given over to a particular area of interest, such as paintings, perfume bottles, jewellery, silver, or glass. However, the majority of sales are general ones.

The large reception area on the ground floor displays sale catalogues, which can be studied free of charge. There are plenty of saleroom assistants on hand to advise potential buyers, and many of them speak English. As always, it is important to familiarise yourself with the terms of sale before deciding how high to bid. They are available in English and include advice on bidding and other auction procedures.

Viewing for all sales takes place from 11.00am to 1.00pm daily. It is essential to make good use of this time, because once an auction has started it is impossible to see the lots clearly. The salerooms close for lunch at 1.00pm, for one hour. Ten minutes or so before they reopen, people can be seen congregating around the doors of each saleroom. Once the doors are open, be prepared for a rush to take seats inside.

There is a pleasant touch of apparent chaos about these sales. This is partly due to the porters, who shout out bids with the auctioneer as a sale progresses, making the whole affair rather noisy. Successful bidders are handed slips of paper showing the lot numbers of the items they have bought, so there is no need to shout out your name to the auctioneer when the hammer comes down on your bid. Bidders can pay for their goods as soon as they are handed their slips of paper, or any time afterwards.

Auction houses

PARIS Nearly all sales in Paris are held at the following address:
Hôtel Drouot 9 rue Drouot, 75009 Paris.
Tel: (1) 48 00 20 42

AIX EN PROVENCE
Hours De Valaurie Chemin de la Vierge Noire, Aix en Provence 13090. *Tel:* 42 64 02 37

ARGENTEUIL
Regis-Thiollet 19 rue Denis Roy, Argenteuil 95100. *Tel:* 39 61 01 50

CALAIS
Pillon 24 rue Delaroche, Calais 62100.
Tel: 21 97 33 76

CANNES
Issaly 69 avenue Félix Fauré, Cannes 06400.
Tel: 93 39 01 35

FONTAINEBLEAU
Osenat 5 rue Royale, Fontainebleau 77300.
Tel: 64 22 27 62

LE HAVRE
Revol 203 bd de Strasbourg, Le Havre 76600.
Tel: 35 21 21 27

MARSEILLE
D'Authier de Sigsaw & Charriaud 19 rue Borde, Marseille 13008. *Tel:* 91 79 46 30

Auctions in Belgium

The prices fetched at Belgian auctions tend to reflect the country's high cost of living. On the whole, it is not a good place for bargain hunters, but if you know what you want and are willing to pay the going price for it, you will find a trip here rewarding — particularly if you are interested in paintings, antiques, jewellery, silver and, of course, lace. Because Belgium is within easy reach of Paris and Amsterdam, sales tend to be highly international in character. Lots tend to be drawn from surrounding countries, but Flemish pieces, in the form of heavy oak furniture, are also much in evidence. This wide and interesting mixture of styles attracts bidders from all over Europe and beyond. One of the most enjoyable aspects of attending Belgian sales, from my own point of view, is seeing how well people of many different nationalities can get on together, even while they are engaged in the potentially explosive activity of competing for the lots on offer.

If you are auction-going in Brussels, don't forget to pay a visit to Grand' Place between viewing and bidding; it is one of the most attractive squares in Europe. If you can, see it either in the morning, when there is a flower market in progress, or at night, when the 15th-century Gothic guildhalls that surround it are floodlit. Antwerp, Belgium's second city, is equally attractive. English is spoken all over the country.

Auction houses

ANTWERP
De Keuster Vrijdagmarkt 4-6, Antwerp 2000.
Tel: (3) 233 8140

Dixy Handelstraat 19, Antwerp 2000.
Tel: (3) 236 3864

BRUSSELS
Beguinage 10 rue de Rouleau, Brussels 1000.
Tel: (2) 218 1742

Auctions in Eire

Although this section has dealt with auctions on the Continent, Eire is also a popular destination within easy reach of British holiday-makers, so I am including it here.

Eire should certainly not be overlooked by bargain hunters. I always have a feeling that if I am going to make a real find at an auction — a Chippendale chair painted white, or something similar — it will be at an Irish sale. Indeed, there are well-documented cases of rare antiques being discovered, dusty and neglected, in farmers' sheds here. Once restored, some of them have gone on to fetch higher and higher sums, until they have ended up as highly prized pieces in American antique showrooms. Irish auctioneers are experts in their fields, though, and very little escapes them. However, I live in hope, and Eire is where I have the most hope!

Eire remains a highly individual and atmospheric country. Auctions are professionally run, but also manage to maintain a charming country atmosphere. Irish humour flows easily from the rostrum, and a certain amount of banter often accompanies the bidding.

Sales in Dublin, especially, attract tourists from all over the world, but prices are often modest. Domestic and ornamental china, country furniture, well-cared-for antiques and craft items represent particularly good value for money. There is also plenty of local history in evidence, as anyone who rummages through the boxes of bric-à-brac will soon discover. Something to suit most tastes invariably turns up at these busy sales, which are a joy to attend. But beware! Even if you enter an Irish saleroom with no intention of bidding, you need a strong will if you are not to be caught up in the excitement.

Auction houses

CAHIR
Fleury's The Square, Cahir. *Tel:* (52) 41226
CORK
Woodwards 26 Cook Street, Cork. *Tel:* (21) 273327
DUBLIN
Thomas P Adams 38 Main Street, Blackrock, Dublin. *Tel:* (1) 2885146
Herman & Wilkinson 161 Lower Rathmines Road, Dublin. *Tel:* (1) 972245

... and finally

Since the first edition of this book, many readers have been kind enough to send me details of their favourite local auctions in Britain. I am most grateful for their interest, and have included as many 'reader recommendations' as possible in this new, updated edition.

The auctions in France, Holland, Belgium and Eire listed in this introduction have been selected because they are within comparatively easy reach of day-trippers and holiday-makers from Britain. All of these auction houses hold regular general sales (and sometimes specialist ones, too).

There must be many auctions that I have missed in Britain, Eire and on the Continent, so I would be grateful to hear from any members of the public who would like to recommend a sale to me. There are forms at the end of this book for readers to use, if they wish to.

As always, may all your bids be bargains.

Eric Geen

· HOW TO USE THIS BOOK ·

The sales in this book are listed in sections under England, Wales, Scotland and Northern Ireland; then alphabetically by county and place. London auctioneers may be found at the end of the section on England.

EXAMPLE OF AN ENTRY

ISLE OF WIGHT

Ryde

Place name.

WAYS

Name of establishment.

Garfield Road.
Tel: (0983) 562255

Address.

500-700 lots.

Approximate number of lots in a sale, which may vary. Most auctioneers sell between 80-100 lots an hour, so this figure can be used as a rough guide to the duration of a sale. Be careful, though. Sometimes an auctioneer will sell more than 100 lots an hour, if there are fewer bids. At some auctions in Scotland, all the items brought to a sale by one vendor may be given the same lot number. As each item will be sold separately, it is important to look at what is being sold, rather than to listen for lot numbers during the bidding.

Established as long ago as 1815, Ways are the oldest auctioneers on the Isle of Wight. Their saleroom, with its sign swinging prominently outside, was once an old Victorian coach house with three stables. The auctions are mainly of antique and modern furnishings, although they also include plenty of smaller lots such as silver and silver plate, jewellery, china and *objets d'art*, all of which make good holiday souvenirs. There may also be some tempting larger items of furniture. These auctions are packed with good-quality items, and they are well attended by buyers who regularly make the journey over from the mainland.

Description of entry.

BUYER'S PREMIUM: *Nil*

The commission charged by auctioneers to successful bidders. It is calculated as a percentage of the 'hammer' price, and varies from auction to auction. It can be 5 or 10 per cent or more, or nothing at all, as in this case. VAT may also be charged on the buyer's premium. Always read auction catalogues thoroughly before a sale, especially the small print. If you are in any doubt, consult the auctioneers before deciding how high to bid.

SALES: *Every five weeks on Thu at 10.30am.*
VIEWING: *Day prior from 10.00am-6.00pm.*

Although every effort has been made to ensure accuracy, these details may be subject to change at short notice. Always confirm details with the auctioneers before setting out on a journey.

REFRESHMENTS: *Own café.*

The establishments listed in this book are not necessarily AA inspected. However, the AA is always pleased to hear of any reader's recommendations (see the forms at the end of this book).

PARKING: *Own car park.*

Details of NCP or other car parks in the area are given where necessary.

STORAGE: *Yes*
TRANSPORTATION: *Yes*
SHIPPING: *Yes*

'Yes' indicates that the auctioneers are willing to *advise* bidders of suitable services; it does not always mean that the auctioneers offer these services themselves.

The auctions described in this book have been selected by the author personally. No financial transactions have been entered into with regard to choice of establishments. The opinions given in each entry are the author's personal view, and are not necessarily shared by The Automobile Association. The Automobile Association cannot accept responsibility for the future quality and range of goods at these auctions, or for any financial transactions entered into by readers. It is always advisable to read the small print in auctioneers' catalogues, and to confirm sale details with them, before making firm plans to attend an auction.

AVON

ALDRIDGES OF BATH

The Auction Galleries, 130/132 Walcot Street.
Tel: (0225) 462830

400-500 lots. This is a long-established, independently run sale less than half a mile from the centre of the attractive city of Bath.

The sale is held in a converted old school with four salerooms, one for paintings, one for porcelain and china, one for the general sale and the other used as needed. Auctions are held on Tuesdays. A fortnightly general sale of household furniture and effects alternates with specialist antiques sales. The categories include clocks and carpets, silver and porcelain, paintings, drawings and prints, collectables and many other specialities. All the sales are interesting and well attended.

Bath

BUYER'S PREMIUM: 10%
SALES: *General: fortnightly on Tue at 10.00am. Antiques (different specialities): fortnightly on Tue at 10.00am (alternate weeks to general).*
VIEWING: *Sat 9.00am-12.00 noon, Mon 9.00am-5.00pm.*
REFRESHMENTS: *Own café.*
PARKING: *Own car park.*
STORAGE: *Yes*
TRANSPORTATION: *Yes*
SHIPPING: *Yes*

GARDINER HOULGATE

The Bath Auction Rooms, Old Malthouse, Comfortable Place, Upper Bristol Road. Tel: (0225) 447933

400-600 lots. Usually there are between three and five sales per month. 'Victoriana and Later Furnishings' is the name given to the general sale, held on the last or penultimate Thursday of the month. This can include up to 100 lots of electrical items such as televisions and audio systems, plus unredeemed pawnbroker pledges like cameras and compact disc players. The jewellery sales are held twice monthly on Wednesdays and also include unredeemed pledges, such as gold, silver and antique jewellery. Prices vary from a few pounds to a few thousand pounds. Four times a year, this sale becomes a special sale of antique jewellery, silver and plate.

Also four times a year, the general sale is replaced by one of antique furniture and works of art. There are special sales of musical instruments four times a year, when instruments of all ages and types can be found. Other speciality sales are held periodically, including popular categories such as books, garden pots and model railways.

Bath

BUYER'S PREMIUM: 10%
SALES: *General: monthly on last or second-to-last Thu of month at 10.30am (replaced by antiques and works of art four times a year in Feb, May, Sep and Nov). Jewellery: twice monthly on Wed at 12.00 noon. Musical instruments: four times a year in Mar, Jun, Sep and Dec on Fri at 1.00pm.*
VIEWING: *General: Sat prior 10.00am-1.00pm, Tue prior 12.00 noon-6.00pm, Wed prior 9.00am-6.00pm. Jewellery: Tue prior 12.00 noon-6.00pm, morning of sale. Musical instruments: day prior, 12.00 noon-7.00pm. All sales: morning of sale from 9.00am.*
REFRESHMENTS: *Own café.*
PARKING: *Charlotte Street public car park.*
STORAGE: *Yes*
TRANSPORTATION: *Yes*
SHIPPING: *Yes*

Bath

BUYER'S PREMIUM: 10%
SALES: *Antiques and
Victoriana: fortnightly on Mon
at 11.00am. Antiques and fine
art: every two months on Mon
at 11.00am.*
VIEWING: *Both sales: Fri
9.00am-5.00pm, Sat
9.00am-1.00pm, morning of
sale from 8.30am.*
REFRESHMENTS: *None
available on the premises.*
PARKING: *Own car park.*
STORAGE: *Yes*
TRANSPORTATION: *Yes*
SHIPPING: *Yes*

Bristol

BUYER'S PREMIUM: 10%
SALES: *General: fortnightly
on Tue at 10.30am. Antique
and Decorative: about eight
times a year on Tue at
10.30am. Antique and Modern
(Wells): monthly on Wed at
1.30pm. Commercial Assets:
fortnightly (days vary) at
10.30am.*
VIEWING: *General: day
prior 12.00 noon-5.00pm.
Antique and Decorative: Sat
prior 9.30am-1.00pm, Mon
prior 9.30am-7.00pm.
Antique and Modern (Wells):
day prior 1.00pm-5.00pm, day
of sale from 9.00am.
Commercial Assets: variable -
check with the auctioneers.*
REFRESHMENTS:
*Available at Commercial Assets
sales only.*
PARKING: *Own car parks.*
STORAGE: *Yes*
TRANSPORTATION: *Yes*
SHIPPING: *Yes*

Bristol

BUYER'S PREMIUM: 10%
SALES: *General: weekly on*

PHILLIPS

1 Old Street. Tel: (0225) 310609

150-500 lots. The saleroom is in a large old building with blue painted doors by the rear entrance to Jolly's Department Store — about quarter of a mile from the abbey, Pump Room and Roman Baths. Like all Phillips auctions, this one is at the upper end of the market. Sales are held most Mondays in various specialist categories. There are fortnightly sales under the heading 'Antiques and Victoriana', and sales of 'Antiques and Fine Art' every two months. All sales include furniture, clocks, rugs, ceramics, glass, silver, jewellery, pictures and deocrative items.

ALLEN AND HARRIS

*Bristol Auction Rooms, St John's Place,
Apsley Road, Clifton. Tel: (0272) 737201*

400-500 lots. The saleroom lies about two miles from the Clifton Suspension Bridge over the River Avon. The company is a member of Royal Life Estates, and associated companies have sales in Wiltshire, Dorset, Hampshire and Somerset. Auctions are held two or three times per month in Bristol. There is a fortnightly general sale, and there are also 'Antique and Decorative' sales about eight times a year. The auctioneer conducting this sale is also responsible for the monthly 'Antique and Modern' sales about 20 miles away at Wells. The address is 66-68 Southover, and you will find a predominance of antiques. Fortnightly sales of 'Commercial Assets' are also held by the auctioneers on behalf of the Official Receivers at their second auction room, which can be found at 2a Greville Road, Ashford, Bristol.

TAVINER'S OF BRISTOL

Prewett Street, Redcliffe. Tel: (0272) 265996

300-400 lots. Taviner's have been established in the area for over 20 years, and hold a general sale every Friday (except

Good Friday and at Christmas). This includes complete house contents, office effects and stock, with a variety of bric-à-brac and other items. Every month on Thursdays Taviner's also have sales in special categories in rotation. 'Antique and Quality Furniture' includes clocks, rugs, boxes and table furniture; 'Ceramics and Collectables' includes glass, metals, silver, jewellery, toys and dolls, medals, coins, scientific and musical instruments, textiles and weapons; 'Postcards' includes cigarette and trade cards, stamps, photographs, albums and ephemera. 'Printed Books and Pictures' includes antiquarian and secondhand books and literary properties, together with paintings, drawings, maps, prints and frames.

WICKS & PIERCE

The Auction Rooms. Tel: (0761) 413060

400-500 lots. The Old Parsonage is one of the oldest and most attractive houses in this pretty little village. It is situated just off the main road where the A37 and A39 meet. The easy access from Bristol, Bath and the coast may be one reason why the sales are so well attended, and another attraction is the beautiful surrounding countryside. The saleroom atmosphere is good too. Sales occur on average every four to six weeks, but may be less frequent in the winter months. This auction is at the more up-market end of the country auction scene. Included are general antiques, Victorian and Edwardian furniture, pine, good quality shipping furniture, good quality china, porcelain, silver, silver plate, metalware, collectables, bygones of various types, oil paintings, watercolour drawings, prints and so on.

WOODSPRING AUCTION ROOMS

Churchill Road. Tel: (0934) 628419

600-800 lots. Churchill Road is a turning off Locking Road, the main route through this seaside resort. Woodspring Auctions hold excellent fortnightly sales of general household furniture and effects, plus periodic special sales of antiques. The general sales sometimes include liquidated stock and goods from office clearances, and free valuations are given on request.

The number attending the general sale noticeably increases during the summer months. There are plenty of other attractions around here, but many visitors enjoy the out-of-the-ordinary atmosphere of a sale. The excitement of bidding for a fine old Royal Doulton tea cup beats walking into a souvenir shop, too.

Fri at 12.00 noon. Special categories: monthly on Thu at 12.00 noon.
VIEWING: *General: morning of sale from 9.00am. All others: day prior 10.00am-7.00pm, morning of sale.*
REFRESHMENTS: *None available on the premises.*
PARKING: *None available on the premises.*
STORAGE: *Yes*
TRANSPORTATION: *Yes*
SHIPPING: *Yes*

Farrington Gurney

BUYER'S PREMIUM: *Nil*
SALES: *About every four to six weeks on Sat at 11.00am.*
VIEWING: *Day prior 2.00pm- 6.00pm.*
REFRESHMENTS: *Own café.*
PARKING: *Own car park.*
STORAGE: *Yes*
TRANSPORTATION: *Yes*
SHIPPING: *Yes*

Weston-Super-Mare

BUYER'S PREMIUM: *10%*
SALES: *Fortnightly on Thu at 10.00am.*
VIEWING: *Day prior 2.00pm-6.00pm, day of sale from 9.00am.*
REFRESHMENTS: *None available on premises.*
PARKING: *None available on premises.*
STORAGE: *Yes*
TRANSPORTATION: *Yes*
SHIPPING: *Yes*

BEDFORDSHIRE

Bedford

BUYER'S PREMIUM: *10%*
SALES: *General: weekly on Sat at 9.30am.*
VIEWING: *Day prior 8.30am-8.00pm.*
REFRESHMENTS: *Own café.*
PARKING: *None available on the premises.*
STORAGE: *No*
TRANSPORTATION: *Yes*
SHIPPING: *Yes*

Luton

BUYER'S PREMIUM: *Nil*
SALES: *Weekly on Wed at 7.00pm.*
VIEWING: *Day of sale from 12.00 noon- 7.00pm.*
REFRESHMENTS: *Own café.*
PARKING: *Own car park.*
STORAGE: *Yes*
TRANSPORTATION: *Yes*
SHIPPING: *Yes*

WILSON PEACOCK

26 Newnham Street. Tel: (0234) 266366

1,000-1,500 lots. Visiting Wilson Peacock's Saturday sale could be an enjoyable and rewarding day out for the whole family. Almost certainly there will be something to interest everyone. Eggs are sold at 9.30am, followed by bicycles, plants, and produce. Household furniture and effects and small items of electrical equipment are sold at 10.30am, when a sale of motor vehicles also takes place outside. Office furniture and heavy goods — windows, doors and lawn mowers — are sold at 11.00am, and the day's bidding is usually over by 3.30pm.

ADELAIDE AUCTION ROOM

Stuart Place, off Adelaide Street. Tel: (0582) 423809

300-400 lots. The saleroom is situated at the rear of 82 Wellington Street and next door to the Driving Test Centre. There are excellent sales here, which normally include bargains in all categories of household furniture and effects and miscellaneous items. The lots are of all ages, and in all kinds of condition, from 'perfect' to 'in need of attention'. There are often good buys among the antique, modern and reproduction furniture, and also among the electrical goods, paintings and prints, china and gardening items. Boxes of miscellanea are always worth inspection — they might contain anything from china and postcards to books and toys. Many local people attend regularly, not necessarily to buy but purely to enjoy the occasion.

LUTON MULTI AUCTIONS

37 John Street. Tel: (0582) 405281

300-500 lots. This evening auction is a well-known local event and a focal point for those looking for bargains. The saleroom is also used as an antique centre whenever an auction is held. Many people just pop in on their way home from work, or while they are on a shopping trip in Luton (the saleroom is opposite the Arndale Shopping Centre in the middle of the town) to look at antiques which can be bought or are on view for a forthcoming auction.

This is a family-run business, and the proprietors, Frank and Shirley Horn, are also responsible for the long-established and very popular regular Sunday antiques auctions at the Village Hall, Slip End. These offer a good day's entertainment for the whole family because the auctions, which begin at 5.30pm, are usually accompanied by an antiques fair from 10.00am onwards.

BUYER'S PREMIUM: *50p per lot.*
SALES: *General: weekly on Thu at 7.00pm; antiques and collectors' items: last Sun of month at 6.00pm; Slip End: first Sun of the month at 5.30pm.*
VIEWING: *General: all week from 10.00am-5.00pm (10.00am-9.00pm Wed); antiques and collectors' items: day of sale; Slip End: day of sale from 2.00pm.*
REFRESHMENTS: *Own café.*
PARKING: *Own car park.*
STORAGE: *Yes*
TRANSPORTATION: *Yes*
SHIPPING: *Yes*

DOWNER ROSS

Old Town Hall. Tel: (0525) 290502 or (0908) 679900

350-450 lots. Woburn's Old Town Hall is difficult to miss. It is an attractive old building in the town centre, standing alone, almost in an island surrounded by roads. Woburn Abbey, the historic home of the Duke of Bedford, with its magnificent collection of furniture and art treasures, is only about three miles away. Woburn Abbey Antiques Centre is one of the largest in the country, with more than 40 independently-run shops under one roof. Combining a trip to the abbey with a visit to an auction makes a very pleasant and interesting day out for the family.

The lots on offer at Downer Ross's auctions are usually of high quality, and cover all sorts of fields: antique, period and later furniture, pictures, prints, ceramics and metalware, ornamental items, silver and glass, and much more besides. The saleroom is attractively set out and there is plenty of room for people to view the lots before the auction. This is conducted in a friendly, efficient manner, which puts people at their ease — despite the fact that some lots fetch five-figure sums. Others are sold for as little as five pounds, so there is something here to suit most people.

The auctioneers also hold fortnightly sales of reproduction and second-hand furniture, china and bric-à-brac at their Moreton Road Saleroom in Buckingham, which are well attended.

BUYER'S PREMIUM: *10%*
SALES: *Usually monthly on Thu at 11.00am. Buckingham: fortnightly on Thu at 11.00am.*
VIEWING: *Day prior, 9.00am-7.30pm. Buckingham: day prior, 9.00am-5.30pm.*
REFRESHMENTS: *Woburn and Buckingham: none available on the premises.*
PARKING: *Public car park 100 yards away. Buckingham: own car park.*
STORAGE: *Both: yes*
TRANSPORTATION: *Both: yes*
SHIPPING: *Both: yes*

BERKSHIRE

Donnington

BUYER'S PREMIUM: 10%
SALES: General: fortnightly on Tue at 10.00am. Specialist: monthly on Wed at 10.30am.
VIEWING: General: Sat prior, 9.30am-12.00 noon, day prior, 9.30am-4.00pm; Specialist: Sat prior, 9.30am-12.00 noon, Mon and Tue prior, 9.30am-4.00pm.
REFRESHMENTS: On sale days.
PARKING: Own car park.
STORAGE: Yes (limited period).
TRANSPORTATION: Yes
SHIPPING: Yes

Reading

BUYER'S PREMIUM: Nil (5% on furniture sales). Shiplake: 10%.
SALES: General: monthly on Sat at 10.00am. Saddlery: first Fri of the month, at 10.30am. Shiplake: every two months (day varies).
VIEWING: General: day prior, 12.00 noon-4.00pm and day of sale from 9.00am; Saddlery: day of sale from 9.00am. Shiplake: times vary.
REFRESHMENTS: Own café. Shiplake: none available on the premises.
PARKING: Both: available on the premises.
STORAGE: Both: yes
TRANSPORTATION: Both: yes
SHIPPING: Both: yes

DREWEATT NEATE

Donnington Priory, near Newbury. Tel: (0635) 31234

400-500 lots. Donnington Priory is an attractive Georgian building set in beautiful grounds, which are well worth visiting in their own right. Dreweatt Neate, established in 1759, have held sales at the Priory for ten years, and before that they operated from premises in Newbury. There are three or four auctions a month to tempt prospective buyers to the Priory; a fortnightly auction, consisting of general household furniture and effects, lesser antiques and Victoriana is held on Tuesdays in Saleroom IV, but there is also a specialist Wednesday sale once or twice a month in the other three salerooms. The latter is usually devoted to one of the following areas: antiques (including clocks and instruments, furniture, rugs, textiles, collectors' items and old toys); silver and jewellery; paintings, books and ceramics. Illustrated catalogues are available for the specialist sales.

THIMBLEBY & SHORLAND

31 Great Knollys Street. Tel: (0734) 508611

1,500-2,000 lots. Once a month, in the same sheds which are used every week for livestock auctions, Thimbleby & Shorland hold massive auctions of antique and modern furniture, household effects, and office furniture. Regularly among the lots are items to be sold by Order of H M Customs and Excise, H M Collector of Taxes, the County Courts, the Official Receiver, other liquidators and the High Sheriff of Berkshire. The proceedings are divided into three separate auctions in order to get through the number of items for sale. Here it is quite possible to end up buying such varied items as brass stair rods, fire surrounds, modern furniture, Victorian coal scuttles, violins, electronic components, packets of biscuits, beds and bedding, and telephone answering machines all in the course of one day. The auctioneers also hold monthly sales of horses and saddlery here, with some 800 lots of harnesses, vehicles, trailers, jumps and so on. Machinery and contractors' sales are also held.

'Paddle' bidding is the order of the day, which means that prospective buyers must register with the auctioneer before the sale so that they can be given a number.

Thimbleby & Shorland have recently acquired Duncan Vincent Chartered Surveyors, and now run sales of antique,

Victorian and later furnishings every two months at Shiplake Memorial Hall, near Henley-on-Thames in Oxfordshire.

HOLLOWAYS
See HOLLOWAYS, Banbury, Oxfordshire

FRESHWATER ASSOCIATES

New Hall. Tel: (0344) 868858

300-500 lots. This auction was recommended to me by a reader of this book, as he made some good buys here. Waltham St Lawrence is a small village, and New Hall is opposite The Star public house, so the saleroom is easily located. Sales usually include a good mixture of around 200 lots of Victorian and Edwardian furniture, as well as antiques. There are also usually around 100-200 'smalls', including domestic and ornamental china, silver and silver plate, and so on. There are also plenty of boxes of miscellaneous items, which are fun to sift through.

ROBIN ELLIOTT CHARTERED SURVEYORS
incorporating CHANCELLORS FINE ART

Charlotte Pratt Memorial Hall, Chavey Down Road. Tel: (0344) 872588

500-700 lots. Chavey Down Road is a very long, quiet country road, and the Charlotte Pratt Memorial Hall is not very well signed. This makes it somewhat difficult to find if you are a stranger to the area. The venue is close to the White Horse public house, and if there is time it is a good idea for first-time bidders to call in at Robin Elliott's 32 High Street, Ascot office in order to pick up a sale catalogue and obtain clear directions. The goods at the Winkfield Row sales reflect, on the whole, the tone of the neighbourhood; the saleroom is close to the Royal Berkshire Polo Club and Royal Ascot Racecourse.

General antiques and good modern furniture are included in these auctions, which are, however, memorable for the range of smaller items that they offer: china, glass, ornaments, silver, jewellery, pictures and so on.

MARTIN & POLE (inc. WATTS & SON)

The Auction Galleries, 12 Milton Road. Tel: (0734) 790460

500-600 lots. Martin & Pole were established in 1846 and have been conducting auctions at this saleroom, just off Wokingham's busy main shopping street, for more than 30

Streatley

Waltham St Lawrence

BUYER'S PREMIUM: 10%
SALES: *On average once every six weeks on Thu at 6.00pm.*
VIEWING: *Day of sale from 1.00pm.*
REFRESHMENTS: *Own café.*
PARKING: *Own car park.*
STORAGE: *No*
TRANSPORTATION: *Yes*
SHIPPING: *Yes*

Winkfield Row

BUYER'S PREMIUM: 10%
SALES: *Monthly on Mon at 10.00am.*
VIEWING: *Sat prior, 10.00am-5.00pm.*
REFRESHMENTS: *Available.*
PARKING: *Some on the premises.*
STORAGE: *No*
TRANSPORTATION: *Yes*
SHIPPING: *Yes*

Wokingham

BUYER'S PREMIUM: *Nil*
SALES: *General sale: once a month on Sat at 10am. Antiques sale: once a month, usually on third Wed of the*

month at 10.00am.
VIEWING: *General: morning of sale from 8.30am; antique: Sat prior, 9.00am-1.00pm, Mon and Tue prior, 9.00am-5.00pm.*
REFRESHMENTS: *None available on the premises.*
PARKING: *None on the premises.*
STORAGE: *No*
TRANSPORTATION: *Yes*
SHIPPING: *Yes*

years. Visitors should note that street parking outside the saleroom is limited to two hours only. Despite this difficulty, Martin & Pole's sales have gained quite a large following over the years and they now attract bidders from all over the country. The saleroom is often overflowing on sale days. There are two main auctions a month: a Saturday sale of general household items, and a Wednesday antique and collector's sale, which includes antique and reproduction furniture, silver and plate, porcelain, pictures, carpets and rugs.

BUCKINGHAMSHIRE

Amersham

AMERSHAM AUCTION ROOMS

Pretty & Ellis, Station Road. Tel: (0494) 729292

400-500 lots. The saleroom is 100 yards from the Metropolitan line tube station, and is a charming single-storey building which at one time was a theatre. It comes complete with resident ghost!

The weekly auction is of antiques and collectables on the first Thursday of the month, but in other weeks this is a general sale. The antiques sale includes better quality items of English and European glass and china, antique and modern silver and jewellery, clocks, watches, barometers, scientific instruments, oil paintings, engravings, prints, furniture and so on. The other auctions are good general household sales.

BUYER'S PREMIUM: *10%*
SALES: *Weekly on Thu at 10.30am (includes antiques sale on first Thu of every month).*
VIEWING:
Tue 2.30pm-4.30pm, Wed 9.30am-7.00pm.
REFRESHMENTS: *None available on the premises.*
PARKING: *Own car park.*
STORAGE: *Yes*
TRANSPORTATION: *Yes*
SHIPPING: *Yes*

As well as a wide range of furniture, there will probably be all types of electrical equipment, gardening tools, kitchen items and assorted bric-à-brac to browse through.

Amersham

SOUTH BUCKS AUCTIONS

British Legion Hall, Whieldon Street. Tel: (0494) 722758

500-600 lots. South Bucks Auctions hold three sales a month in Amersham, a charming old town. All of these are very much looked-forward-to local events, especially as they take place on Saturdays. Twice a month there are sales of general household furniture and effects and miscellanea at the British Legion

BUYER'S PREMIUM: *10%*
SALES: *General: twice monthly on Sat at 1.00pm. Antiques: third Sat of the month at 1.00pm.*
VIEWING: *General: day*

Hall, but on the third Saturday of the month there is a special antiques auction. The latter takes place at the Conservative Centre in Church Street. Both venues can become quite crowded at times.

BOURNE END AUCTIONS

Station Approach. Tel: (0628) 531500

500-600 lots. This auction, recommended by a reader of this book, is a good place for bargain hunters. There is a wide variety of lots, which might include virtually anything, from household items to good-quality antiques. The saleroom is next to Bourne End railway station and is situated in a brick-and-flint building, on the first floor. The auctions are privately owned and run, and have a friendly atmosphere. They are very popular with local people, and you can usually find something for everyone. Apart from the usual fortnightly sales, there are also special sales of antiques at intervals throughout the year.

DOWNER ROSS

See DOWNER ROSS, Woburn, Bedfordshire

GEO WIGLEY & SONS

12 Market Square. Tel: (0296) 712717

600-700 lots. Winslow is a quiet little town with neat thatched cottages and an attractive market square surrounded by Georgian buildings. This is where you will find Geo Wigley & Son's estate agency, and the saleroom is just behind that. This is a good general sale which offers the possibility of picking up some bargains. It takes place on the last Friday of each month, and is of general household furniture and effects, including antiques. There are three salerooms. The auction starts in the one with the better quality items. The more run-of-the-mill goods and larger pieces of furniture such as wardrobes and dressers are in the biggest saleroom. The third saleroom is for bric-à-brac and smaller miscellanea.

prior, 6.00pm-11.00pm, morning of sale from 9.00am-1.00 pm. Antiques: Thu prior, 6.00pm-11.00pm, Fri prior, 10.00am-11.00pm, morning of sale from 9.00am-1.00pm.
REFRESHMENTS: *Own café.*
PARKING: *Public car park near by.*
STORAGE: *Yes*
TRANSPORTATION: *Yes*
SHIPPING: *Yes*

Bourne End

BUYER'S PREMIUM: *10%*
SALES: *General: fortnightly on Wed at 10.30am. Special sales of antiques: approximately four times a year on Wed at 10.30am.*
VIEWING: *General: Mon and Tue prior 9.30am-7.00pm. Special sales of antiques: Mon and Tue prior, 9.30am-7.00pm.*
REFRESHMENTS: *None available on the premises.*
PARKING: *Ample near by.*
STORAGE: *Yes*
TRANSPORTATION: *Yes*
SHIPPING: *Yes*

Buckingham

Winslow

BUYER'S PREMIUM: *Nil*
SALES: *Monthly on last Fri of month at 10.00am.*
VIEWING: *Day prior 9.30am-4.00pm, day of sale from 9.00am.*
REFRESHMENTS: *Own café.*
PARKING: *Ample parking near by.*
STORAGE: *Yes*
TRANSPORTATION: *Yes*
SHIPPING: *Yes*

CAMBRIDGESHIRE

Cambridge

BUYER'S PREMIUM: *10%*
SALES: *General household: weekly on Thu at 11.00am. Victoriana/books and prints: every six weeks on Thu at 11.00am (replaces general household sale). Rural and domestic bygones: four times a year on Sat at 10.30am.*
VIEWING: *All sales: day prior 2.00pm-7.00pm, morning of sale from 9.00am.*
REFRESHMENTS: *On day of sale only.*
PARKING: *Available in old cattle market near by.*
STORAGE: *Yes*
TRANSPORTATION: *Yes*
SHIPPING: *Yes*

Littleport

BUYER'S PREMIUM: *Nil*
SALES: *Weekly on Thu at 11.00am.*
VIEWING: *Day of sale from 9.00am.*
REFRESHMENTS: *Available on the premises*
PARKING: *Own car park.*
STORAGE: *Yes*
TRANSPORTATION: *Yes*
SHIPPING: *Yes*

March

BUYER'S PREMIUM: *5%*
SALES: *Weekly on Wed at 10.00am.*
VIEWING: *Tue prior, 2.00pm-5.00pm.*
REFRESHMENTS: *None available on the premises.*
PARKING: *None available on the premises.*
STORAGE: *Yes*
TRANSPORTATION: *Yes*
SHIPPING: *Yes*

CHEFFINS, GRAIN & COMINS

Cambridge Salerooms, 2 Clifton Road. Tel: (0223) 213343

300-400 lots. Cheffins, Grain & Comins are old-established auctioneers dating back to 1825. Every week on Thursday there is a sale of general household furniture and effects, including antiques and quality second-hand furniture, miscellaneous items, china and glass. Every six weeks the Thursday sale is devoted to Victoriana, including decorative furniture, furnishings and effects. Three times a year this becomes a book and print sale.

There are also four sales a year, on Saturdays, of rural and domestic bygones, which may include anything from old kitchen equipment to disused farming implements and scientific instruments. Dates for each type of sale are available from the auctioneers on request.

CHEFFINS, GRAIN & COMINS

Portley Hill Saleroom. Tel: (0353) 860832

850-1,000 lots. This is a typical country auction, colourful and noisy, with garden produce and poultry as well as general items being auctioned. Two separate sales begin at 11.00am. Outside the saleroom is the sale of 'deadstock' — a term often used in this part of England to describe such lots as bundles of timber, paving stones, rolls of wire netting, gardening tools, and perhaps window frames or doors. At the same time, produce and poultry are auctioned in a smaller undercover area. The auctioneer of the sale that finishes first will then start selling the lots in the general sale, which does not usually begin until around 12.30pm.

COLLINGWOODS

The March Weekly Auctions, Palace Hall Auction Rooms, Broad Street. Tel: (0354) 52488

200-300 lots. Established in 1884, this is a very popular and always interesting general auction, held in an attractive former cinema. It is in the middle of March, just off the High Street. The sale day is Wednesday, which is also market day, and the market stalls are just five minutes away. All types of good quality household furniture are sold, including antique, period and modern, together with various collectables, bygones, and a wide range of other items. There are usually some of the oddities that make country auctions so endearing: a bundle of bicycle mudguards perhaps, or a quantity of old tools including a scythe, or a horsedrawn cart jack and a pair of blacksmith's bellows from around 1878. At a typical sale, 20 bicycles were sold 'by order of Cambridgeshire Constabulary', at well below shop prices. Garden produce is sold first, including bulbs, shrubs and other plants. The main part of the auction begins at around 11.00am and takes about two hours. Payment is made on the spot: whereas at most auctions there is usually a short delay, here you should be prepared to hand over the cash as soon as a successful bid is made.

GROUNDS

Market Yard, Elwyn Road. Tel: (0354) 52502

300-400 lots. The motto of Grounds' auctioneer, Richard Barnwell, is to accept all sorts of goods for sale, even those that others might reject. Being a collector himself, he is aware that some people will make a collection out of the most unlikely objects. One of his satisfied customers was a collector of cardboard milk bottle tops showing the dairy's name, which were used after the Second World War.

Much has been written about the luck of buyers coming across bargains at auctions, but less is heard about the luck of the vendor. On one occasion a glass bowl was put up for sale at Grounds. It was valued at around £15, but the bidding started at £20, and the price went up...and up...until a bemused auctioneer found himself knocking it down for £1,370. Two London dealers were attending the auction and both had spotted its true value.

March

BUYER'S PREMIUM: 5%
SALES: *Monthly on Tue at 12.00 noon.*
VIEWING: *Morning of sale from 9.00am-12.00 noon.*
REFRESHMENTS: *None available on the premises.*
PARKING: *Own car park*
STORAGE: *Yes*
TRANSPORTATION: *Yes*
SHIPPING: *Yes*

L SHAW & SON

75 New Street. Tel: (0480) 472097 and 474550

250-500 lots. The auction is carried out with a great deal of gusto and friendly banter, and is ideal for those new to auction-going. The prices usually stay within reach of most pockets, and it would be difficult not to find something to bid for in one of the lots of bric-à-brac, furniture, china, pottery, bicycles, television sets, pots and pans, garden ornaments and furniture, boxes of books, beds, paintings and so on. The saleyard is on the outskirts of town, near the common.

Selling starts with fruit and vegetables at 11.00am, followed by eggs and poultry at 12.00 noon and flowers at 12.30pm. The furniture and general sale begins at around 1.00 to 1.30pm.

On Mondays and Fridays there are special fruit and vegetable sales beginning at 2.00pm. Sales finish at around

St Neots

BUYER'S PREMIUM: *Nil*
SALES: *Weekly on Thu at 11.00am.*
VIEWING: *Wed prior 4.00pm-5.00pm.*
REFRESHMENTS: *Van selling snacks.*
PARKING: *Room for a few cars in the saleyard, or park on the common.*
STORAGE: *No*
TRANSPORTATION: *Yes*
SHIPPING: *No*

3.30pm, leaving plenty of time to take a walk down to the river to see the old paper mill, which first produced machine-made paper in 1798.

Wisbech

BUYER'S PREMIUM: 10%
SALES: *Weekly on Wed and Sat at 10.00am.*
VIEWING: *Day prior and morning of sale.*
REFRESHMENTS: *Saturday only, van selling snacks.*
PARKING: *Own car park.*
STORAGE: *Yes*
TRANSPORTATION: *Yes*
SHIPPING: *Yes*

MAXEY & SON

Cattle Market. Tel: (0945) 584609

500-2,000 lots. Maxey & Son has been established for over 130 years, and two members of the Maxey family plus two other partners now run one of the largest auctions in this area. It is situated just off the busy Chapel Road, where on Wednesdays and Saturdays there is always an interesting range of good antique, period and modern furniture on offer, in addition to other household effects, china, glassware, jewellery, pictures, implements, machinery and so on.

The lots often include collectables, such as locally found old bottles and old woodworking tools. Wisbech was built as a port, and as well as seeing some large coasters lying alongside the quays, you will often find articles connected with boating and fishing among the lots. There are also daily auctions of fruit, vegetables and flowers at 4.00pm and twice weekly sales of nursery stock, bulbs and plants, on Wednesday and Saturday at 10.00am.

Auctions of fruit, vegetables and flowers are held nearby at The Chase Auction Hall, Chapel Road, by Clifford F Cross (Wisbech) Ltd, Horticultural Auctioneers, tel: (0945) 583398, on Monday, Wednesday and Thursday at 4.00pm. Nursery stock is auctioned on Wednesday and Saturday at 10.00am.

CHANNEL ISLANDS

GUERNSEY
St Peter Port

BUYER'S PREMIUM: *Nil*
SALES: *Weekly on Thu at 2.00pm.*
VIEWING: *Tue and Wed, 9.00am-12.00 noon and 2.00pm-5.00pm. Morning of sale, 9.00am-12.00 noon.*
REFRESHMENTS: *None available on the premises.*
PARKING: *None on the premises.*
STORAGE: *Yes*
TRANSPORTATION: *Yes*
SHIPPING: *Yes*

ALLEN'S ESTATE AGENCY & AUCTION CENTRE LTD

Auction Rooms, Les Amballes. Tel: (0481) 24526

250-300 lots. St Peter Port is the capital of Guernsey. It has plenty to offer visitors, but it is also well worth putting an hour or two aside from sight-seeing to sample some of the local auctions. Allen's is a short distance away from the shopping centre, and offers pleasant, unhurried auctions of general household furniture and effects, antiques and innumerable miscellaneous items.

Anything from a stamp to a car can be sold here, and 'island bygones', ideal for holiday souvenir hunters, are a speciality. Smaller items are usually kept back and sold towards the end of the auction.

MARTEL MAIDES & LE PELLEY LTD

12 Allez Street. Tel: (0481) 713463
200-250 lots. The auction room, converted from an old bakehouse, is within easy reach of St Peter Port's main shopping centre. Twice yearly, usually at the beginning and end of the year, the company holds special antiques auctions in place of their fortnightly sales of general household furniture and effects (although these sales also include some antiques). The quality of lots is good, reflecting the overall standard of living in the Channel Islands.

H W MAILLARD & SON

Glencoe. Tel: (0534) 37291
300-350 lots. Although attending an auction may not be a priority for many of Jersey's tourists, a trip to one of H W Maillard's sales (which have become almost a tradition of island life) could well turn out to be one of your holiday highlights. The auctions which take place here have a real island flavour, and many of Jersey's local characters will be found at them, together with farm workers, retired professionals and Charlie Hungerford-type millionaire immigrants. Many of those present regard the sales as social gatherings as well as opportunities to buy goods. The lots on offer range from farm equipment and livestock to vehicles, plants, antique and good quality furniture and household effects. The goods are sold in a field and adjoining saleroom. Once a year, on a Saturday in April, Maillard run a popular sale of boating, fishing and marine equipment.

CHESHIRE

WRIGHT-MANLEY

Beeston Castle Sales Centre, Beeston Cattle Market.
Tel: (0829) 260318
500-600 lots. The large, pleasant saleroom nestles at the foot of Beeston Castle. There is ample seating for the public and a good loudspeaker system means the auctioneer can be heard in all parts. A sale of general household furniture and effects is held fortnightly on Wednesdays. Every six weeks on Thursdays there is a sale of antiques and fine art, and

St Peter Port

BUYER'S PREMIUM: 5%
SALES: *Fortnightly on Thu at 2.15pm.*
VIEWING: *Wed prior, 9.00am-5.30pm. Day of sale from 9.00am.*
REFRESHMENTS: *None available on the premises.*
PARKING: *None on the premises.*
STORAGE: *Yes*
TRANSPORTATION: *Yes*
SHIPPING: *Yes*

JERSEY
St Lawrence

BUYER'S PREMIUM: *Nil*
SALES: *Fortnightly on Wed at 2.00pm; annual boating equipment sale in Apr on a Sat at 10.30am.*
VIEWING: *On day of sale.*
REFRESHMENTS: *Available from mobile vans.*
PARKING: *Available on the premises.*
STORAGE: *No*
TRANSPORTATION: *Yes*
SHIPPING: *No*

Beeston

BUYER'S PREMIUM: *Nil (general sales), 10% (antique sales).*
SALES: *General: twice monthly on first and third Wed of month at 10.00am. Antiques and fine art: every six weeks on Thu at 10.30am.*
VIEWING: *General: day*

prior 9.00am-5.00pm, morning
of sale from 9.00am. Antiques: in
week prior, Sun
10.00am-4.00pm, Mon
9.00am-5.00pm, Tue
9.00am-7.30pm, Wed
9.00am-12.00 noon; morning of
sale by appointment.
REFRESHMENTS: Own café.
PARKING: Own car park.
STORAGE: No
TRANSPORTATION: Yes
SHIPPING: Yes

Chester

BUYER'S PREMIUM: 10%
SALES: General: weekly on
Tue at 10.30am and 2.00pm.
Antiques and collectors' sale:
monthly on first Tue of month
at 10.30am (collectors' sale)
and 2.00pm (antiques).
VIEWING: Sat
9.00am-12.00 noon, Mon
9.00am-5.00pm.
REFRESHMENTS: Not
available on the premises.
PARKING: Ample car
parking space.
STORAGE: Yes
TRANSPORTATION: Yes
SHIPPING: Yes

Chester

BUYER'S PREMIUM: 10%
SALES: 'Gallery' sales:
fortnightly on Mon at 10.30am.
Specialist: at regular intervals.
VIEWING: 'Gallery' sales :
Fri prior, 10.00am-4.00pm,
Sat 9.00am-12.00 noon.
Specialist: at least two days prior
to sale, 10.00am-4.00pm.
REFRESHMENTS: None
available on the premises.
PARKING: Own car park.
STORAGE: Yes
TRANSPORTATION: Yes
SHIPPING: Yes

excellent buys are to be had at both sales. Wright-Manley are particularly known for their 'on-site' sales: sales of the complete contents of farms and farmhouses, which take place in the house, in a marquee or partly in the house and gardens and partly in nearby fields. These sales take place at irregular intervals, but are held frequently, particularly from spring onward.

ROBERT I HEYES & ASSOCIATES

Hatton Building, Lightfoot Street, Hoole. Tel: (0244) 328941

400-500 lots. The saleroom is just behind the railway station of this most picturesque of English cities. A special antiques and collectors' sale is held on the first Tuesday of the month. Every Tuesday there is also a sale of general household furniture and effects, which will include sitting room, dining room and bedroom suites, garden equipment, cookers, refrigerators and other electrical goods, china, porcelain, bric-à-brac and miscellaneous items. There is no particular order to the sale, except that the morning session ends with outside effects such as gardening tools and equipment. Viewing and sales times are the same for both types of sale. There is a break from around 1.00pm until 2.00pm for lunch, and the selling finishes around 4.00 to 4.30pm.

PHILLIPS

New House, 150 Christleton Road. Tel: (0244) 313936

300-600 lots. The Phillips saleroom is about one and a half miles out of the city, heading towards Whitchurch on the A41. 'Gallery' sales are held every fortnight on Mondays. These are of Victorian, Edwardian and reproduction furniture, ceramics, glass and miscellaneous items. Specialist sales of furniture, paintings, silver, jewellery and golfing memorabilia are also held regularly.

WHITTAKER & BIGGS

Macclesfield Road Saleroom. Tel: (0260) 273241

400-500 lots. Whittaker & Biggs saleroom is next to the livestock market, which they also run. The weekly auction takes place on a Friday or Saturday, and one auction a month is devoted to antiques. Otherwise this is a general auction of household furniture and effects.

The firm also holds special antiques auctions twice a year on Thursdays, at Meerbrook Village Hall, Meerbrook, Leek, Staffordshire.

Congleton

BUYER'S PREMIUM: *10%*
SALES: *Weekly general: Fri or Sat at 10.00am. Monthly antiques: Fri at 5.00pm. Special antiques: twice a year on Thu at 10.00am.*
VIEWING: *All sales: day prior 5.00pm-7.00pm, and one hour before start of sale.*
REFRESHMENTS: *Own café.*
PARKING: *Own car park.*
STORAGE: *Yes*
TRANSPORTATION: *Yes*
SHIPPING: *Yes*

FRANK R MARSHALL

Marshall House, Church Hill. Tel: (0565) 653284

400-600 lots. The saleroom, which is close to the railway station, is a large, red-brick building which was at one time the Egerton School. Sales are held twice a month and usually alternate between general and antiques. Occasionally there is no antiques sale, in which case a second general sale is held. Both types of sale start in the first-floor saleroom with smaller items such as various collectables, silver and jewellery. At around 12.30pm the sale moves to the ground floor for the auctioning of furniture and larger items.

Six miles away at Chelford Agricultural Centre, Chelford, tel: (0625) 861122, Frank R Marshall hold sales of another sort which are full of interest. These are more for the wholesale trade and are devoted to cut flowers and potted plants, shrubs and conifers, potatoes and other vegetables, eggs, dressed poultry and the like — all in a busy day of cattle and sheep selling. Sales are weekly on Monday at 9.15am, Wednesday at 12.00 noon, and Thursday at 10.30am and 7.00pm. A horse and tackle sale is held on the last Friday of the month, with times as follows: saddlery and tack 10.15am; warranted horses and ponies, 12.15pm, followed by unwarranted horses and ponies at 2.00pm. Times may change in March and September sales.

Knutsford

BUYER'S PREMIUM: *10%*
SALES: *Twice monthly on Tue at 10.00am (general sales usually alternate with antiques).*
VIEWING: *General and antiques: day prior 10.00am-6.30pm.*
REFRESHMENTS: *None available on the premises.*
PARKING: *Own car park.*
STORAGE: *No*
TRANSPORTATION: *Yes*
SHIPPING: *No*

Nantwich

BUYER'S PREMIUM: 10%
SALES: *Weekly on Thu at 11.00am (fine art and Victoriana every two months).*
VIEWING: *Day prior 10.00am-4.00pm, day of sale from 9.00am. Fine art: at least two days prior, and day of sale from 9.00am.*
REFRESHMENTS: *Own café.*
PARKING: *Own car park.*
STORAGE: *Vendors only.*
TRANSPORTATION: *Yes*
SHIPPING: *No*

PETER WILSON

Victoria Gallery, Market Street. Tel: (0270) 623878

500 lots. The saleroom is a good conversion from an old school, and is near the town centre, at the rear of the bus station. The auctioneers were formerly known as Henry Spencer & Sons. They now hold weekly sales of household and shipping goods, while catalogued sales of fine art and antiques are held about every two months.

Sandbach

BUYER'S PREMIUM: 10%
SALES: *Weekly on Wed at 10.00am (replaced quarterly by antiques and picture sale).*
VIEWING: *day prior 9.30am-4.30pm.*
REFRESHMENTS: *None available on the premises.*
PARKING: *Ample parking near by.*
STORAGE: *Yes*
TRANSPORTATION: *Yes*
SHIPPING: *Yes*

ANDREW, HILDITCH & SON LTD

Hanover House, The Square. Tel: (0270) 767246

300-500 lots. The saleroom is opposite one of this quaint old town's remarkable landmarks: two Saxon crosses which stand in the market place and are said to mark a royal wedding. The proprietor of the auction is Mr Thomas Spencer Andrew, who started it as a 16-year-old 'one man band' after developing an interest in Old Master paintings. Now his hobby has grown into a thriving business with a reputation far beyond the local area. The weekly sale is of general household furniture and effects, and is replaced at quarterly intervals by special sales of pictures and antiques. There are three separate sales galleries. The general auction begins in the smaller China Room, which holds bric-à-brac, silver, china, jewellery, ornaments and other small items. The sale of general goods and furniture begins in the main gallery, always after 1.00pm. The quarterly sale is held in the first-floor gallery.

Warrington

BUYER'S PREMIUM: *General: nil. Antiques: 10%.*
SALES: *Weekly on Thu at 10.30am; specialist antiques and collectors' sale: Tue and Sat (times vary).*
VIEWING: *Both sales: day prior 10.00am-8.00pm.*
REFRESHMENTS: *Own café.*
PARKING: *Own car park.*
STORAGE: *Yes*

LITTONS (CHESHIRE) LTD

Guardian Street. Tel: (0925) 572199

400-500 lots. The saleroom is on the edge of the town centre, by the rear entrance of Warrington General Hospital. This is an interesting weekly sale of general household furniture and effects, which may include antiques. Specialist sales of antiques and collectors' items take place regularly on Tuesdays and Saturdays. There are over 10,000 sq ft of floor space, divided into two salerooms, making this one of the largest auction areas in the north of England. Only one saleroom is used at a time, while the other is prepared for the next week's sale. The general sale starts with 'white goods', such as dishwashers, refrigerators, spin driers, freezers and so on. Any motor vehicles among the lots are always sold in the middle of the sale, around lunch time. The saleroom is so large than even these are sold under cover. Better quality goods including antiques are kept for the later part of the sale.

CLEVELAND

SANDERSONS AUCTION ROOMS

Andrew Street. Tel: (0429) 275406

200-400 lots. This is a long-established general sale operated by a well-known local firm, Sanderson Removals. In addition to these two activities, the firm has a retail shop where new and second-hand furniture is sold. You go through the shop to get to the auction saleroom. The sale is held once a fortnight, and typically will offer household furniture in a variety of styles, ages and conditions, including upholstered lounge suites and easy chairs, dining room and bedroom suites, kitchen cabinets, dressers and so on. There could also be ornamental and domestic china such as teapots, cups, and porcelain plates, with candlesticks, glass, lamps, children's toys, and books, plus office furniture, hand tools, electrical tools, bicycles and other items.

CLEVELAND AUCTION ROOMS

345 Linthorpe Road. Tel: (0642) 82984

300-350 lots. Proprietor David Lomas and his six helpers run a fortnightly sale from the Linthorpe Road saleroom. This can be very rewarding to attend. As the sales are held on Friday evenings, there are usually plenty of private buyers, as well as browsers, in evidence. The absence of large numbers of dealers at these sales means that it is possible to find bargains at reasonable prices. Although a private buyer can usually afford to pay more for something than a dealer (dealers do, after all, have to consider the resale price of anything they buy, including their expenses and business overheads), dealers nevertheless tend to know the true value of goods. This means that private buyers are less likely to find really good bargains when dealers are present at a sale.

David Lomas usually starts the proceedings by auctioning miscellaneous items in boxes. These may contain books, children's toys and games, china, odd pieces of cutlery and ornaments. There is often a fair amount of china of varying

TRANSPORTATION: *Yes*
SHIPPING: *Yes*

Hartlepool

BUYER'S PREMIUM: *12%*
SALES: *Fortnightly on Sat at 1.00pm.*
VIEWING: *Day prior 10.00am-1.00pm.*
REFRESHMENTS: *Own café.*
PARKING: *Own car park.*
STORAGE: *Yes*
TRANSPORTATION: *Yes*
SHIPPING: *Yes*

Middlesborough

BUYER'S PREMIUM: *10%*
SALES: *Fortnightly on Fri at 6.00pm.*
VIEWING: *Mon-Fri 9.00am-5.00pm.*
REFRESHMENTS: *None available on the premises.*
PARKING: *Ample near by.*
STORAGE: *Yes*
TRANSPORTATION: *Yes*
SHIPPING: *Yes*

quality, as well as silver, brass, jewellery, carpets, rugs and pictures. There are also plenty of collectables, such as old cameras, books and photo albums. The lots may be of any age, and in all types of condition. Cars and outside effects such as gardening equipment are also a part of the sale.

Saltburn-by-the-Sea

BUYER'S PREMIUM: *10%*
SALES: *Weekly on Wed at 9.30am (includes antiques and collectors' sale every six to eight weeks).*
VIEWING: *Sat prior 9.00am-4.00pm, Mon and Tue 9.00am-5.00pm.*
REFRESHMENTS: *None available on the premises but several cafés near by.*
PARKING: *Ample parking near by.*
STORAGE: *Yes*
TRANSPORTATION: *Yes*
SHIPPING: *Yes*

J C SIMMONS & SON

Saltburn Salerooms, Diamond Street. Tel: (0287) 622366

400-450 lots. The saleroom is in the centre of this pleasant seaside town and adjoins the fine old three-storey building which houses the firm's offices. Opposite are the equally large storerooms. The salerooms were established in the 1920s and since 1947 have been run by the Simmons family, John Charles Simmons (now retired) and his son John. It is a very popular, well-attended auction, ideal for those wanting to furnish a house. Decorative china, ornamental items, electrical goods, bicycles, garden equipment and other household effects are sold in the morning session, which finishes at around 12.00 noon. At 1.00pm the sale continues with traditional, reproduction and quality modern furnishings. Every six to eight weeks the general sale is replaced by a special antiques and fine art sale.

Stockton

BUYER'S PREMIUM: *10%*
SALES: *Fortnightly on Tue at 10.00am.*
VIEWING: *Fri, Sat and Mon prior 9.30am-4.30pm.*
REFRESHMENTS: *None available on the premises.*
PARKING: *Swallow Hotel multi-storey car park.*
STORAGE: *Yes*
TRANSPORTATION: *Yes*
SHIPPING: *Yes*

STOCKTON AUCTION ROOMS

17 Bridge Road. Tel: (0642) 607473

400-450 lots. Stockton is an industrial town on the bank of the tidal River Tees. The auction rooms are a minute's walk from the wide High Street, which has been the scene of an open-air market since 1310 (market days are Wednesday and Saturday). This is a pleasant and unintimidating sale. It is well run and has been under the proprietorship of the same family for the past 70 years. There are good buys in all categories of general household furniture and effects, including antiques. The general sale starts with 'smalls': glass, domestic and ornamental china, boxes of assorted bric-à-brac, books, children's toys and so on. A typical sale will also have craft goods and general tools of various kinds, electrical goods, gas appliances and televisions. The selling of furniture always starts at 1.00pm and usually includes some excellent 1930s and 1940s pieces, as well as modern and antique. The auctioneer ends the sale by returning to any 'smalls' that are left. A special sale of antiques and fine art replaces the general sale at irregular intervals, whenever enough lots of particularly high quality have been amassed.

LITHGOW SONS & PARTNERS

The Auction House, Station Road. Tel: (0642) 710158
600-1,000 lots. Lithgow Sons & Partners have been independent auctioneers since 1868 and are one of the largest auctioneers in the county. There is one sale per week, and although this will be well advertised locally, it is usually necessary to contact the auctioneers to find out what type of goods are to be sold. General sales of furniture and household effects are held about every four to six weeks, on Friday at 10.30am. Sales of tools and machinery, including small hand tools for the DIY enthusiast, are held every two to three weeks, on Wednesday at 10.30am. Office furniture and equipment and catering equipment sales occur monthly on average, also on Wednesday, but usually starting at 12.00 noon. Other sales, often of liquidated stock, are held at irregular intervals as the need arises. They usually take place in the saleroom, but occasionally will be held 'on site' — in the actual factory, office or shop which has gone into receivership. These sales could be of anything from brand new clothing to jewellery to boats, and offer excellent bargains. There are also sales of fine wines twice a year in December and June or July, on a Wednesday at 12.00 noon.

Stokesley

BUYER'S PREMIUM: *10%*
SALES: *Weekly on various days at 10.30am or 12.00 noon (ring to check type of goods).*
VIEWING: *Sales starting at 10.30am: day prior 10.00am-4.00pm. Sales starting at 12.00 noon: day of sale from 9.30am.*
REFRESHMENTS: *Own café.*
PARKING: *Own car park.*
STORAGE: *Yes*
TRANSPORTATION: *Yes*
SHIPPING: *Yes*

CORNWALL

ERIC DISTIN CHARTERED SURVEYORS
See ERIC DISTIN CHARTERED SURVEYORS, Plymouth, Devon

Callington

KITTOWS

41 Fore Street. Tel: (0579) 83585
500-600 lots. Situated opposite Callington's imposing parish church, Kittows was established in 1850. Over the years they have gained a well-founded reputation for being a friendly but efficient saleroom: light hearted but well run, with an atmosphere that would certainly not intimidate a new auction-goer. The monthly sales offer all types of goods: antique, period and modern furniture, which includes dining suites, bedroom suites, tables, soft furnishings, bureaux and pine; electrical goods; outside effects; large amounts of bric-à-brac and miscellaneous effects, and garden and hand tools. Some lots go for as little as 50p, while in the same sale a George III mahogany bureau bookcase could fetch £2,000.

Callington

BUYER'S PREMIUM: *Nil*
SALES: *Monthly on Mon at 10.30am.*
VIEWING: *Day of sale from 8.30am.*
REFRESHMENTS: *None available on the premises.*
PARKING: *In centre of town, a few minutes walk away.*
STORAGE: *Yes*
TRANSPORTATION: *Yes*
SHIPPING: *Yes*

Camborne

BUYER'S PREMIUM: 10%
SALES: General: weekly on
Thu at 6.00pm. Antiques and
collectors' items: about every
two months on Sat at 11.00am.
Tools,machinery and marine:
monthly on Sat at 11.00am.
VIEWING: Day of sale from
9.00am.
REFRESHMENTS: Yes.
PARKING: Own car park.
STORAGE: Yes
TRANSPORTATION: Yes
SHIPPING: Yes

Lostwithiel

BUYER'S PREMIUM: 10%
SALES: Weekly, monthly and
three-monthly sales all on Wed
at 10.00am at either the
Lostwithiel or the Wadebridge
salerooms.
VIEWING: Lostwithiel: Tue
10.00am-1.00pm,
2.00pm-4.00pm. Wadebridge:
Mon and Tue 9.00am-
1.00pm, 2.00pm-5.00pm.
REFRESHMENTS: Tea on
the premises.
PARKING: None available
on the premises.
STORAGE: Yes
TRANSPORTATION: Yes
SHIPPING: Yes

Penzance

BUYER'S PREMIUM: 10%
SALES: Antiques: alternate
months at 10.30am, usually on
Tue and Wed. Pictures and
prints: alternate months at
10.30am, usually on Thu.
Specialist collectors' items: twice
a year in spring and autumn on
Fri at 6.30pm and on Sat at
10.30am. Books: twice a year
in spring and autumn on Fri at
6.30pm and Sat at 10.30am.
VIEWING: All sales: Sat
prior 9.30am-12.30pm, day
prior 9.00am-1.00pm,
2.00pm-7.00pm, and morning

MGA AUCTIONS

West Charles Street. Tel: (0209) 711065

300-500 lots. MGA Auctions have been established for many years and are an excellent example of a good country auction. The atmosphere is pleasant, and there seems no limit to the type and variety of goods. There will be quality furniture, paintings, cutlery, crockery and electrical goods, including videos, hi-fis and televisions. Roughly every two months a sale of antiques and collectors' items is held. The monthly sale of tools, machinery, plant and marine items is also popular and well attended.

JEFFERYS

5 Fore Street. Tel: (0208) 872245

1,200 lots. Jefferys were established in 1865, and today they hold popular weekly sales of modern and Victorian household furniture and effects, and other items. Lostwithiel is a picturesque old town, which attracts visitors for its salmon and trout fishing. Jefferys also have premises at The Belmont Auction Rooms, Wadebridge, tel: (0208) 812131. The weekly sales alternate between the Lostwithiel and Wadebridge salerooms. There are sales of antique and oriental furniture, textiles, works of art and ceramics once a month, again alternating between the two premises. The Belmont Auction Rooms at Wadebridge hold three collectors' sales a year, of stamps, postcards and cigarette cards. Wadebridge itself is a clean, bright town, worth visiting for its river scenery and bridge.

W H LANE & SON

65 Morrab Road. Tel: (0736) 61447

More than 1,500 lots. The saleroom is just a few minutes' walk from the promenade and sea front, and is easily recognisable as an ex-Victorian school. A large L-shaped saleroom has been created out of the ground floor, with the second floor used for storage. The sales have a reputation far beyond the borders of Cornwall. There are sales here every month, alternating between antiques and objets d'art one month and pictures and prints the next. There are also twice-yearly book sales and specialist collectors' sales, which could include Dinky toys, coins, medals, railway memorabilia, nautical artefacts and so on.

The sea around Penzance is notorious, and there are special

sales of items brought up from shipwrecks, such as old coins, parts of boats and even the odd cannon. These sales go under titles such as 'Sunken Treasure' and do not occur very often, but are well worth attending. Over the years W H Lane have also built up a reputation for their sales of West Country art, including the Newlyn and St Ives' schools of painting.

DAVID LAY ASVA

The Penzance Auction House, Alverton. Tel: (0736) 61414
1,000-1,500 lots. The monthly Tuesday sale is of general Victorian, good quality modern and reproduction furniture, pine, and household effects. Every eight weeks there is a two-day sale of general antiques, ceramics, silver, jewellery, plated ware, rugs and commemorative ware. Even classic cars sometimes appear for sale. In the two-day sales, furniture usually starts the afternoon session at around 1.30pm on Friday. In addition to these sales there is a three-monthly sale of paintings (mainly Newlyn and St Ives schools).

Twice yearly David Lay holds special sales of collectors' items, including books, coins, stamps, post and cigarette cards, and toys. No one should ever be surprised at what can be bought at David Lay's. A recent sale included an entire late-Victorian conservatory. The conservatory was still attached to a house, and the successful purchaser was responsible for dismantling and removing it.

The saleroom holds the provincial record for a non-art lot: £230,000 for a Georgian bookcase. Not all prices are in these realms, however.

ERIC DISTIN CHARTERED SURVEYORS

See ERIC DISTIN CHARTERED SURVEYORS, Plymouth, Devon

PETER KEMP AUCTIONS

Parish Hall, Ladock. Tel: (0326) 375735
400-500 lots. Cornwall is unusual in that many auctions do not have regular salerooms but move week by week to various parish and church halls around the county. Peter Kemp's sale is one of these — it is most often in Ladock, but check the location in the local press or by telephone. (All correspondence should be sent to the auctioneers at 5 Park Hill, Falmouth.) Vendors can bring in goods right up to the moment of sale, which adds to the excitement. Prices vary greatly, with one lot going for £1, the next for £1,000 and the next for £20. A typical sale will have modern, reproduction,

Penzance

of sale from 8.30am.
REFRESHMENTS: Available on the premises.
PARKING: Unrestricted parking near by.
STORAGE: Yes
TRANSPORTATION: Yes
SHIPPING: Yes

BUYER'S PREMIUM: 10%
SALES: General: monthly on Tue at 10.00am. Antiques: every eight weeks on Thu and Fri at 10.00am. Paintings and prints: every three months on Thu at 10.00am. Collectors' items: twice a year on Tue at 10.00am.
VIEWING: Sat prior 11.00am-4.00pm, day prior 9.00am-7.30pm, day of sale from 8.30am.
REFRESHMENTS: Own café.
PARKING: Large car park.
STORAGE: Yes
TRANSPORTATION: Yes
SHIPPING: Yes

Saltash

Truro

BUYER'S PREMIUM: 10%
SALES: General: fortnightly on Sat at 2.00pm (time varies). Harness and saddlery every three months, usually on Mon at 6.30pm.
VIEWING: General (Sat): morning of sale. General (Thu) and harness and saddlery: day of sale from 2.00pm.
REFRESHMENTS: Own café.
PARKING: Own car park.

STORAGE: *No*
TRANSPORTATION: *Yes*
SHIPPING: *Yes*

Victorian, Edwardian, and Georgian furniture, including a notable amount of pine, plus china, jewellery, general household items and bric-à-brac. The quarterly sales of harness and saddlery include virtually everything to do with horses, from whips and saddles to brasses, books and paintings.

Truro

BUYER'S PREMIUM: 5%
SALES: *Periodically (day varies) at 11.00am.*
VIEWING: *On day of sale — times vary.*
REFRESHMENTS: *Van selling snacks.*
PARKING: *Ample near by.*
STORAGE: *No*
TRANSPORTATION: *No*
SHIPPING: *No*

LODGE & THOMAS

58 Lemon Street. Tel: (0872) 72722

300-500 lots. Truro is a cathedral city and also has a small port at the head of the river. The lots at Lodge & Thomas's sales are either from private sources or from bankrupt stock, ensuring a wide and interesting range of goods. There is no one regular saleroom. The auctions are held at various locations in the Truro area, such as village halls which have been hired especially for the sale — the main venues are the Community Hall at Playing Place, a village near Truro, and Leedstown Village Hall, between Hayle and Helston. The sales cover the entire range of modern, Victorian, reproduction and antique furniture, general household furniture and effects. Miscellaneous items, including gardening equipment and tools, china (both sets and single pieces), ornaments, glass, brass and electrical goods, are also sold. Interesting lots of bric-à-brac and collectables, and catering and office equipment, are also available. These sales are busy and well attended.

Wadebridge

JEFFERYS

See JEFFERYS, Lostwithiel, Cornwall

Wadebridge

LAMBRAYS

Polmorla Walk. Tel: (0208) 813593

BUYER'S PREMIUM: 10%
SALES: *Fortnightly on Mon at 11.00am (includes antiques and fine art sale five times a year, starting 12.00 noon). End of Year Sale: New Year's Eve (or Fri/Mon if at weekend) at 12.00 noon.*
VIEWING: *General: Sat prior 9.00am-12.00 noon, morning of sale from 9.00am. Antiques and fine art: Thu prior 6.30pm-8.30pm, Fri prior 9.00am-5.00pm, morning of sale from 9.00am. End of Year Sale: morning of sale from 9.00am.*
REFRESHMENTS: *Own café.*

400-500 lots. Buying at auction is such a way of life in Cornwall that local people needing an item of household furniture or perhaps a gift for a friend are just as likely to visit an auction as a shop. The Lambrays auctions are particularly good for the odd little gift, because they start with perhaps 200-250 lots of trays of small miscellaneous items. There will usually be something enticing on one of the trays, such as a piece of china, a small ornament or a book. The saleroom is large, around 4,000 sq ft, and is situated in a new shopping complex in the centre of the town. Items in forthcoming sales are displayed in a large window overlooking the street (there are occasionally displays of work by local crafts people and artists here instead).

The fortnightly sale is of general household furniture and

effects, including china, jewellery, paintings and many other items of all ages and values. Around five times a year this sale is devoted to antiques and fine art instead. A particularly popular sale is the 'End of the Year Sale' which is held on New Year's Eve (except when it falls at the weekend, when the sale is on the Friday or Monday). It begins at noon and covers the gambit of modern, antique, Victorian, Edwardian, pine, collectors' items, memorabilia and so on. This sale has become an annual must for locals and visitors over the years.

PARKING: *None available on the premises.*
STORAGE: *Yes*
TRANSPORTATION: *Yes*
SHIPPING: *Yes*

CUMBRIA

HARRISON COWARD
See HARRISON COWARD, Millom, Cumbria

Broughton-in-Furness

CUMBRIA AUCTION ROOMS

12 Lowther Street. Tel: (0228) 25259

500-800 lots. Carlisle is the centre for many remote villages and houses, which is one reason why there are so many excellent auctions in the area. The city is also the seat of a bishop: if time allows, take a look at the cathedral, which has stained glass to rival any at York Minster.

This sale was established in 1876 and is still held close to the original site. The present saleroom is part of an interesting building which was once the Hope & Bendle bottling factory. Past lots in the weekly general sale have included Victorian mahogany desks, wash stands, tables, chests of drawers, Edwardian bedroom suites, deal cupboards, oak bureaux and china cabinets, extending tables, Victorian day beds and cane chairs, plus electrical goods, china and glass, metalwork, silver plate, pictures and prints, carpets and soft furnishings.

About every eight to ten weeks the general sale is replaced by a catalogued sale of antiques. Items in this sale in the past have ranged from oak, Georgian and Victorian furniture to 19th- and 20th-century paintings, ceramics, silver, jewellery and collector's items.

Carlisle

BUYER'S PREMIUM: *General: Nil. Antiques: 10%*
SALES: *Weekly on Mon at 10.00am (includes catalogued antiques sale every eight to ten weeks).*
VIEWING: *Fri prior 9.00am-5.00pm, Sat prior 9.00am-12.00 noon.*
REFRESHMENTS: *Cellar café.*
PARKING: *Civic Centre public car park.*
STORAGE: *Yes*
TRANSPORTATION: *Yes*
SHIPPING: *Yes*

ROBERT DALTON & SONS LTD

Daltons Mart, Botchergate. Tel: (0228) 21102

600-700 lots. This auction has been established for over 100 years, and has become something of a local institution. The weekly sales generally have a wide range of goods and are enormously popular and entertaining. The Saturday sale

Carlisle

BUYER'S PREMIUM: *Nil*
SALES: *General: weekly on Sat at 9.30am. Timber and building equipment: weekly on Fri at 1.00pm.*

begins with an assortment of miscellaneous items, which might include bicycles, general tools, work benches, gardening equipment and machinery, household electrical equipment such as washing machines and refrigerators, sinks, panel doors, ladders and heaters. Around lunch time, depending on the number of lots in the first section, the sale generally continues with specialist sales in various categories such as antiques, office furniture, marine objects, horse tack, vintage plant, plant and machinery, and so on. There is also a weekly Friday sale of timber and various building equipment, which might include slates, gates, boards and beams, and is ideal for the DIY enthusiast. Every two or three weeks throughout the growing season there are also Wednesday sales of bulbs and shrubs, starting at 1.00pm. Sales of dressed and oven-ready poultry are held on the Wednesday, Thursday and Friday nearest to Christmas, at 12.00 noon.

VIEWING: *General: day prior 3.00pm-5.00pm, day of sale from 8.00am. Others: day of sale from 8.00am.*
REFRESHMENTS: *Van selling snacks.*
PARKING: *Tait Street public car park.*
STORAGE: *No*
TRANSPORTATION: *Yes*
SHIPPING: *Yes*

Carlisle

BUYER'S PREMIUM: *Nil*
SALES: *Weekly on Thu at 10.30am (includes periodic catalogue sale of antiques and collectors' items).*
VIEWING: *Day prior 9.00am-5.00pm.*
REFRESHMENTS: *Own café.*
PARKING: *Own car park.*
STORAGE: *Yes*
TRANSPORTATION: *Yes*
SHIPPING: *Yes*

HARRISON & HETHERINGTON LTD

Borderway Mart, Rosehill. Tel: (0228) 26292

300-400 lots. The weekly sale takes place in the Rosehill Furniture Hall within the Borderway Mart, a very large complex which houses livestock sales during the week. It is outside the city centre, close to Junction 43 of the M6. This is a good location for an auction, and a good auction is what it is. The popular and well-run general sale offers a wide and varied range of modern household furniture and effects, which may include 1930s and 1940s pieces, cottage furniture, reproductions, curios and bygones, china, ornaments and so on. Periodically the general sale is replaced by special catalogue sales of antiques, curios and collectors' items.

Carlisle

THOMSON, RODDICK & LAURIE
See THOMSON, RODDICK & LAURIE, Wigton, Cumbria

Cartmel

BUYER'S PREMIUM: *£1 per lot.*
SALES: *Monthly on Fri at 10.00am.*
VIEWING: *Day prior 2.00pm-5.00pm.*
REFRESHMENTS: *Available near by.*
PARKING: *Ample parking near by.*

HACKNEY & LEIGH

The Village Hall. Tel: (05395) 33316

400-500 lots. Hackney & Leigh is one of the largest independent auctioneers in the area, holding periodic sales in various Lake District locations but principally at Cartmel. Cartmel is two miles west of Grange-over-Sands, and is rather like a cathedral city in miniature, with a fine old priory church. The village hall is a couple of minutes' walk away. Plenty of china and porcelain, glass, bric-à-brac, good quality household items and a selection of antiques are included in most sales.

Typical sales in the past have included antiques and period furniture, collections of pictures, china, porcelain and cut glass, brass lamps and horse brasses, chairs, clocks, books, jewellers' silver and gold, electrical equipment, garden tools and furniture, carpets and so on. Sales of shop and hotel contents and other specialities are held regularly.

STORAGE: *Yes*
TRANSPORTATION: *Yes*
SHIPPING: *Yes*

MITCHELLS

The Furniture and Fine Art Hall, Station Street.
Tel: (0900) 822016 and 827800

Cockermouth

500-600 lots. Cockermouth is famous as the birthplace of William Wordsworth, and the house in which he was born is kept by the National Trust as a place of literary pilgrimage. The saleroom is an impressive Victorian building in the centre of the town, directly opposite the cattle market. The same firm is also responsible for livestock sales, which are held on Monday and Wednesday. Within the saleroom an octagonal sale ring displays 'smalls' such as china, porcelain, glass, silver and plated ware. Larger items in the general sale might include dining room and bedroom suites, wardrobes, occasional tables, and three-piece suites. Also to be found are paintings and other pictures, mirrors, bed and table linen and other soft goods, carpets, rugs, electrical goods, kitchen utensils and gardening tools. There will usually be some antiques, but particularly good items are kept back for the special antiques sales which replace the general sale about every six to eight weeks.

BUYER'S PREMIUM:
Antiques: 10%. Others: nil
SALES: *Weekly on Thu at 10.00am.*
VIEWING: *Day prior 2.30pm-4.30pm, morning of sale from 9.00am.*
REFRESHMENTS: *Own café.*
PARKING: *Public car park near by.*
STORAGE: *Yes*
TRANSPORTATION: *Yes*
SHIPPING: *No*

JAMES THOMPSON

64 Main Street. Tel: (05242) 71555

Kirkby Lonsdale

1,200-1,300 lots. There are two James Thompson sales in the town. The monthly two-day antiques and fine art sale takes place in a clearly marked saleroom behind the post office. The sale of pictures is held every two months, in the Royal Barn in New Road. Both rooms are well-known local landmarks and the sales attract buyers from a wide area, including many from Scotland.

The antiques sale is usually on the first Wednesday and Thursday of the month. Up for auction on the first day are silver and plate, jewellery, brass, copper and other metalware, glass and china. The second day is devoted to books, prints, rugs, furniture and miscellaneous items, which can include almost anything that is old: musical instruments, cameras, telescopes, tinplate toys, old games and dolls. Clocks of all types, including grandfather clocks, are always sold at 1.30pm.

The picture sale is also held on a Wednesday but is usually

BUYER'S PREMIUM: *Nil*
SALES: *Antiques: monthly on first Wed and Thu of month at 9.30am. Pictures: every two months on Wed at 9.30am.*
VIEWING: *Day prior 9.30am-3.00pm.*
REFRESHMENTS: *None available on the premises.*
PARKING: *Ample parking near by.*
STORAGE: *No*
TRANSPORTATION: *Yes*
SHIPPING: *Yes*

towards the end of the month. There may be some 300-350 lots of paintings and other pictures in this sale.

Millom

HARRISON COWARD

St George's Hall, Lapstone Road. Tel: (0229) 772314

200-300 lots. St George's Hall, which is hired for the sale, is just down the road from the company's office at 24 Lapstone Road, and next door to an infants' school. There are numerous old country houses in the area, and the sale often has good country furniture, including antiques and various interesting household and personal effects such as photograph albums, old toys, dolls and so on.

In addition to the Millom sale, Harrison Coward also hold monthly general sales at the County Auction Rooms, County Square, Ulverston, tel: (0229) 52056, and at Victory Hall, Broughton-in-Furness (same telephone number). The Ulverston sale tends to involve the contents of complete house clearances, while individual vendors are more likely to bring items to the Broughton-in-Furness sale. All the goods put in for auction by one vendor are given the same number, which makes it difficult to judge how many individual lots are for sale. However, it is a system which keeps buyers on their toes during the proceedings.

BUYER'S PREMIUM: *Nil*
SALES: *Millom: every six weeks on Wed. Ulverston: monthly on Tue. Broughton-in-Furness: Tue or Wed. All at 10.30am.*
VIEWING: *Millom: day prior 2.00pm-7.00pm. Ulverston: day prior 10.00am-4.00pm. Broughton-in-Furness: day prior 2.00pm-5.00pm.*
REFRESHMENTS: *Millom: own café. Others: none available on the premises.*
PARKING: *All: ample parking available.*
STORAGE: *All: yes*
TRANSPORTATION: *All: yes*
SHIPPING: *All: yes*

Penrith

PENRITH FARMERS & KIDDS PLC

The Castlegate Saleroom, Castlegate. Tel: (0768) 890781

600-800 lots. The ancient town of Penrith is the gateway to the Lake District from the north, and owes much of its turbulent history to the fact that the visiting Scots were not always as friendly as they are now. Today quite a few Scots regularly find their way to these sales. The saleroom is a large Victorian building near the railway station. The weekly Wednesday sales are devoted to general household furniture and effects, such as modern furniture in all styles, cottage and reproduction furniture, jewellery, ornaments, china, toys, tools, machinery and bicycles.

Once a month this general sale is replaced by a collective sale of antiques, Victoriana and shipping goods (as well as 1930s and 1940s items). This sale can also include 18th and 19th-century and later furniture, and other articles from these periods.

BUYER'S PREMIUM: *Nil*
SALES: *Weekly on Wed at 9.30am (includes monthly collective sale of antiques).*
VIEWING: *Day prior 3.30pm-6.00pm.*
REFRESHMENTS: *Available near by.*
PARKING: *Ample parking near by.*
STORAGE: *Yes*
TRANSPORTATION: *Yes*
SHIPPING: *Yes*

MICHAEL C L HODGSON

The Memorial Hall. Tel: (0539) 721375

300-450 lots. The sale is to be found about a mile from the M6 at Junction 36. The general sale includes antique and reproduction furniture as well as good quality household furniture and effects. Items sold in past sales have included cane chairs, dining suites of various types, bedroom and lounge furniture, mirrors, china, glass, silver and plate, jewellery (including costume jewellery), various electrical goods such as vacuum cleaners, kettles and cookers, curtains, bed linen, pictures, and some collectable items like cigarette card and postcard albums.

The best items are put into special sales of antiques, which are held in place of the general sale whenever enough high quality goods have been gathered.

Preston Patrick, near Kendal

BUYER'S PREMIUM: *Nil*
SALES: *Monthly on Wed at 12.00 noon (includes periodic antiques sale).*
VIEWING: *Morning of sale from 9.00am.*
REFRESHMENTS: *None available on the premises.*
PARKING: *Ample parking available.*
STORAGE: *Yes*
TRANSPORTATION: *Yes*
SHIPPING: *Yes*

HARRISON COWARD

See HARRISON COWARD, Millom, Cumbria

Ulverston

HOPE'S AUCTION CO LTD

93 High Street. Tel: (06973) 42202

500-600 lots. Wigton is an attractive little town with a fine 18th-century church and an interesting fountain. The saleroom, a large brick building, stands on the Cockermouth side of the town. This is a very local auction in the sense that it is popular with many people in the area and attracts a great many regulars (most of whom come to look, rather than buy). Over the years Hope's has also become a favourite meeting-place for friends.

These sales contain a whole range of items — from antiques and quality furniture and collectors' items to more run-of-the-mill lots from house clearances. The latter may include bicycles, lawnmowers, wheelbarrows and other gardening tools. Potential buyers should note that all the items supplied by one vendor will be allocated the same lot number. This can make bidding a little confusing at times, but it also adds to the interest of the sale.

Wigton

BUYER'S PREMIUM: *Nil*
SALES: *Monthly on Mon at 10.30am.*
VIEWING: *Day of sale from 9.30am.*
REFRESHMENTS: *Own café.*
PARKING: *Own car park.*
STORAGE: *Yes*
TRANSPORTATION: *Yes*
SHIPPING: *Yes*

THOMSON, RODDICK & LAURIE

25 King Street. Tel: (06973) 43348

200-300 lots. The monthly Friday sale is of general household furniture and effects. About every three months, again on a Friday, there is a sale of antiques, fine art and collectors' items.

Special fine art sales which include oil paintings,

Wigton

BUYER'S PREMIUM: *10% (selected sales).*
SALES: *Wigton (general): monthly on Fri at 10.30am. Wigton (antiques): quarterly on*

watercolours and prints, silver, silver plate and jewellery, are held quarterly at the Swallow Hilltop Hotel, Carlisle. The hotel is on the A6 between the M6 at Junction 42 and the city centre. Thomson Roddick & Laurie also hold regular auctions in Dumfries and Annan in Scotland, and have a department specialising in book sales.

For information on all Thomson, Roddick & Laurie's sales except those in Wigton, contact the firm's office at 24 Lowther Street, Carlisle, tel: (0228) 28939.

DERBYSHIRE

NEALES

The Derby Salerooms, Becket Street. Tel: (0332) 43286

300-500 lots. Neales are Chartered Surveyors, Fine Art Auctioneers and Valuers founded in 1840. Their Derby saleroom is an attractive, double-fronted building in the centre of the city. Neales' fortnightly Tuesday general sales are uncatalogued and include English and Continental furniture, selected reproduction furnishings, clocks, metalwork, paintings, drawings, prints, books, ceramics, glass, Art Nouveau and Art Deco.

'Derbyshire Sales', which are devoted to particular themes and have catalogued lots, take place four times a year, again on Tuesdays. These sales usually include 300-400 lots of fine paintings, drawings and prints, Derby porcelain, European and Oriental ceramics, silver, furniture and collectors' items. Like many other auctioneers, Neales also organise 'Discovery Mornings' at which experts are on hand to identify and value items brought in by the public. In the Derby saleroom these are held every Wednesday, from 9.00am to 11.00am.

RICHARDSON & LINNELL

The Cattle Market, Chequers Road. Tel: (0332) 296369

500-600 lots. The sales take place in the Cattle Market, a massive 10-acre complex just off the A52 between Derby and Nottingham. They are excellent general sales with an established following locally. Usually there are around 70 lots of antiques, plus about 200 lots of jewellery, pictures and prints, collectables and china, which include plenty of Crown Derby. The boxes of miscellaneous items are always worth rummaging through, and goods sold as liquidated stock are also possible sources of bargains, ranging from cookers to clothing. Unclaimed police lost property can also be a good source of finds. If you are interested in general household furniture and effects you will find plenty to interest you at these entertaining sales.

REFRESHMENTS: *Mobile van.*
PARKING: *Own car park.*
STORAGE: *Yes*
TRANSPORTATION: *Yes*
SHIPPING: *Yes*

BURY & HILTON
See BURY & HILTON, Leek, Staffordshire

Osmaston, near Ashbourne

ARMSTRONG'S AUCTIONS

Swadlincote

Aults Industrial Estate, Midland Road. Tel: (0283) 550326
300-400 lots. Until recently this auction travelled around nearby villages and was held in various village halls. Then a permanent home was found in the small complex of industrial buildings in the centre of Swadlincote. John Walker, the auctioneer, has been wielding the hammer for over 20 years and the firm has been in existence for over 40. The sale has become a meeting place for old friends, and there is plenty of cheerful banter, with many of the 'audience' known to the auctioneer by Christian name. Typical lots might be galvanised corn bins, circular saws and garden urns, with the occasional piece of high-quality furniture, fine jewellery or porcelain waiting to be discovered among more run-of-the-mill lots.

BUYER'S PREMIUM: *Nil*
SALES: *Weekly on Wed at 11.00am.*
VIEWING: *Day prior 2.30pm-4.30pm, morning of sale from 9.00am.*
REFRESHMENTS: *Own café.*
PARKING: *Own car park.*
STORAGE: *Yes*
TRANSPORTATION: *Yes*
SHIPPING: *Yes*

DEVON

MICHAEL J BOWMAN

Chudleigh

The Town Hall. Tel: (0626) 872890
350-400 lots. Mr Bowman hires the Town Hall at Chudleigh specially for his auctions, which usually take place on Mondays. He prides himself on offering a personal service to buyers and vendors, and he is usually on hand to discuss the lots and to give advice at the viewing and on the day of the sale (prior to the beginning of the auction). Each sale is accompanied by a colour catalogue. There is often a mix of good quality items in these sales, ranging from antique and reproduction furniture to china, glass, porcelain, paintings, jewellery and so on. The auction usually begins with ceramics and glass, and ends with furniture.

BUYER'S PREMIUM: *10%*
SALES: *On average monthly on Mon (days can vary) at 2.00pm.*
VIEWING: *Day prior 4.30pm-8.00pm.*
REFRESHMENTS: *None available on the premises.*
PARKING: *Ample near by.*
STORAGE: *Yes*
TRANSPORTATION: *Yes*
SHIPPING: *Yes*

Dartmouth

BUYER'S PREMIUM: 5%
SALES: *Fortnightly on Thu at
11.00am (includes antiques and
collectables sale in Feb, May and
Oct).*
VIEWING: *General: day prior
9.00am-5.00pm. Antiques:
three days prior 9.00am-5.00pm.*
REFRESHMENTS: *None
available on the premises.*
PARKING: *None available on
the premises.*
STORAGE: *Yes*
TRANSPORTATION: *Yes*
SHIPPING: *Yes*

FULFORDS (incorporating LETCHER & SCORER)

9 South Embankment. Tel: (0803) 832223

500-600 lots. Mrs Daphne Scorer has been the auctioneer in this saleroom for 30 years. She likes to keep the atmosphere light-hearted, and tries to make the sales a good day out for the would-be buyers.

The location of the saleroom is a wonderful asset: Dartmouth is one of the most picturesque towns in Britain, and the saleroom stands directly on the waterfront. Daphne Scorer sees the auctioneer's challenge as ensuring that both buyer and vendor are satisfied with the prices reached. If the sale price is too low vendors will be reluctant to place goods in future sales, but if it's too high buyers will be put off. We have a good balance here, which reflects the interests of both parties. The auctions are well attended, and usually offer plenty of interesting household furniture, effects and bric-à-brac.

Special sales of antiques and collectables are also held in October, February and May. These are larger than the general sales and usually include around 700 lots. The times of sale remain the same as for the general sale, although there is extended viewing.

Exeter

BUYER'S PREMIUM: 10%
SALES: *Okehampton Street:
general weekly on Fri at
10.30am; Specialist: twice
monthly on Thu at 10.30am.
Queens Road: fortnightly on
Wed at 10.30am.*
VIEWING: *General: day prior
9.00am-5.30pm. Specialist:
2.30pm-5.30pm.*
REFRESHMENTS: *Own
café.*
PARKING: *Ample parking
near by.*
STORAGE: *Yes*
TRANSPORTATION: *Yes*
SHIPPING: *Yes*

WHITTON & LAING

32 Okehampton Street. Tel: (0392) 52621

400-500 lots. Whitton & Laing have two salerooms in Exeter. The Okehampton Street saleroom has weekly Friday sales of general household furniture and effects, plus two special Thursday auctions each month. One of these special sales is of antiques; the other may be of pictures and carpets, or silver and jewellery.

About once every six months there will also be special sales of coins and medals, and of books. No general sale is held during weeks with a specialist sale.

The other saleroom is Queens Road Auctions, Queens Road, Exeter, tel: (0392) 56256, which has fortnightly sales of general household furniture and effects. These may include bankrupt stock. On a typical day the saleroom will be set out with chairs and three-piece suites, tables displaying china, bric-à-brac and so on, but the complete contents and stock of a shop or company that has gone out of business could also be up for sale.

BONHAMS WEST COUNTRY

Dowell Street. Tel: (0404) 41872

400-500 lots. Dowell Street is on the road to Cullompton, a short distance from the town centre. There is one two-day sale a month at Bonham's large saleroom complex. Usually on the last Thursday of the month there is a general auction of Victorian, Edwardian and modern household furniture and other goods, ranging from electric cookers to wardrobes, china and even step ladders. This takes place in the downstairs saleroom. On the last Friday of the month the upstairs saleroom is the setting for a sale of furniture and works of art in the morning, followed by silver and jewellery in the afternoon (or ceramics, rugs, paintings, watercolours and prints in the afternoon on alternate months). Specialist sales also take place on a regular basis: categories include oil paintings, silver and jewellery, art in the West Country, toys and fishing equipment.

Honiton

BUYER'S PREMIUM: *10%*
SALES: *Monthly on the last Thu and Fri of the month at 11.00am.*
VIEWING: *Day prior 9.00am-5.00pm (and sometimes Sat prior 10.00am-1.00pm).*
REFRESHMENTS: *Own café.*
PARKING: *Car park next door.*
STORAGE: *Yes*
TRANSPORTATION: *Yes*
SHIPPING: *Yes*

TAYLORS

Honiton Galleries, 205 High Street. Tel: (0404) 42404

300-500 lots. Honiton consists mainly of one long street, with a number of pleasant Georgian houses. The Honiton Galleries are set at the lower end of the High Street. They were once an old cinema and the building is easily recognisable, with its four yellow Art Deco arches.

Auctions take place here every three or four weeks and are of two alternating types. (Both are of rather up-market items, however.) The first is a general sale with antiques, furniture, clocks, silver, china and porcelain, copper and brass, plus Art Nouveau, Art Deco and other collectable items. The second auction is a specialist sale, devoted to pictures and consisting of oil paintings, watercolours and prints.

Honiton

BUYER'S PREMIUM: *10%*
SALES: *Every three to four weeks on Thu at 11.00am.*
VIEWING: *Day prior 9.00am-5.00pm.*
REFRESHMENTS: *Snack bar.*
PARKING: *Own car park.*
STORAGE: *Yes*
TRANSPORTATION: *Yes*
SHIPPING: *Yes*

KINGSBRIDGE AUCTION SALES

Market Hall, 85 Fore Street. Tel: (0548) 856829

600-700 lots. Kingsbridge is a busy market town at the head of the tidal estuary extending up from Salcombe. It is an ideal area for fishing, sailing and windsurfing, and many of the lots in the sale reflect these activities. Kingsbridge is also the main centre for many villages, and as most of the lots come from private vendors, this ensures there is always an interesting range of articles. The furniture will include modern, Victorian, reproduction and antique, in all conditions and of all values. There is usually a good selection of carpets, electrical goods and, best of all, miscellanea, which could

Kingsbridge

BUYER'S PREMIUM: *5%*
SALES: *Monthly on Thu at 10.00am (includes quarterly antiques and fine arts sale, usually Mar, Jun, Sep and Dec).*
VIEWING: *Wed prior, 9.00am-4.30pm.*
REFRESHMENTS: *None available on the premises.*
PARKING: *None available on the premises.*
STORAGE: *Yes*
TRANSPORTATION: *Yes*
SHIPPING: *Yes*

include a collection of walking sticks or handbags, a box of dolls' furniture or dolls, an old Monopoly set or perhaps a camera. Four times a year, usually in March, June, September and December, special antiques and fine art sales are held in place of the general sale.

Modbury

BUYER'S PREMIUM: 5%
SALES: *Irregular intervals on Wed at 10.30am.*
VIEWING: *Day prior 1.00pm-7.00pm.*
REFRESHMENTS: *Own café.*
PARKING: *Public car park opposite.*
STORAGE: *Yes*
TRANSPORTATION: *Yes*
SHIPPING: *No*

FIELDENS CHARTERED SURVEYORS

South Hams Auction Rooms, Poundwell Square.
Tel: (0548) 830494

600-700 lots. Modbury is a small town on the main Plymouth to Kingsbridge road, the A379. There are three salerooms, in a building converted from an old factory in the centre of town, opposite the main car park. The sale usually begins in the saleroom which holds outside items, such as gardening equipment, lawn mowers and hand tools. Smaller lots such as china, ornaments, pottery, ceramics, books and so on are displayed on shelves in the central saleroom. The main saleroom has the furniture, which ranges from antique to modern. Like many other country auctioneers Fieldens also conduct outside sales, which may take place in a house, factory or store. There are no regular dates for these sales, but it is worth ringing to check if any are coming up.

Newport

BUYER'S PREMIUM: 10%
SALES: *Days and times vary; check first.*
VIEWING: *Days and times vary; check with the auctioneers.*
REFRESHMENTS: *None available on the premises.*
PARKING: *None available on the premises.*
STORAGE: *Yes*
TRANSPORTATION: *Yes*
SHIPPING: *Yes*

SOUTH STREET AUCTIONS

South Street. Tel: (0271) 78858 and 850337

250-300 lots. The saleroom is a two-storey building with a pleasant public house — The Rose and Crown — next door, to which bidders flock at suitable intervals on sale days. In 1990 David Watts took over the company, which has grown from strength to strength. There are two regular sales a month; one of antiques and collectables, in the evening, and the other of general, household and leisure goods, which takes place in the morning. The offices are open seven days a week, from 10.00am to 12.00 noon, for those wishing to make enquiries, and they are usually busy.

Newton Abbot

BUYER'S PREMIUM:
General: 5%. Boat auctions: Nil
SALES: *General: about 30 a year on Thu (occasionally Tue) at 10.00am. Boat auctions: usually in Apr, May and Oct, on Sat at 9.00am.*
VIEWING: *General: day*

CHERRY'S AUCTION ROOMS

Newton Abbot Racecourse. Tel: (0626) 56489

400-1,000 lots. Cherry's Auction Rooms hold about 30 auctions a year, mostly on Thursdays but occasionally Tuesdays. The sales are of general household furniture and effects of all periods, and often include commercial goods as well, such as the complete contents of a shop. Cherry's also hold celebrated boat auctions, usually in April and May and then again in October. These sales include everything to do with boats and boating, such as dinghies, engines, chandlery, trailers and so on. Some of the sales are held at The Racecourse, Newton Abbot, while others take place on Shaldon Beach, at the tip of the Teign estuary. There is a real carnival atmosphere at these sales, with the lots set out on the beach and on the pavement alongside. The auction starts at 9.00am, but it is wise to get there before 8.30am.

MID DEVON AUCTIONS

2 Market Street. Tel: (0837) 52594

1,400-1,500 lots. Mr and Mrs R Crabtree have been the proprietors of Mid Devon Auctions, which was first established in 1925, for over 16 years. They have built it up into possibly the largest one-day auction of antiques and general goods in the county. It has a tremendous reputation and quite a following among local dealers, private buyers and casual browsers. Up to 700 people have been known to visit the saleroom in one day.

Auctions typically follow a set pattern. In the morning the auctioneers will sell off smaller items such as brass, china, gold, silver and pottery. Then, at about two or three o'clock in the afternoon, the remaining lots come under the hammer. One auctioneer will sell off antique and better quality items, while another takes bids for general goods such as electric cookers, gardening equipment and other outside effects. These sales appeal to anyone looking for a good day out.

AUSTINS

5 Curledge Street. Tel: (0803) 557112

700-800 lots. The saleroom is a large building close to the town's main bus centre. Different rooms are used for various parts of the auction. The sale is advertised as 'Victorian and Modern', and practically anything can be bought, from a grandfather clock to a box of assorted china, from a Welsh dresser to Victorian glass goblets, from a Royal Doulton baluster vase to a step ladder or bicycle. The auctions start in the upstairs saleroom with linen, bedding and bedroom suites, followed by a break at around 12.15pm for lunch. At 2.15pm the selling begins again in the yard with outside effects such as lawn mowers, gardening tools and bikes. The auctioneer and crowd then move into the Vestibule for the sale of cookers, refrigerators and general kitchen equipment. The auction ends in Saleroom B with antiques and paintings.

---

prior 11.00am-4.00pm, morning of sale. Boat auctions: morning of sale.
REFRESHMENTS: *Van selling snacks.*
PARKING: *Own car park.*
STORAGE: Yes
TRANSPORTATION: Yes
SHIPPING: Yes

Okehampton

BUYER'S PREMIUM: 10%
SALES: *Monthly on Wed at 10.30am.*
VIEWING: *Day prior 2.00pm-7.30pm, morning of sale from 9.00am.*
REFRESHMENTS: *Own café.*
PARKING: *Own car park.*
STORAGE: Yes
TRANSPORTATION: Yes
SHIPPING: Yes

Paignton

BUYER'S PREMIUM: 10%
SALES: *Fortnightly on Thu at 10.00am.*
VIEWING: *Day prior 9.30am-7.00pm.*
REFRESHMENTS: *Own café.*
PARKING: *Ample car parking near by.*
STORAGE: Yes
TRANSPORTATION: Yes
SHIPPING: Yes

Paignton

BUYER'S PREMIUM: 10%
SALES: *Fortnightly on Tue at 10.00am.*
VIEWING: *Day prior 9.00am-6.00pm.*
REFRESHMENTS: *None available on the premises.*
PARKING: *Public car park about 20 yards away.*
STORAGE: *Yes*
TRANSPORTATION: *Yes*
SHIPPING: *Yes*

D T BEESLEY

262 Torquay Road. Tel: (0803) 522222

500-600 lots. Paignton is a flourishing seaside resort, where the resident population of around 30,000 is easily doubled at the peak of the holiday season. The auction has a loyal local following, but the summer influx is easy to see at the sales. D T Beesley is a family firm, established for over 50 years, and their saleroom is in the Preston area, just out of the town centre. The sales are mixed and include both modern and antique items, with occasional reminders that the area is known for fishing and boating. There is no regular order of sale: a large and valuable item of furniture might be followed by a cheap box of china or a pile of local interest books. This haphazard method keeps prospective buyers on their toes, and some people find it helps them to focus on articles they missed during the viewing.

Plymouth

BUYER'S PREMIUM: *Nil*
SALES: *General: weekly on Sat at 10.30am (location varies between all three branches in Devon and Cornwall). Furniture: fortnightly on Fri at 10.30am (in lower floor Plymouth saleroom). Antiques: monthly on Sat at 10.30am. Coins, stamps and medals: monthly on Mon at 6.00pm.*
VIEWING: *Day of sale from 9.00am, except coins, stamps and medals sales: day of sale 4.00pm-6.00pm*
REFRESHMENTS: *None available on the premises.*
PARKING: *Public car parks near each branch.*
STORAGE: *Yes*
TRANSPORTATION: *Yes*
SHIPPING: *Yes*

ERIC DISTIN CHARTERED SURVEYORS

2 Bretonside. Tel: (0752) 663046

200-500 lots. The auctioneers have premises in Plymouth, but also in Saltash and Callington, and their weekly general Saturday sales rotate between all three salerooms. Plymouth is the main venue, though, as it has two salerooms where there are regular fortnightly sales of general furniture on Fridays (in the lower saleroom), and a monthly Saturday sale of antiques (on the first floor). The first-floor Plymouth saleroom is also the setting for a monthly Monday night collectors' sale of coins, stamps and medals. The Saltash saleroom is at 54 Fore Street, tel: (0752) 843768. The Callington premises, at 7 New Road, tel: (0579) 83322, are close to a public car park. All three branches attract regulars to their sales.

Plymouth

BUYER'S PREMIUM: 5%
SALES: *General: weekly on Wed at 10.00am. Antiques and fine art: every two or three weeks on Wed at 1.30pm (after general sale).*
VIEWING: *Day prior 9.00am-5.00pm.*

G S SHOBROOK & CO

20 Western Approach. Tel: (0752) 663341

300-600 lots. The G S Shobrook sale is popular with locals and those travelling into town from nearby villages, with many people popping briefly into the saleroom during a day's shopping to see if there is anything they want. The weekly sale includes a fine array of general household furniture and effects, gardening tools and equipment, china of all types, brass, ornaments, bric-à-brac, kitchenalia, paintings, mirrors and so on. The sale finishes around 12.30pm as a rule, but every two or three weeks it continues after lunch with antiques and fine art. There are good bargains to be had in both sales. The saleroom is in the centre of the city in a large new complex on two floors: the ground floor is the home of the general sale, and the first floor is used for the antiques. Just across the road is an enclosed market packed with stalls selling clothes, fruit and vegetables, antiques, bric-à-brac and local crafts.

REFRESHMENTS: *None available on the premises.*
PARKING: *None available on the premises.*
STORAGE: *Yes*
TRANSPORTATION: *Yes*
SHIPPING: *Yes*

Seaton

LYME BAY AUCTION GALLERIES

Harbour Road. Tel: (0297) 22453

700-1,000 lots. Seaton is a small, pleasant resort with a shingle beach and a long Esplanade. The saleroom can be found directly opposite Lyme Bay Holiday Village, and, as might be imagined, the saleroom is particularly busy during the holiday season. Auctions of antique and collectors' items take place on two floors. The lots on the ground floor are lesser-quality items, and they are sold at the beginning of the day. At around midday the auction moves upstairs to the first-floor saleroom, where antiques are up for bidding. Throughout the year (but at no set intervals) sales are held within specialist categories, such as paintings, memorabilia and coins. Visitors to past auctions have been offered a whole host of goods, from fridges and soft furnishings to tools, windsurfing boards and cars.

BUYER'S PREMIUM: 10%
SALES: *Monthly on Mon at 10.00am.*
VIEWING: *Thu prior 9.00am-8.00pm, Fri prior 9.00am-5.00pm, Sat and Sun prior 10.00am-4.00pm.*
REFRESHMENTS: Yes.
PARKING: *Own car park.*
STORAGE: Yes
TRANSPORTATION: Yes
SHIPPING: Yes

Sidmouth

POTBURYS

Temple Street. Tel: (0395) 515555

600-700 lots. The auction room is close to the town centre at the junction of Winslade Road and Temple Street. There are sales every two to three weeks, and a good selection of general and antique household furniture and effects is usually offered. A special auction of antique and reproduction furniture replaces the general sale several times a year. Most auctions take place over two days (Wednesday and Thursday), but if a sale only lasts one day it takes place on a Thursday. The Wednesday part of the sale starts at 2.00pm, and linen, bedding, carpets and garden tools are sold. The bulk of the sale is on Thursday, though, when all kinds of goods, including furniture, are sold from 10.30am.

BUYER'S PREMIUM: 10%
SALES: *General: every two to three weeks on Wed at 2.00pm and Thu at 10.30am (or on Thu only at 10.30am). Antique and reproduction furniture: several times a year (replaces general sale) on Wed at 2.30pm and Thu at 10.30am (or on Thu only at 10.30am).*
VIEWING: *All sales: first day of sale from 9.00am (or day prior from 9.00am if sale is on Thu only).*
REFRESHMENTS: *None available on the premises.*
PARKING: *Own car park.*
STORAGE: Yes
TRANSPORTATION: Yes
SHIPPING: Yes

Tavistock

BUYER'S PREMIUM: 10%
SALES: Fortnightly on Thu at 10.00am.
VIEWING: Wed prior 1.00pm-6.00pm.
REFRESHMENTS: Café adjoining saleroom.
PARKING: Public car parks near by.
STORAGE: No
TRANSPORTATION: Yes
SHIPPING: Yes

WARD & CHOWEN

Tavistock Auction Rooms, Market Road. Tel: (0822) 612603

400-500 lots. With a population of around 10,000 people, Tavistock is an ancient market town set astride the River Tavy. Tavistock's Goose Fair, held on the second Wednesday of October, attracts visitors from afar, and so do the sales of general household furniture and effects held by Ward & Chowen in the Tavistock Auction Rooms. The saleroom, an old, attractive building that was at one time a meat warehouse, is part of the Pannier Market complex. Auctioning is a way of life for many in the West Country, and the sales provide a popular venue. They are also fascinating to visitors from other parts of the UK and abroad.

Ward & Chowen are also auctioneers at the town's cattle market. Sales are held every Friday and on the second Wednesday in every month (except December and February).

Teignmouth

BUYER'S PREMIUM: 5%
SALES: Fortnightly on Thu at 10.00am and 2.00pm.
VIEWING: Tue and Wed prior 9.30am-12.30pm and 2.00pm-4.30pm.
REFRESHMENTS: None available on the premises.
PARKING: Brunswick Street public car park opposite.
STORAGE: Yes
TRANSPORTATION: Yes
SHIPPING: Yes

LEWIS & ROWDEN

24 Brunswick Street. Tel: (0626) 770279

500-750 lots. The saleroom is a large building with a 'shop front' directly opposite Brunswick Street public car park. The fortnightly auctions are conducted on two floors: downstairs the saleroom is full of lesser-quality items, such as kitchen equipment, gardening tools, modern furniture, beds and bedding, while the upstairs saleroom contains the better-quality lots. These are sold off after the lunch break, usually at around 2.00pm.

Torquay

BUYER'S PREMIUM: 10%
SALES: Collective: every two weeks on Tue. Specialist: send or telephone for details. Starting times depend on the number of lots.
VIEWING: Sat prior 9.30am-12.30pm, Mon and Tue prior 9.30am-5.00pm.
REFRESHMENTS: Own café.
PARKING: Own large car park.
STORAGE: Yes
TRANSPORTATION: Yes
SHIPPING: Yes

BEARNE'S

Rainbow, Avenue Road. Tel: (0803) 296277

500-1,000 lots. Bearne's Rainbow saleroom is off Avenue Road, between Torre Station and the seafront, less than a mile from Torquay Station.

The saleroom is in a large, imposing mansion standing in its own wooded grounds, which was converted into an auction house in 1977. Every two weeks Bearne's hold a collective sale which always includes Georgian, Victorian and Edwardian furniture. There are also either pictures, silver and jewellery or (in alternate sales) ceramics and glass, works of art and collectors' items.

Specialist sales are held regularly in the following categories: pictures, furniture, works of art and collectors' items, silver and jewellery, and ceramics and glass. Additional specialist sales are held throughout the year. In the past these have included Art Nouveau and Art Deco, veteran and classic cars, distinctive number plates and automobilia. There are no regular dates for these sales, but they are generally very popular and worth finding out about. Refreshments are available on sale days in the summer house next to the car park.

McCALLUM-ASHWEEK

Alexandra Road, Ellacombe. Tel: (0803) 291097
500-600 lots. The auction is well known locally, and is used as a meeting-place for friends. Situated about a quarter of a mile from the town centre, the saleroom is housed in a square white building, conspicuous for its size. On sale days it is a hub of noise, with the auctioneer calling out during the bidding and other people wandering around at will, inspecting the goods and discussing bids. The sale offers a mixture of antiques and general household effects, and there will usually be something to suit most pockets in each of the categories. These range from furniture to china, pictures, local craft items, jewellery, silver and collectables.

Torquay

BUYER'S PREMIUM: *10%*
SALES: *Fortnightly on Wed at 12.00 noon.*
VIEWING: *Day prior 9.00am-5.00pm.*
REFRESHMENTS: *None available on the premises.*
PARKING: *Ample near by.*
STORAGE: *Yes*
TRANSPORTATION: *Yes*
SHIPPING: *No*

WEST OF ENGLAND AUCTIONS

3 Warren Road. Tel: (0803) 211266
400-600 lots. The saleroom has three sale galleries. The first-floor gallery and downstairs outer gallery are used for the general sale, with the main ground-floor gallery reserved for antiques. The general sale is usually held monthly, with general goods sold in the morning and antiques, works of art, silver and jewellery in the afternoon. This is a very busy auction, popular with both dealers and private buyers, and its reputation extends well beyond the borders of Devon.

Torquay

BUYER'S PREMIUM: *10%*
SALES: *Monthly on last Mon at 11.00am.*
VIEWING: *Sat prior 9.00am-12.00 noon, Sun prior 2.00pm-6.00pm, morning of sale from 9.00am.*
REFRESHMENTS: *Own refreshment area.*
PARKING: *Multi-storey car park close by in Abbey Road.*
STORAGE: *Yes*
TRANSPORTATION: *Yes*
SHIPPING: *Yes*

DORSET

BLANDFORD AUCTION ROOMS

1a Alfred Street. Tel: (0258) 452454
400-500 lots. Blandford Forum is a Georgian market town on the Stour. Sales take place here at four-weekly intervals as opposed to once a month, which makes life a little more

Blandford Forum

BUYER'S PREMIUM: *10%*
SALES: *Every four weeks on Wed at 10.00am.*

VIEWING: *Day prior 9.30am-7.30pm.*
REFRESHMENTS: *Snacks available.*
PARKING: *Free car park 50 yards away.*
STORAGE: *Yes*
TRANSPORTATION: *Yes*
SHIPPING: *Yes*

Bournemouth

BUYER'S PREMIUM: *10%*
SALES: *At five-weekly intervals on Sat at 10.30am.*
VIEWING: *Sat prior 9.30am-1.30pm and 2.30pm-4.30pm, Mon-Fri prior 10.00am-1.30pm and 2.30pm-5.00pm, morning of sale 8.00am-10.00am.*
REFRESHMENTS: *Saleroom has adjoining cafeteria/restaurant.*
PARKING: *Richmond Gardens car park, in the town centre.*
STORAGE: *Yes*
TRANSPORTATION: *Postal service available.*
SHIPPING: *Postal service for small lots.*

Bournemouth

BUYER'S PREMIUM: *10%*
SALES: *Fortnightly on Tue and Wed at 10.00am.*
VIEWING: *Mon prior 9.30am-3.30pm.*
REFRESHMENTS: *None available on the premises.*
PARKING: *Public car park near by.*
STORAGE: *Yes*
TRANSPORTATION: *Yes*
SHIPPING: *Yes*

complicated for visitors planning a trip to one. However, these sales are a good introduction to the world of auctions. 'We like to give a friendly welcome to people,' says auctioneer Rob Warry.

The proceedings are informal and there is usually a wide variety of antiques, general household furniture and effects on offer, often with plenty of small china and glass objects. These are interesting for both collectors and casual browsers.

DALKEITH AUCTIONS

Dalkeith Hall, 81b Old Christchurch Road. Tel: (0202) 292905

1,000 lots. Sales take place at the Hinton Suite, Hinton Road, Bournemouth, which is part of the Charles Forte complex, but viewing is at Dalkeith Hall, 81b Old Christchurch Road. These auctions are of particular interest to those who enjoy browsing and have an interest in anything nostalgic. No furniture is sold. The sales are of collectors' items, including stamps, postcards, autographs, coins, cigarette cards, medals, old toys and dolls, militaria and banknotes. The lots include things that people have been throwing out for years, but which have since become valuable. A moment or two spent browsing around the lots in any sale will demonstrate that. One lot, a large box, sold by the auctioneers recently, was crammed with more than 3,700 assorted postcards.

Sales are divided into seven sessions: stamps; picture postcards; cigarette cards, cameras, photographic and scientific instruments, coins and banknotes; military medals, pop, stage and screen memorabilia and autographs; sport, railwayana and transport collectables, toys, prints and ephemera; jewellery, ceramics, glass and other collectors' items; and finally books and manuscripts. Sales end between 5.00pm and 6.00pm.

HOUSE & SON

11/16 Lansdown House, Christchurch Road. Tel: (0202) 298044

600-800 lots. The enthusiastic auction-goer is certainly not deprived of excellent venues in Bournemouth. House & Son's premises are part of a parade, and they usually boast a long window display of lots in their forthcoming two-day sales, held fortnightly.

House & Son are a long-established firm and they enjoy an excellent reputation. In their two-day auctions you can be sure that you will find a wide range of interesting lots. The first day of such an auction usually has a morning-only sale. Any motor vehicles on offer are sold first, then come carpets and beds. These are followed by oil paintings and watercolours, books, photographs, postcards and prints, antique, Victorian and reproduction furniture, and household effects. The second day starts with pottery and porcelain, and goes on to include glass, silver and plate. Selling begins again in the afternoon at 2.15pm, when jewellery and watches, *objets d'art*, collectors' items, copper, brass, bronzes and metalware are offered.

RIDDETTS OF BOURNEMOUTH

Bournemouth

The Auction Galleries, 26 Richmond Hill, The Square. Tel: (0202) 555686

1,000-1,200 lots. There are separate salerooms on each floor of Riddetts' tall, attractive premises. On the first floor there are sales of paintings, watercolours and prints, Persian carpets and rugs, books and specialist sales of toys. On the ground floor there are sales of antiques, silver and plated wares, fine art, porcelain, glass and jewellery. Outside, in the covered car park, there are also sales of general chattels, electrical goods, televisions, gardening equipment and tools.

Every fortnight there is a two-day sale, starting with small items, porcelain and pottery on Tuesday morning. The afternoon is usually taken up with antique furniture. On Wednesday morning, silver, silver plate, jewellery, paintings, watercolour drawings and prints are auctioned, followed by modern and reproduction furniture, lounge suites, bedroom suites, soft furnishings, beds, pine, televisions and electrical goods.

BUYER'S PREMIUM: *10%*
SALES: *Fortnightly on Tue and Wed at 10.00am and 2.00pm.*
VIEWING: *Mon prior 10.00am-8.00pm.*
REFRESHMENTS: *Available sometimes.*
PARKING: *Own car park.*
STORAGE: *Yes*
TRANSPORTATION: *Yes*
SHIPPING: *Yes*

WILLIAM MOREY & SONS

Bridport

St Michael's Lane. Tel: (0308) 22078

500-600 lots. Bridport lies nearly two miles from the port of West Bay, in magnificent countryside. It is a pleasant old rope-making town, with a wide street of fine, red-brick houses. The saleroom is close to the bus and coach station and was at one time part of the cattle market (now sadly defunct). The Morey family began the cattle market in 1870 and a branch of the same family is responsible for the antiques auctions that take place in the town today. The auctions are very popular events, which many local people attend purely to be entertained by the humour and chit-chat that flows back and forth between the auctioneer and the crowd. One of the auctioneers is also the Town Crier, and is a very well-known local character.

The sale is divided into two sections, which each attract different types of buyers. The first section, of cheaper outside effects, begins the auction. This is where cycles, old lawn

BUYER'S PREMIUM: *10%*
SALES: *Every three to five weeks on Thu at 9.30am.*
VIEWING: *Day prior 9.00am-6.00pm.*
REFRESHMENTS: *Own canteen.*
PARKING: *None available on the premises.*
STORAGE: *No*
TRANSPORTATION: *Yes*
SHIPPING: *Yes*

mowers, timber and other items are offered. The second section of the sale lasts through the afternoon and is held indoors. Here there are lots of modern household furniture, plus antiques. It used to be the custom in this area for craftsmen to visit houses to ensure that all the carving on furniture matched, and they would carry out their work *in situ*. A past sale included an example in the form of a magnificent hand-carved, five-piece oak bedroom suite. At the same sale an old RAC emergency telephone box that had been used as a garden shed for a number of years was also sold, demonstrating that these sales have a wide range of lots.

Christchurch

BUYER'S PREMIUM: *10%*
SALES: *Weekly on Wed and Thu at 10.00am (includes antiques sale twice a month on Thu).*
VIEWING: *Tue prior, 10.00am-5.00pm.*
REFRESHMENTS: *None available on the premises.*
PARKING: *Own car park.*
STORAGE: *Yes*
TRANSPORTATION: *Yes*
SHIPPING: *Yes*

BULSTRODES AUCTIONS

13 Stour Road. Tel: (0202) 482244

500-600 lots per day. Situated next to Christchurch railway station, Bulstrodes' premises were originally part of the railway outbuildings, but they have since been converted into modern salerooms. There are two separate salerooms, but one is used for storing the following week's sale items. The auctioneers take it in turns to conduct the proceedings, and the sales are divided into morning and afternoon sessions.

On Wednesday mornings there are sales of outside effects, such as garden furniture and tools, plus electrical household equipment such as cookers, fridges and washing machines. The Wednesday morning sales often include dinghies, yachts and windsurfing equipment, too. The Wednesday afternoon sales are usually of modern furniture and beds.

On Thursdays there is a sale of carpets, modern and office furniture, and twice a month the afternoon is given over to antique furniture, silver and other small, good quality items.

Dorchester

BUYER'S PREMIUM: *10%*
SALES: *Dorchester: every six weeks on Thu at 10.30am, or on Thu at 12.00 noon and Fri at 10.30am (two-day sales). Weymouth: twice a month on Tue at 10.30am.*
VIEWING: *Dorchester: Mon prior 9.30am-5.00pm, Tue prior 9.30am-7.00pm, Wed prior 9.30am-5.00pm. Weymouth: Mon prior 9.00am-5.00pm.*
REFRESHMENTS: *Dorchester and Weymouth:*

HY. DUKE & SON

Dorchester Fine Art Saleroom, Weymouth Avenue. Tel: (0305) 265080

400-600 lots. Hy. Duke & Son have been holding auctions in Dorset since 1823. They are members of Royal Life Estates, which has associated companies holding sales in Avon, Hampshire, Wiltshire and Somerset. Here there are rather up-market sales, on average every six weeks. Sales take place on Thursdays, and sometimes on Fridays as well.If the sale is a one-day, Thursday event, there will be 400 lots of paintings, ceramics and silver, dolls and toys, clocks, musical instruments, rugs, carpets and English and Continental furniture, but when the sale extends over two days these goods are sold on the Friday, and the Thursday sale becomes a specialist auction, devoted to jewellery and silver, or to ceramics, or paintings.

Hy. Duke & Son also run interesting sales of Victorian and modern furniture and effects. These are held on average twice a month, and take place at The Weymouth Salerooms, Nicholas Street, Weymouth, tel: (0305) 761499.

JEFFS & SON

Northernhay Saleroom, Northernhay. Tel: (0305) 262552

200-250 lots. Dorchester is a charming old-English town on the River Frome. Jeffs & Son were established over 90 years ago and are an independently owned, family-run business. The auctions are held about every six weeks in what was a wartime dance hall. If you are hoping to furnish your house by going to one of these sales, or simply wish to collect something, you'll have fun bidding or simply browsing here. You will find almost anything and everything on sale, from china, paintings, jewellery and clocks to vacuum cleaners, beds and old brass taps.

POOLE FURNITURE SALEROOMS

13 St Peter's Road, Parkstone. Tel: (0202) 748567

700-750 lots. Regular monthly sales of antiques and modern furniture, silver, silver plate, jewellery, linen, china, glass, gardening equipment and other effects have been held in this saleroom (once a Victorian school) since 1945. The sales, which are very popular, usually start with outside effects, including bicycles, and then continue with furniture. In the afternoon better-quality lots are offered, such as antiques, pictures, jewellery and silver. Sometimes a sale is extended over a second day. The pace of selling at these auctions is fast, but if you are unused to bidding there will usually be a helpful saleroom attendant present who can offer advice.

CHAPMAN, MOORE & MUGFORD

Lyons Walk Gallery. Tel: (0747) 52400

300-350 lots. The sales here are in a delightful setting. The stone building was converted about 20 years ago and has a panelled ceiling, exposed roof timbers and an attractive gallery. It lies just off the High Street, and is approached by a courtyard behind the auctioneers' offices at 9 High Street. The auctions include antique furniture, silver, jewellery, paintings and musical instruments, and lots can be bought from a few pounds upwards. Although nothing is given away, interesting items

none available on the premises.
PARKING: *Dorchester: own car park. Weymouth: none available on the premises.*
STORAGE: *Both: yes*
TRANSPORTATION: *Both: yes*
SHIPPING: *Both: yes*

Dorchester

BUYER'S PREMIUM: *10%*
SALES: *Usually every six weeks on Thu at 10.30am.*
VIEWING: *Day prior 10.00am-4.00pm.*
REFRESHMENTS: *None available on the premises.*
PARKING: *None on the premises.*
STORAGE: *Yes*
TRANSPORTATION: *Yes*
SHIPPING: *Yes*

Poole

BUYER'S PREMIUM: *10%*
SALES: *Monthly on Tue at 10.00am.*
VIEWING: *Sat prior 10.00am-12.00 noon, Mon prior 10.00am-4.00pm.*
REFRESHMENTS: *Available.*
PARKING: *None available on the premises.*
STORAGE: *Yes*
TRANSPORTATION: *Yes*
SHIPPING: *Yes*

Shaftesbury

BUYER'S PREMIUM: *Nil*
SALES: *Every six to eight weeks on Fri at 6.00pm.*
VIEWING: *Day of sale from 10.30am.*
REFRESHMENTS: *None available on the premises.*
PARKING: *Main town car park is 100 yards away.*
STORAGE: *Yes*
TRANSPORTATION: *Yes*
SHIPPING: *Yes*

from country homes in the area can be found at very reasonable prices. A tremendous amount can be learnt from just viewing an auction, where you may freely inspect the goods and enjoy the atmosphere, even if you are unsuccessful in the bidding.

Shaftesbury

BUYER'S PREMIUM: *Nil*
SALES: *Monthly on the last Mon of the month (or a week prior if the last Mon of the month is a Bank Holiday) at 10.30am.*
VIEWING: *Day of sale from 9.00am.*
REFRESHMENTS: *Available.*
PARKING: *Own car park.*
STORAGE: *Yes*
TRANSPORTATION: *Yes*
SHIPPING: *Yes*

SOUTHERN COUNTIES AUCTIONEERS

Christy's Lane Livestock Market. Tel: (0747) 51735

400-500 lots. Southern Counties Auctioneers hold a monthly sale of goods of all types and ages from their premises at the Livestock Market. They also hold weekly livestock sales on Thursdays, and there are calf pens adjacent to the saleroom. The general auction has real atmosphere, partly due to its setting and partly due to the range of characters to be found wandering around the saleroom, many of whom are on first-name terms with the auctioneer and use the premises as a place to meet friends. Among the lots on offer are antiques. Large pieces of furniture such as wardrobes, beds, chests of drawers and dressers are placed around the edge of the saleroom; they are sold at the beginning and end of the proceedings. The main part of the sale is taken up by small items, such as china, brass, jewellery, books, craft items, collectors' items and bric-à-brac. These objects are set out on tables in the centre of the room.

Sherborne

BUYER'S PREMIUM: *10%*
SALES: *Two a month, on Tue at 11.00am.*
VIEWING: *Fri prior 2.30pm-7.30pm, Sat prior 10.00am-1.00pm, Mon prior 10.00am-4.00pm and morning of sale from 9.00am.*
REFRESHMENTS: *Own café.*
PARKING: *None available on the premises.*
STORAGE: *Yes*
TRANSPORTATION: *Yes*
SHIPPING: *Yes*

PHILLIPS

Long Street Salerooms, Long Street. Tel: (0935) 815271

300-400 lots. Sherborne is a historic town, set among green hills. It has many old houses, some dating back to the 15th century. Phillips' premises were once an old chapel and school, and can be found just off Cheap Street. The mellow stone building has decorative leaded windows with a neat grass verge to the front. It makes a comfortable setting for the two sales that take place here every month. One of the sales comprises Victoriana and pictures. The others are specialist sales of antiques, works of art, ceramics and glass, jewellery, silver and collector's items. There are sales in each of these categories at least four times a year.

Wareham

BUYER'S PREMIUM: *10%*
SALES: *Antique and later furniture and effects: fortnightly on Tue at 10.00am. For details*

COTTEES

The Market, East Street. Tel: (0929) 552826

700-800 lots. Wareham is a delightful town with broad streets and fine churches. It is also near heath, sea, and river. In the Saxon church of St Martin there is a figure of T E Lawrence in

Arab attire, sculpted by Eric Kennington — unfortunately not for sale. However, there should be enough goods at these busy auctions to satisfy most people who are looking for something interesting to buy.

The saleroom is about 300 yards from the only set of traffic lights in Wareham, and the proceedings begin with bidding both inside and outside the auctioneers' premises. Antique and later furniture, porcelain, silver and plate, pictures, books, carpets and rugs, collectors items and miscellanea are always included. On some Saturdays during the year Cottees also hold special sales of marine items, old agricultural equipment, and toys and childhood memorabilia.

HY. DUKE & SON
See HY. DUKE & SON, Dorchester, Dorset

DURHAM

ADDISONS

13 Galgate. Tel: (0833) 38094
900-1000 lots. Barnard Castle is an excellent centre for exploring Teesdale. It is a delightful old market town with wide streets and castle ruins which stand impressively above the river. The business was established over 110 years ago, and stands in the centre of the town opposite the post office. In the summer it is packed with visitors, and during sales and viewing days the large hall has a good display of furniture and household articles. The monthly Thursday sale is of general household furniture, effects and miscellaneous items. Quarterly sales are devoted to collectables, including high quality brass, china, glass, metalware, furniture and others. The general sales are packed with bargains, although probably as much as 90 per cent of the furniture goes to the same group of buyers. The sale starts with 'smalls' — items of china, glass and so on — and then goes on to pieces of furniture, such as chairs. Bedroom furniture is sold next, followed by dining room suites and lounge suites, with upholstered furniture completing the sale.

DENIS EDKINS FSVA

The Auckland Auction Rooms, 58 Kingsway. Tel: (0388) 603095
200-500 lots. The saleroom is a newish brick building at the rear of the town's main shopping centre, in the same street as

of other sales, contact the auctioneers direct.
VIEWING: *Day prior 2.00pm-5.00pm, and 6.00pm-8.00pm.*
REFRESHMENTS: *Own café.*
PARKING: *Own car park.*
STORAGE: *Yes*
TRANSPORTATION: *Yes*
SHIPPING: *Yes*

Weymouth

Barnard Castle

BUYER'S PREMIUM: *10%*
SALES: *Monthly on Thu at 10.00am (includes quarterly sales of collectables).*
VIEWING: *Day prior 10.00am-4.00pm, 6.30pm-7.30pm. Day of sale from 9.30am.*
REFRESHMENTS: *None available on the premises.*
PARKING: *Ample parking near by.*
STORAGE: *Yes*
TRANSPORTATION: *Yes*
SHIPPING: *No*

Bishop Auckland

BUYER'S PREMIUM: *5%*
SALES: *Weekly on Thu at 11.00am.*

VIEWING: *Day prior 10.00am-12.00 noon, 2.00pm-5.00pm.*
REFRESHMENTS: *None available on the premises.*
PARKING: *Limited.*
STORAGE: *Yes*
TRANSPORTATION: *Yes*
SHIPPING: *Yes*

the football ground. Sale day is Thursday, which is also one of the town's two market days, and there are stalls selling all sorts of interesting things in the Market Square, only a short walk from the saleroom. (The other market day is Saturday.)

The weekly sale tends to run to a theme: one week it might be of better quality household furniture and effects, the next could be for office furniture such as desks, filing cabinets, typist's chairs and so on, the next week modern furniture and effects, and then the following week plant and machinery, including small DIY hand tools. Sometimes the sales are of older furniture, which may include antiques, shipping furniture (1930s-1940s) and smaller general goods such as old china, porcelain and collectables.

All the lots put into the sale by one vendor are given the same lot number, instead of being numbered individually. This means that a wide variety of goods may share the same number, making it more important than ever to note down the specific details of items that interest you, not just the lot number.

Darlington

BUYER'S PREMIUM: *10%*
SALES: *General: weekly on Mon at 10.00am. Antiques and collectables: monthly on Mon at 4.00pm.*
VIEWING: *Both sales: Fri prior 1.00pm-5.00pm, Sat prior 8.30am-5.00pm.*
REFRESHMENTS: *Vending machine.*
PARKING: *Commercial Street public car park opposite.*
STORAGE: *Yes*
TRANSPORTATION: *Yes*
SHIPPING: *Yes*

HUNT BROTHERS

12 King Street. Tel: (0325) 352328

300-400 lots. The saleroom is near the centre of this busy industrial and market town, which George Stephenson put on the map by opening the first passenger railway here in 1825. The No. 1 Locomotive which drew the first passenger train at a speed of 13mph is on display at Bank Top Station, south-east of the town centre. There is a wide variety of goods in Hunt Brothers' weekly general sale, with something to interest most bidders. The sale starts with electrical goods such as cookers, refrigerators, freezers, televisions, video machines and so on. Next to be sold are boxes of miscellaneous items such as odd pieces of china and glass, books, pots and pans. Most sales will also include beds and carpets, modern furniture, better quality china such as Royal Doulton and other well-known makes, jewellery and antique furniture. Once a month this sale is followed at 4.00pm by a sale of antiques and collectables.

Darlington

BUYER'S PREMIUM: *10%*
SALES: *Fortnightly on Tue at 10.00am (includes periodic antiques sale).*
VIEWING: *Sat, morning prior and Mon prior 9.00am-5.00pm.*

THOMAS WATSON & SON

The Gallery Saleroom, Northumberland Street.
Tel: (0325) 462559

350-450 lots. The saleroom is large and purpose-built, and stands within the town's inner ring road. Thomas Watson & Son are one of the oldest established auctioneers in the area, having recently celebrated their 150th anniversary. Buyers from as far away as Leeds and Newcastle regularly attend the fortnightly general sale. Typically this will have china, pottery, pictures and garden equipment, as well as a variety of furniture. This sale is sometimes replaced by what the firm describes as a periodic sale of antiques, including good quality Edwardian and Victorian furniture and effects.

REFRESHMENTS: *None available on the premises.*
PARKING: *Town centre car parks.*
STORAGE: *No*
TRANSPORTATION: *Yes*
SHIPPING: *No*

LANGLEY MOOR AUCTION ROOMS

Langley Moor

Little Burn Lane. Tel: (091) 378 2009

400-600 lots. This is an excellent weekly general auction. The auctioneers can boast that they have helped to furnish and equip many homes in the neighbourhood, and that they have helped many young collectors with their hobbies. The general hustle and bustle of the saleroom adds to the excitement of the day's events at these auctions. Smaller items such as china, ornaments and knick-knacks are laid out on tables and usually receive a great deal of attention at the start of the sales. Paintings, prints and 'boxed lots' are sold off afterwards. The boxed lots consist of a whole assortment of items — and invariably there will be some rubbish among them. It is usually worthwhile spending some time checking them out, though, in case there is something hidden of particular value or interest. All types of general household furniture, including a large number of electrical goods, are sold during the afternoon. There are some excellent buys to be had, even for those of modest means.

BUYER'S PREMIUM: 10%
SALES: *Weekly on Tue at 10.00am.*
VIEWING: *Sat 9.00am-1.00pm, Mon 9.00am-4.00pm.*
REFRESHMENTS: *None available on the premises.*
PARKING: *Yes*
STORAGE: *No*
TRANSPORTATION: *Yes*
SHIPPING: *Yes*

SOUTH HETTON & WINGATE AUCTIONS

Station Town, near Wingate

Station Lane. Tel: (0429) 837245

300-350 lots. This is a busy evening sale, popular with local people. Many of the lots come from houses in the nearby villages, and there is usually a great deal of furniture which has been well looked after. Vendors also bring in unwanted knick-knacks and ornaments.

The selling starts with a very popular section: perhaps 100 lots of 'smalls' such as assorted china, boxes of mixed ornaments, and various items of kitchen equipment. Pictures, including prints, oils and watercolours, are sold next, followed by jewellery. There are usually some valuable hallmarked gold and silver pieces such as watches, pendants, rings and brooches. Furniture completes the sale, with the entire proceedings finishing around 8.30 to 9.00pm.

BUYER'S PREMIUM: 10%
SALES: *Fortnightly on Wed at 6.00pm.*
VIEWING: *Day of sale from 9.00am.*
REFRESHMENTS: *Own café.*
PARKING: *Ample parking near by.*
STORAGE: *Yes*
TRANSPORTATION: *Yes*
SHIPPING: *Yes*

EAST SUSSEX

Battle

BUYER'S PREMIUM: *Abbey Auction Galleries: 5%.
Granary: nil*
SALES: *Abbey Auction Galleries: furniture, monthly on Wed at 11.00am, paintings monthly on Wed one week after furniture sale at 6.30pm. Granary: furniture, monthly on Wed at 10.30am, tools monthly on Sat at 1.00pm.*
VIEWING: *Abbey Auction Galleries: furniture, day prior 9.00am-8.00pm, paintings, day of sale 9.00am-6.30pm. Granary: furniture, day prior 9.00am-7.00pm, tools morning of sale.*
REFRESHMENTS: *Vending machine.*
PARKING: *Own car park.*
STORAGE: *Yes*
TRANSPORTATION: *Yes*
SHIPPING: *Yes*

Bexhill-on-Sea

BUYER'S PREMIUM: 10%
SALES: *Fortnightly on Tue at 10.00am. Sales are on Wed in Bank Holiday weeks.*
VIEWING: *Day prior 9.00am-7.00pm, morning of sale from 9.00am.*
REFRESHMENTS: *Food available at Rother Arms public house, adjacent in same building.*
PARKING: *Own car park.*
STORAGE: *Yes*
TRANSPORTATION: *Yes*
SHIPPING: *Yes*

Brighton

BUYER'S PREMIUM: 8%
SALES: *About every five weeks on Mon at 9.30am.*
VIEWING: *Fri and Sat prior 9.30am-4.00pm.*

BURSTOW & HEWETT

Abbey Auction Galleries, Lower Lake. Tel: (0424) 772374

700-800 lots. Burstow & Hewett are a busy firm holding four sales a month in two salerooms (both at the station end of the town). The Abbey Auction Galleries hold a monthly Wednesday sale of 'Antique and Fine Furniture, Silver, Jewellery, Ceramics and Metalware'. The following week a sale of 'Antique and Modern Oil Paintings, Watercolours, Engravings, and Postcards' takes place.

The Granary saleroom five minutes away in Station Road has a monthly Wednesday sale of 'Antique and Modern Furniture, Silver, Ceramics, Metalware and all types of Household Furnishings', and a monthly Saturday afternoon special sale of 'Gardening, Builders', Carpenters' and Mechanics' Tools and Accessories', including such equipment as mowers and rotavators.

FRYER'S AUCTION GALLERIES

Terminus Road. Tel: (0424) 212994

500-600 lots. Bexhill-on-Sea is a holiday and residential town. The saleroom is an impressive ex-railway terminal with a clock tower, just west of Town Hall Square. The auctions reflect somewhat the resort's sedate reputation, and occur fortnightly on a Tuesday. In weeks with a Bank Holiday the sale is put back until Wednesday. Auctions go under the heading 'Antique and Modern Household Furniture and Effects'. The sale starts at 10.00am (lunch break 1.00pm-1.45pm) and includes good quality 1930s and Edwardian furniture, china, pottery, glass and so on.

RAYMOND P INMAN

The Auction Galleries, 35/40 Temple Street. Tel: (0273) 774777

400-500 lots. The pleasant, unintimidating atmosphere at this auction should be encouraging for new or nervous auction-goers. The reason for it is probably that this is very much a family concern. Proprietor Raymond Inman is the son of the founder, and shares the selling duties with his own son Robert, while wife Maureen Inman takes charge of the mound of office work. The sales are held on three floors in an attractive building off Western Road in the Hove direction. The lots tend to be towards the upper end of the general market, and usually include antiques and reproduction furniture, china, silver, jewellery, paintings and so on. Successful bids range from £1 to many hundreds or even thousands — the record price for a single lot here is £90,000.

REFRESHMENTS: *None available on the premises.*
PARKING: *Own small car park.*
STORAGE: *Yes*
TRANSPORTATION: *Yes*
SHIPPING: *No*

EDGAR HORN'S AUCTION GALLERIES

The Auction Galleries, 46/50 South Street. Tel: (0323) 410419

1,000 lots. Every five weeks Edgar Horn's Auction Galleries hold a popular, well-attended two-day sale at their large saleroom complex, which is in the centre of the town. On the morning of the first day, soft furnishings and Victorian, Edwardian and later bedroom furniture are sold. In the afternoon better-quality lots are auctioned. These might include furniture, clocks, textiles, Oriental carpets and rugs. On the second day, china (such as Staffordshire figures and Royal Doulton tea sets), glass, metalware and miscellaneous collectors' items are sold. Past auctions have included a Kodak Box Brownie camera, silk postcards, telescopes and glass vials used by chemists. Paintings, watercolours and prints, or silver and jewellery, come up for bidding in the afternoon of the second day.

Eastbourne

BUYER'S PREMIUM: 5%
SALES: *On average every five weeks on Tue and Wed at 10.30am and 2.00pm.*
VIEWING: *Fri prior 9.30am-6.00pm, Sat prior 9.30am-4.00pm.*
REFRESHMENTS: *None available on the premises.*
PARKING: *Available near by*
STORAGE: *Yes*
TRANSPORTATION: *Yes*
SHIPPING: *Yes*

PHOENIX AUCTION ROOMS

124 Pevensey Road. Tel: (0323) 645007

250-500 lots. Spend time browsing around the lots on offer at this sale. The large old Victorian saleroom is packed with assorted antiques and general household furniture and effects. Dotted about the room and sold in no particular order there will usually be plenty of domestic and ornamental china, porcelain, electrical goods, televisions, radios, outside effects like gardening equipment, furniture, collectables, and endless miscellaneous items of all ages and values. Even if you don't have time to take advantage of the two viewing days, it is permitted to wander around looking at the lots while the sale is in progress, which many people do.

The auction is close to Eastbourne's Grand Parade, and is one which summer visitors eagerly look forward to. The excitement generated between friends after a successful bid (or even an unsuccessful one) makes the noise level quite high at times. This informality is why many people like the sale.

Eastbourne

BUYER'S PREMIUM: 10%
SALES: *Every three weeks on Wed at 10.00am.*
VIEWING: *Mon and Tue prior 8.30am-12.45pm, 2.00pm-4.00pm, day of sale.*
REFRESHMENTS: *None available on the premises.*
PARKING: *None available on the premises.*
STORAGE: *Yes*
TRANSPORTATION: *Yes*
SHIPPING: *Yes*

Hove

BUYER'S PREMIUM: 8%
SALES: *Monthly two-day sale on Thu and Fri at 10.30am.*
VIEWING: *Tue prior 10.00am-4.30pm and 6.00pm-8.00pm, Wed prior 10.00am-4.30pm.*
REFRESHMENTS: *None available on the premises.*
PARKING: *None available on the premises.*
STORAGE: *Yes*
TRANSPORTATION: *Yes*
SHIPPING: *Yes*

GRAVES SON & PILCHER FINE ARTS

Palmeira Auction Room, Holland Road. Tel: (0273) 735266

600-800 lots. Graves Son & Pilcher Fine Arts hold good, traditional auctions; the company was established in 1897. The monthly two-day sale is a rather up-market affair, and some unusual items can be found among the lots. The auctioneers sell mainly antiques, although good quality reproductions can sometimes be found. If you are looking for quality furniture, though, you will have fun browsing and bidding here. The first day of the sale includes smaller items such as china, jewellery, silver and silver plate and brass, while paintings and furniture are sold on the second. Bidding is usually over on both days by 4.00pm.

Lewes

BUYER'S PREMIUM: 5%
SALES: *Approximately every two months on Tue and Wed at 10.30am.*
VIEWING: *Fri prior 11.00am-5.00pm, Sat prior 10.00am-5.00pm.*
REFRESHMENTS: *None available on the premises.*
PARKING: *None available on the premises.*
STORAGE: *Yes*
TRANSPORTATION: *Yes*
SHIPPING: *Yes*

CLIFFORD DANN AUCTION GALLERIES

20/21 High Street. Tel: (0273) 480111

800-1,000 lots. Lewes is an ancient town; one of its main tourist attractions, the Norman castle, is just a short walk up the hill from Clifford Dann's saleroom.

About once every two months the auctioneers hold a two-day sale of antiques and fine art at their High Street premises. The first day of the sale concentrates on furniture and paintings; smaller items such as ceramics, glass, porcelain, china, silver and jewellery are sold on the second. Every second or third sale will be divided into specialist categories, such as paintings, books, fabrics, toys and games and collectors' items.

Lewes

BUYER'S PREMIUM: 5%
SALES: *On average every six weeks on Tue, Wed and Thu (and sometimes Fri) at 10.00am or 10.30am.*
VIEWING: *Fri and Sat prior 10.00am-5.00pm.*
REFRESHMENTS: *None available on the premises.*
PARKING: *Own car park.*
STORAGE: *Yes*
TRANSPORTATION: *Yes*
SHIPPING: *Yes*

GORRINGE'S AUCTION GALLERIES

15 North Street. Tel: (0273) 472503

2,500-3,000 lots. Gorringe's are a long-established, independent company whose three- (or sometimes four-) day sales attract buyers regularly from all over the world. The first day of the auction is devoted to furniture — longcase clocks and barometers are also included, plus about 100 lots of rugs and carpets. Metalware, porcelain, glass and miscellaneous items are sold on the second day, when you might find cloth-bound photograph albums, mahogany wig stands, painted silk fans and much more besides. On the third day the sale is given over to silver and plate, jewellery, textiles, oil paintings, watercolours and prints. If there is a large number of textiles and paintings, the sale will run on for a fourth day, when vintage and inexpensive wines may also be offered.

There is a short break for lunch each day; this may begin at any time between 12.00 noon and 1.45pm.

LEWES AUCTION ROOMS (JULIAN DAWSON)

Garden Street. Tel: (0273) 478221
600-800 lots. The saleroom is close to the railway station and next to the cattle market. This is one of the largest weekly general auctions in the county, and is certainly an ideal starting place for new auction-goers — friendly and, at times, a little noisy. The variety of lots is very wide: the hammer will come down on successful bids ranging from £1 to over £1,000. A range of goods is set out in the crowded saleroom, and includes the entire range of antique and modern furniture, general household effects and miscellanea. At roughly six-weekly intervals, Mr Dawson holds special antique sales. These take place on Thursdays.

ASCENT AUCTION GALLERIES

11/12 East Ascent. Tel: (0424) 420275
550-700 lots. The busy general sale of furniture, household effects and miscellanea is held every two weeks. There is also a quarterly sale of good quality antiques. The general sale alternates between East Ascent and the saleroom just around the corner, the Mews Galleries at 1 Mews Road. This allows one sale to be prepared while another is in progress. Both salerooms are near the seafront and lie behind one of St Leonards-on-Sea's landmarks, the Marine Court.

All the items offered are from private sources. Lots sell from a few pounds upwards in the general sale, and the usual selling order is carpets, linen and blankets, kitchen and garden effects, furniture, books and pictures. Next are clocks, brass, silver and silver plate, and then ornamental and domestic china and glass: there is usually a good selection in all these categories. Catalogues are available on request.

ESSEX

BRENTWOOD AUCTIONS

45 North Road. Tel: (0277) 224599
200-400 lots. The auctioneer is Wendy Wood, one of the few professional lady auctioneers in the business. Brentwood

Lewes

BUYER'S PREMIUM: *Nil*
SALES: *General: weekly on Mon at 11.00am. Antiques: about every six weeks on Thu at 10.30am.*
VIEWING: *Sat prior 9.00am-1.00pm, morning of sale. Antiques also day prior 9.00am-7.30pm.*
REFRESHMENTS: *Available in cattle market.*
PARKING: *Own car park.*
STORAGE: *Yes*
TRANSPORTATION: *Yes*
SHIPPING: *Yes*

St Leonards-on-Sea

BUYER'S PREMIUM: *10%*
SALES: *General: every two weeks on Thu at 10.00am. Antiques: quarterly on Thu at 11.00am.*
VIEWING: *Day prior 9.00am-6.30pm.*
REFRESHMENTS: *Own café.*
PARKING: *Grand Parade public car park.*
STORAGE: *Yes*
TRANSPORTATION: *Yes*
SHIPPING: *Yes*

Brentwood

BUYER'S PREMIUM: *10%*
SALES: *Weekly on Mon at 11.00am.*

VIEWING: *Sat
10.00am-2.00pm, day of sale
from 9.00am.*
REFRESHMENTS: *Own
tea room.*
PARKING: *Large public car
parks near by.*
STORAGE: *Yes*
TRANSPORTATION: *Yes*
SHIPPING: *Yes*

Auctions' general weekly sale is a mixture of everything under the sun, including household furniture, collectors' items, electrical goods, jewellery, china and the odd unexpected lot, such as a stuffed mongoose or fox. In addition to the general sales, Brentwood Auctions hold specialist antiques sales throughout the year.

Chelmsford

BUYER'S PREMIUM: *10%*
SALES: *General: weekly on
Tue at 10.00am. Outside
effects: weekly on Fri at
10.00am. Antiques and fine
art: every two months on Wed
at 10.30am.*
VIEWING: *General and
outside effects: morning of sale
from 8.30am. Antiques and
fine art: day prior
2.00pm-8.00pm, morning of
sale from 9.00am.*
REFRESHMENTS: *Own
buffet bar.*
PARKING: *Own car park.*
STORAGE: *Yes*
TRANSPORTATION: *Yes*
SHIPPING: *Yes*

COOPER HIRST AUCTIONS

The Granary Sale Room, Victoria Road. Tel: (0245) 260535

300-400 lots. The saleroom has been well adapted from what was a factory warehouse. It is just out of the centre of Chelmsford, opposite the ice rink and about 10 minutes' walk from the railway station. The weekly Tuesday sale consists of general household furniture and effects, and might include wardrobes, dining tables, sideboards, chests of drawers and other furniture, plus cookers, refrigerators and other electrical goods. Typically there will be boxes containing interesting assortments of miscellaneous items, such as children's books, or toys, kitchen equipment and ornaments. There are usually bundles of linen and various china items, perhaps plates from an old violet-pattern dinner set, a box of assorted tea pots, a blue-and-white jug and basin, various vases, decanters and so on.

The weekly Friday sale is of what might be described as outside effects, and includes such items as bundles of timber, machinery of all types and various gardening tools. It takes place on the ground floor.

The bi-monthly antique and fine art sale takes place in a pleasant first-floor saleroom, and includes Georgian, Victorian, Edwardian and reproduction furniture of a high quality.

Chelmsford

S H ROWLAND, CHELMSFORD AUCTIONS

42 Milmay Road. Tel: (0245) 354251

BUYER'S PREMIUM: *Nil*
SALES: *General: fortnightly
on Wed at 10.00am. Antiques
and fine art: every two months
on Wed at 10.00am.*
VIEWING: *General: day
prior 9.00am-4.30pm, morning
of sale from 9.00am. Antiques
and fine art: day prior
2.00pm-8.00pm, morning of*

400-500 lots. The saleroom is on the London side of the city, close to the Army and Navy roundabout. Despite being only some 30 miles from London, Chelmsford is surrounded by attractive villages, including Writtle, scene of Marconi's first experiments with the wireless. It is from private houses in these villages that many of the lots on sale will have originated. Antique and fine art sales are slotted between the general sales, and while vendors are pleased with the high prices gained at auction, buyers also find that prices compare well with those in shops. Chelmsford Auctions was established in 1946 and draws vendors and buyers from a wide area. They are also the official auctioneers for the Sheriff of Essex. The sales are informal and friendly, and helpful staff are always on hand to answer any queries.

E J GILDERS & CO

The Mart, High Street. Tel: (0255) 423592
250-300 lots. E J Gilders & Co was established in 1887. This is an interesting seaside sale with all the atmosphere of a good country auction. The sales include a wide range of articles, some of which may have come from house clearances. There are usually also some antiques, but best of all are the lots of miscellaneous items bundled together to give a minimum value. One successful bid could find you the proud owner of a box containing a great deal of excellent kitchen equipment, or four or five good-quality gardening tools. The sale is conducted in a very informal, friendly manner, and there is nothing to intimidate those new to auctions.

WILLIAM H BROWN

Paskells Rooms, 11/14 East Hill. Tel: (0206) 868070
300-400 lots. Situated on one of the main approach roads into the town, this long-established auction room has weekly sales of antique and modern household furniture and effects. Lots include Georgian, Victorian, Edwardian and modern furniture, oil and watercolour paintings, china, porcelain and glass. Also included in the weekly sales are kitchenalia, garden tools and the like.

A monthly specialist 'cabinet' sale includes small items such as jewellery, silver, *bijouterie*, watches, figurines, pottery and glass.

ESSEX & SUFFOLK MARKET AUCTIONS/WILLIAM H BROWN

Wyncolls Road. Tel: (0206) 842156
2,000 lots. The sales take place in the cattle market, close to the A12 on the London side of Colchester. This is a busy and traditional country auction, where the sale area may have as many as five separate auctions taking place at the same time.

The general weekly sale is all that a country auction should be: here are auctioned farm produce, fruit and vegetables, eggs, poultry, rabbits, timber, bicycles, cars and 'deadstock' — a term used to describe a huge range of items which cannot be

sale from 9.00am.
REFRESHMENTS: *Own café.*
PARKING: *Own car park.*
STORAGE: Yes
TRANSPORTATION: Yes
SHIPPING: Yes

Clacton-on-Sea

BUYER'S PREMIUM: *Nil*
SALES: *About every six weeks on Thu at 9.30am.*
VIEWING: *All day Wed.*
REFRESHMENTS: *None available on the premises.*
PARKING: *None available on the premises.*
STORAGE: No
TRANSPORTATION: Yes
SHIPPING: No

Colchester

BUYER'S PREMIUM: 10%
SALES: *General: weekly on Tue at 10.00am. Cabinet sale: first Mon of month at 1.00pm.*
VIEWING: *Both: Sat 9.00am-1.00pm*
REFRESHMENTS: *None available on the premises.*
PARKING: *None available on the premises.*
STORAGE: No
TRANSPORTATION: Yes
SHIPPING: No

Colchester

BUYER'S PREMIUM: *Nil*
SALES: *General: weekly on Sat at 9.45am. Horse and tackle: monthly on first Sat of month at 10.00am.*
VIEWING: *General: sale day only. Horse and tackle: morning of sale.*
REFRESHMENTS: *Own café, licensed bar.*
PARKING: *Own car park.*

STORAGE: *Yes*
TRANSPORTATION: *Yes*
SHIPPING: *Yes*

classified as livestock or produce or as anything else. The sale is conducted almost entirely in the open, and starts with timber at about 9.45am, followed by 'deadstock' at about 10.00am, which could include rolls of wire netting, lawn mowers, kitchen sinks, Victorian mangles, the odd piece of furniture, old tins containing somebody's store of screws or nails, boxes of boots, DIY tools, boxes of children's toys, saucepans, building equipment, lamps, assorted bric-à-brac, and so on. The sale of cars takes place at 11.00am.

On the first Saturday of the month, there is also a horse and tackle sale in the very large auction rooms. It starts at 10.00am with horse tackle and other equipment, followed at 12.30pm by the sale of horses in the sale ring. The sales finish at around 2.30 to 3.00pm. There are also Tuesday sales of cattle, pigs and sheep, at 11.00am, and regular sales of nursery produce and garden furniture.

Colchester

BUYER'S PREMIUM: *10%*
SALES: *General: weekly on Wed at 10.00am. Cabinet sale: monthly on last Tue of month at 6.00pm.*
VIEWING: *General sale: Tue 9.00am-7.00pm. Cabinet sale: day of sale 9.00am-6.00pm.*
REFRESHMENTS: *Own café.*
PARKING: *St Mary's car park.*
STORAGE: *Yes*
TRANSPORTATION: *Yes*
SHIPPING: *Yes*

REEMAN, DANSIE, HOWE & SON

12 Head Gate. Tel: (0206) 574271

300-350 lots. Midweek is a busy time for auction-goers in Colchester, with this sale every Wednesday and the William H Brown sale every Tuesday at East Hill, about half a mile away. It is worth making time to look at the Norman castle and Roman wall, however. Colchester is England's oldest recorded town, and dates from the Iron Age. The first sale at Head Gate took place on 6 July 1881, and it has been a saleroom ever since.

The Wednesday auction is an excellent general sale, and includes a wide range of clean, high-quality antique, period and modern furniture, and miscellaneous effects. The lots are laid out with plenty of space for prospective buyers to study them, and the staff are helpful. There is also a monthly 'cabinet' sale of jewellery, silver, china, pottery and glass, at which you can expect to find gold and silver pendants, necklaces, brooches, rings, silver spoons, jewel and cigarette boxes, tea services, art pottery, candlesticks, decorative jars, cutlery, fountain pens and propelling pencils, pocket watches and the like.

Grays Thurrock

BUYER'S PREMIUM: *10%*
SALES: *Fortnightly on Fri at 6.30pm.*
VIEWING: *Day prior 12.00 noon-6.00pm and day of sale 11.00am-6.30pm.*
REFRESHMENTS: *Own café.*

GRAYS AUCTION ROOMS

Alfred Street. Tel: (0375) 381181

300-350 lots. The saleroom is at the rear of 118 William Street, and is a little difficult to find. Only antiques are sold, but here the category includes good, clean pre-1930s items. Glass, pottery, collections of Staffordshire figures and cottages, English porcelain, Oriental ceramics and works of art, rugs, dolls, silver, pictures and many other items can be found. Regular faces turn up week after week, giving the saleroom a club-like atmosphere, and although in the past dealers out-numbered private buyers, it is noticeable now that the numbers have evened out.

HAMPTONS FINE ART (J M WELCH & SON)

Great Dunmow

Chequers Lane. Tel: (0371) 873014

200-800 lots. The Chequers Lane saleroom has a growing reputation for collectables, which are sold on every third Wednesday of every month, together with upmarket modern and reproduction furniture and effects. The main sales are of antiques and fine art and take place every two months. The saleroom is near Great Dunmow's police station.

PARKING: *Free street parking.*
STORAGE: *No*
TRANSPORTATION: *Yes*
SHIPPING: *Yes*

BUYER'S PREMIUM: *10%*
SALES: *General furniture and collectables: monthly on third Wed of the month at 12.00 noon. Antiques and fine art: every two months on Mon at 10.00am.*
VIEWING: *General furniture and collectables: day prior 9.00am-7.00pm. Antiques and fine art: Fri and Sat prior 10.00am-4.00pm.*
REFRESHMENTS: *In saleroom at antiques and fine art sale only.*
PARKING: *Own car park; public car park opposite.*
STORAGE: *Yes*
TRANSPORTATION: *Yes*
SHIPPING: *Yes*

JOHN STACEY & SONS LTD

Leigh-on-Sea

86/90 Pall Mall. Tel: (0702) 77051

400-500 lots. This is a family-run firm, which has seen three generations of family involvement. The Staceys have been in the antiques trade since the 1930s. They were originally dealers, and today they are often asked to give lectures on antiques and the art of buying at auction. No modern furniture is sold at their auctions, which concentrate instead on antiques, works of art, silver, glass, jewellery, Victorian bric-à-brac, music boxes, and paintings. Very rarely, reproductions are sold. The saleroom has been in existence since 1960, and was converted from a church. There are two large floors, with plenty of room for lots to be displayed. Leigh-on-Sea is an old fishing village, which was well known long before Southend-on-Sea became popular.

BUYER'S PREMIUM: *10%*
SALES: *Fortnightly on Tue at 10.30am.*
VIEWING: *Sat and Mon prior 10.00am-4.00pm, day of sale from 9.00am.*
REFRESHMENTS: *None available on the premises.*
PARKING: *Own car park.*
STORAGE: *Yes*
TRANSPORTATION: *Yes*
SHIPPING: *Yes*

BLACK HORSE AGENCIES AMBROSE

Loughton

Loughton Auction Room, 149 High Road. Tel: (081) 502 3951

350-400 lots. This is a monthly auction of antique and high

BUYER'S PREMIUM: *6%*

SALES: *Monthly on last Thu of month at 11.00am.*
VIEWING: *Sat prior 9.00am-4.00pm, Mon prior 9.00am-5.00pm, Tue prior 9.00am-7.00pm.*
REFRESHMENTS: *None available on the premises.*
PARKING: *Available near by.*
STORAGE: *Yes*
TRANSPORTATION: *Yes*
SHIPPING: *Yes*

Saffron Walden

BUYER'S PREMIUM: *10%*
SALES: *General: weekly on Tue at 10.00am. Antiques and fine art: about every six weeks on Fri at 10.30am.*
VIEWING: *General: morning of sale from 8.30am. Antiques and fine art: day prior 10.00am-5.00pm, morning of sale from 8.30am.*
REFRESHMENTS: *Antiques sale days only.*
PARKING: *None available on the premises.*
STORAGE: *No*
TRANSPORTATION: *Yes*
SHIPPING: *No*

Westcliff-on-Sea

BUYER'S PREMIUM: *10%*
SALES: *Fortnightly on Thu at 2.30pm.*
VIEWING: *Wed prior 2.30pm-4.30pm, day of sale 8.00am-1.00pm.*
REFRESHMENTS: *None available on the premises.*
PARKING: *Ample parking near by.*
STORAGE: *Yes*
TRANSPORTATION: *Yes*
SHIPPING: *Yes*

quality furniture, gold, silver and jewellery, oil paintings, watercolours, porcelain, glass and ceramics, clocks, watches, barometers, and all collectable items and memorabilia. The sale always starts at 11.00am, ending at around 3.30-4.00pm. The sale is long established and well organised, with equal appeal to collectors, professional dealers and those looking for the odd handsome old piece of furniture. Potential buyers are quickly put at their ease. Loughton is on the edge of Epping Forest, with easy access from the M11/M25 interchange.

SAFFRON WALDEN AUCTIONS

Auction Sale Room, 1 Market Street. Tel: (0799) 513281

200-250 lots. The sale day is Tuesday, which is also one of Saffron Walden's two market days — and as the market is immediately outside the saleyard, things can become a little hectic. The sale takes place entirely under cover, and the saleroom itself is a much-extended old coach house. Eggs, produce and poultry are sold, as well as modern and household furniture and effects, garden tools and equipment, and a wide variety of miscellaneous items. About every six weeks there is also an antiques and fine art sale. The calendar for this Friday sale is arranged at the start of each year and is available from the sales office. Saffron Walden is worth the trip — it is an attractive jumble of medieval houses, ancient inns and Victorian public buildings. Close by is Audley End, a lavishly decorated Jacobean house which is open to the public.

CHAPEL & CHAPEL

453 London Road. Tel: (0702) 347594 and 343734

200-300 lots. This is a good general auction with an excellent mixture of modern, reproduction and antique furniture, as well as china, porcelain, paintings, various collectables and so on. As most of the goods come from private houses, there will usually be some unexpected, unusual items too: perhaps a Victorian aneroid barometer or a 19th-century grained pine door, or an Italian mandolin. Lots are sold in the order in which vendors have brought them, rather than in categories. The saleroom is open for viewing at 8.00am on the day of sale but closes for lunch, so arrive early or go the day before to look round. It is usually acceptable to move about quietly while the auction is in progress.

GLOUCESTERSHIRE

TAYLER & FLETCHER

The British Legion Hall, off Lansdown Road. Tel: (0451) 820913
400-500 lots. Tayler & Fletcher hold monthly sales of antique
and household furniture, which take place either on a Tuesday
or a Saturday. Lots may come from local houses and cottages,
and include pine, Victorian and Edwardian furniture.
Specialist sales are also held throughout the year. These may be
devoted to sporting equipment and associated items, pictures
and prints, or other subject areas.

Spring and autumn sales of nursery stock are also held by the
auctioneers in March and November. The stock at these sales
includes shrubs, hedging plants, ornamental trees and bedding
plants.

Bourton-on-the-Water

BUYER'S PREMIUM: *Nil*
SALES: *General: monthly on
Sat at 10.00am or Tue at
2.00pm. Specialist sales on Sat
at 10.00am. Nursery stock:
twice a year on Fri at 2.00pm.*
VIEWING: *Monthly Sat sale:
day prior, 3.00pm-6.00pm,
and morning of sale. Monthly
Tue sale: day of sale from
12.00 noon. Nursery stock:
day of sale.*
REFRESHMENTS: *Yes*
PARKING: *Yes*
STORAGE: *By arrangement.*
TRANSPORTATION: *Yes*
SHIPPING: *Yes*

HOBBS & CHAMBERS

Chapel Walk. Tel: (0242) 513722
300-400 lots. Hobbs & Chambers hold fortnightly Tuesday
auctions at their Chapel Walk saleroom in Cheltenham, but
they also host monthly auctions on Fridays at the Bingham
Hall, King Street, Cirencester. Antique, Victorian and
Edwardian furniture, clocks and barometers, Oriental
carpets and rugs, *objets d'art*, pottery, porcelain and glass are
all regularly sold at these events. Many of the sales are
organised in specialist areas, covering silver, jewellery, oil
paintings, watercolours, toys, dolls and models, weapons
and militaria, and other collectables. Art Deco and Art
Nouveau items appear at these auctions with some
regularity, as do scientific instruments, stamps, coins and
medals, and post and cigarette cards.

Cheltenham

BUYER'S PREMIUM: *10%*
SALES: *Fortnightly on Tue at
11.00am (or on Wed at
11.00am in weeks when there is
a Bank Holiday); monthly on
Fri at 9.30am (Cirencester
saleroom).*
VIEWING: *Mon prior,
10.00am-5.00pm and day of
sale; Thu prior,
10.30am-8.00pm (Cirencester
saleroom).*
REFRESHMENTS:
*Available on the premises at
Cirencester only.*
PARKING: *None on the
premises.*
STORAGE: *Yes*
TRANSPORTATION: *Yes*
SHIPPING: *Yes*

MALLAMS
See MALLAMS, Oxford, Oxfordshire

Cheltenham

HOBBS & CHAMBERS
*See HOBBS & CHAMBERS, Cheltenham,
Gloucestershire*

Cirencester

Wotton-under-Edge

BUYER'S PREMIUM: 10%
SALES: Monthly on Tue and Wed at 10.30am.
VIEWING: Mon prior, 10.00am-6.00pm.
REFRESHMENTS: Own café.
PARKING: Own car park.
STORAGE: Yes
TRANSPORTATION: Yes
SHIPPING: Yes

SANDOE LUCE PANES

Wotton Auction Rooms, Tabernacle Road. Tel: (0453) 844733

900-1,000 lots. Sandoe Luce Panes hold monthly antiques sales lasting two days at their main saleroom in Tabernacle Road, Wotton-under-Edge. The bidding is arranged so that smaller lots, such as ceramics, clocks and barometers, watches, jewellery, silver, silver plate, glass, brassware, pictures and books are auctioned on the first day (Tuesday), leaving larger items of antique and quality furniture and effects to be sold on the second day (Wednesday).

GREATER LONDON

Crayford

BUYER'S PREMIUM: Nil
SALES: Weekly on Wed at 10.00am.
VIEWING: Tue prior 4.30pm-8.30pm and day of sale from 9.00am.
REFRESHMENTS: Own café.
PARKING: None available on the premises.
STORAGE: Yes
TRANSPORTATION: Yes
SHIPPING: Yes

ALBERT ANDREWS AUCTIONS & SALES

Farm Buildings, Maiden Lane. Tel: (0322) 528868

350-400 lots. Crayford is only 30 minutes away from central London by train, or 40 minutes away by car. These excellent weekly auctions, which have been well known locally for more than 20 years, are held in attractively converted farm buildings. They include a wide choice of goods, and plenty of household furniture and effects. Antiques and paintings may also appear among the lots. Selling begins with smaller items, and then moves on to furniture. China, glass, paintings, jewellery and collectables are auctioned next, followed by more furniture. There is usually plenty of bric-à-brac, plus kitchenalia, gardening equipment and books. The lots are well worth browsing through.

Croydon

BUYER'S PREMIUM: 10%
SALES: Weekly on Sat at 10.00am and on Wed at 11.00am.
VIEWING: Sat sale: Fri prior 9.00am-4.45pm and day of sale from 9.00am. Wed sale: day of sale from 9.00am-11.00am.
REFRESHMENTS: Own café.

ROSANS & COMPANY

Croydon Auction Rooms, 144/150 London Road. Tel: (081) 688 1123

500-1,000 lots. Croydon is a mini-Houston; it has skyscrapers and flyovers, and one of the greatest concentrations of offices outside central London. London Road is in the (as yet) unmodernised part of town, and Rosans & Company have a very large saleroom next door to Croydon General Hospital. These auctions have been popular locally since they were first established over 30 years ago. Almost anything is sold here, from general household furniture to antiques and bankrupt stock. There is no particular order to the sales; typewriters and office equipment might be sold before or after china and antique furniture.

PARKING: *Plenty on street.*
STORAGE: *No*
TRANSPORTATION: *Yes*
SHIPPING: *Yes*

BAINBRIDGE'S

Ruislip

The Great Barn, Bury Street. Tel: (081) 579 2966

500-600 lots. Bainbridge's were brought to my attention by a reader of this book, and I shall certainly be going to their sales again in future. The saleroom is a beautiful, converted barn dating from the 14th century. It is part of an attractive complex which includes a library and some tea rooms at the top of the main shopping street in Old Ruislip. The auctions are packed with interest and constantly surprising; they comprise a wide range of goods, from antiques to general household furniture and effects. Prices may range from £10 to many thousands.

Sales usually follow a set pattern: pictures are followed by small items and bric-à-brac (china, glass, toys, old radios and so on), jewellery and silver. When these are sold there is an hour-long break before the furniture auction begins.

There is a 'paddle' bidding system in operation, which means that potential bidders are required to register before the sale begins. They are then allocated a number on a card (or 'paddle') which must be raised during the bidding. It is a good idea to register even if you go in with no intention of buying, as you may well find something that you would like to bid for as you browse through the lots, and you will also be able to receive notification of future sales.

BUYER'S PREMIUM: *10%*
SALES: *On average every six weeks on Thu at 10.30am.*
VIEWING: *Day prior 1.00pm-7.00pm, and day of sale from 9.30am.*
REFRESHMENTS: *Café in complex.*
PARKING: *Own car park.*
STORAGE: *Yes*
TRANSPORTATION: *Yes*
SHIPPING: *Yes*

GREATER MANCHESTER

JOHN ARNOLD & COMPANY

Altrincham

Arnolds Yard, Old Market Place. Tel: (061) 928 3724

500-600 lots. Although Altrincham looks like a part of Greater Manchester on the map, the locals insist that it is in Cheshire. Wherever it is, the saleroom is in the oldest part of town where the roads are still cobbled, and it may be a little difficult to find for the newcomer. The best landmark is the Unicorn Hotel, a large white building. The entrance to the saleroom is along Albert Place, the small narrow road beside the hotel. Once found, the sale is packed with goods of all

BUYER'S PREMIUM: *Nil*
SALES: *Fortnightly on Wed at 10.30am.*
VIEWING: *Day prior 10.30am-4.30pm, 7.30pm-8.30pm.*
REFRESHMENTS: *None available on the premises.*
PARKING: *Own car park.*
STORAGE: *Yes*

TRANSPORTATION: *Yes*
SHIPPING: *Yes*

types, and it is a wonder that everything will be sold by the end of the day.

Starting the auction are domestic electrical appliances, refrigerators, cookers, freezers, gardening equipment, perhaps the odd garden gate, carpets, and any large item which doesn't fit into the furniture category. This part of the sale takes around one-and-a-half hours, and is followed by a 30-minute break for lunch. At 12.30pm the selling of furniture and other general household items begins, including antiques. The sale finishes with *objets d'art*.

Bury

BUYER'S PREMIUM:
10% (vehicles 5%).
SALES: *Often on Wed at 10.00am, but check with auctioneer.*
VIEWING: *Day prior 12.00 noon-7.30pm.*
REFRESHMENTS: *Own café.*
PARKING: *Own car park.*
STORAGE: *Yes*
TRANSPORTATION: *Yes*
SHIPPING: *No*

J R PARKINSON SON & HAMER AUCTIONS

Auction Rooms, Rochdale Road. Tel: (061) 761 1612

600-700 lots. The saleroom building is a converted church, just off Junction 2 of the M66, heading towards Bury Town. This is an interesting auction because the type of lots varies so much from week to week. The frequency of sales varies too: there are often two or three in a week, but in some weeks no sale is held. About 50 sales are held in total per year. The firm are bonded auctioneers for the county courts, Inland Revenue, HM Customs and Excise, the Official Receiver and various liquidators, so in addition to furniture and household items you may find motor vehicles, office furniture (such as desks, typewriters and filing cabinets), or perhaps new clothing, jewellery and sewing machines. The bankrupt stock from a single company often warrants a sale of its own.

Eccles

BUYER'S PREMIUM: *Nil*
SALES: *Weekly on Mon at*

STEPHEN SHAWCROSS & SON (AUCTIONEERS) LTD

103/105 Church Street. Tel: (061) 789 3537

250-300 lots. The auction was established in 1870 and is now a weekly sale. Local people, private buyers and dealers rush around to study the lots with the anticipatory air of excitement shown by any gold prospector shaking his sieve. You can bid for almost anything here — general household furniture and effects, electrical goods of all kinds, kitchen items, garden tools and equipment, bric-à-brac and so on. You will also find cutlery and china, jewellery and books, with bargains in all departments.

Every four weeks the general sale is replaced by a sale of antiques, including furniture, paintings, porcelain, silver and silver plate, jewellery, furniture and collectables. The variety of lots offered is as rich as in the general sale, but the goods in the antiques sale are older.

AUCTION INTERNATIONAL (MANCHESTER)

Manchester

51a Broughton Lane, Strangeways. Tel: (061) 832 2400

300-500 lots. The saleroom is to the north of the city, close to Strangeways Prison, and has a massive selling space of 10,000 sq ft. Sales are aimed at the trade rather than private buyers. If an item comes to the sale in packs of 12, then that is how it will be sold. However, there are bargains to be had, even if you are a private buyer.

The fortnightly Thursday sale is of 'fancy goods', which can include clothes, toys, domestic cookware and other items. On the last Tuesday of each month except December a catering sale is held. This offers catering, baking, banqueting, canteen, restaurant and shop equipment, utensils and furnishings.

BUYER'S PREMIUM: 5%
SALES: *Fancy goods: fortnightly on Thu at 11.00am. Catering Equipment: monthly on last Tue of month (except Dec) at 10.30am.*
VIEWING: *Both sales: day prior 9.00am-4.00pm.*
REFRESHMENTS: *Own café.*
PARKING: *Own car park.*
STORAGE: *No*
TRANSPORTATION: *Yes*
SHIPPING: *Yes*

CAPES DUNN & CO

Manchester

The Auction Galleries, 38 Charles Street. Tel: (061) 273 1911

500-600 lots. Charles Street is off Princess Street and close to Piccadilly Railway Station. The firm was established in 1826, and holds two busy, comprehensive auctions per week. Every Monday there is a sale of Victorian and later furniture and effects, which means general household articles, often from complete house clearances. This sale is held on the ground floor. Every Tuesday, on the first or second floor, there are specialist sales in various categories such as ceramics and glass, fine furniture, musical instruments, oil paintings and watercolours, jewellery, silver, textiles and costume, books and prints, collectables and many others.

BUYER'S PREMIUM: 10%
SALES: *General: weekly on Mon at 12.00 noon. Specialist: weekly on Tue at 12.00 noon.*
VIEWING: *General: morning of sale from 10.00am. Specialist: day prior 10.00am-4.00pm and morning of sale from 10.00am.*
REFRESHMENTS: *None available on the premises.*
PARKING: *Charles Street NCP.*
STORAGE: *Yes*
TRANSPORTATION: *Yes*
SHIPPING: *Yes*

Also at top of right column (continued):

1.00pm (includes antiques sale every four weeks).
VIEWING: *Day of sale from 9.30am.*
REFRESHMENTS: *None available on the premises.*
PARKING: *Own car park.*
STORAGE: *No*
TRANSPORTATION: *Yes*
SHIPPING: *Yes*

Stalybridge

BUYER'S PREMIUM: 10%
SALES: General: weekly on Sat at 10.00am. Antiques: every three weeks on Tue at 11.00am. Fancy goods: every three weeks on Wed at 11.00am. Oldham trade auctions: every three weeks on Thu at 11.00am.
VIEWING: Day of sale from 9.00am.
REFRESHMENTS: Own café.
PARKING: Own car park.
STORAGE: No
TRANSPORTATION: Yes
SHIPPING: Yes

Stockport

BUYER'S PREMIUM: 5%
SALES: About 10 times a year on Thu at 6.30pm.
VIEWING: Day of sale from 1.00pm in hotel, or two days prior from 11.00am-4.00pm at A F Brock Ltd's premises.
REFRESHMENTS: Own café.
PARKING: Own car park.
STORAGE: Yes
TRANSPORTATION: Yes
SHIPPING: Yes

Stockport

BUYER'S PREMIUM: Nil
SALES: At frequent intervals.
VIEWING: Usually day prior 10.00am-3.30pm and day of sale from 9.30am, but telephone to check.

HIGHAMS

Waterloo House, Waterloo Road. Tel: (061) 338 8698

400-500 lots. Highams are a large and well-known firm holding a series of sales in Stalybridge and at Southgate Court, Southgate Street, Oldham. Although the public are welcome, the Oldham sales are mainly for trade and include plant and machinery, bankrupt or fire-damaged goods, catering equipment and so on. A fortnightly sale of private saloon cars and commercial vehicles is also held here, on Saturdays at 11.00am.

The building in Stalybridge is next door to the bus centre, and is a massive place with three separate salerooms. Saleroom 3 is where the popular weekly Saturday auctions are held, for general bric-à-brac, household sundries, furniture, televisions, electrical goods, gardening equipment and so on. The other two salerooms are used for midweek auctions, which take place every three weeks.

In saleroom 1, every third Tuesday, there is an auction of good antiques, including paintings and jewellery. In saleroom 2, every third Wednesday, the sale is of office furniture, toys and all types of fancy goods. This is mainly aimed at dealers but can be interesting for others.

A F BROCK LTD

269 London Road, Hazel Grove. Tel: (061) 456 5050

500-600 lots. There is no furniture in this auction, which is mainly of collectables — coins, jewellery, cigarette cards, porcelain, silver and silver plate, postage stamps, autographs, ephemera, jewellery, medals and so on, with prices ranging from a pound or two up to a couple of thousand.

The sales take place about 10 times a year at the Acton Court Hotel, 187 Buxton Road, Stockport. There is always something of interest, and a visit makes an entertaining evening out for bargain hunters and collectors alike.

PHILIP DAVIES & SONS

The Auction Centre, Newby Road, Hazel Grove.
Tel: (061) 483 2637

Up to 500 lots. This is another auction in Stockport which is out of the normal category but worth a visit. The regular sales are mainly of liquidated stock with an emphasis on office furniture — desks, typewriters, filing cabinets, photocopying machines, chairs, computers and so on — but almost anything can come up. Vehicles, musical instruments, wood-working machinery, tools and building materials have all featured, and one sale contained 15 full-size snooker tables. As the items are from insolvency-related cases, all lots are offered without reserve prices.

The auctioneer will advise on the types of goods to be sold, so make an enquiry before setting out on a journey. The saleroom is a large warehouse about three miles from the centre of the town. The firm also holds auctions at the premises of companies based throughout the region, on behalf of insolvency practitioners.

REFRESHMENTS: *Own café.*
PARKING: *Own car park.*
STORAGE: *Yes*
TRANSPORTATION: *Yes*
SHIPPING: *Yes*

HAMPSHIRE

ANDOVER SALEROOM

41a London Street. Tel: (0264) 364820

700-800 lots. The fortnightly Monday sale is always a busy event at this most cheerful saleroom. Bob Herbert, the auctioneer, exchanges jokes with the crowd, many of whom he is on first-name terms with. This is an ideal place to begin for those worried by the thought of buying at auction, and there is always a wide variety of goods here. The Monday sale begins in a building outside the main saleroom and might include stripped pine furniture, beds, electrical goods, lawn mowers, gardening tools and so on. Waxed pine furniture is usually sold in the main saleroom, followed by 1930s and 1940s furniture, brass, porcelain, copper and silver. The sale finishes with antique furniture.

The fortnightly sale on the previous Saturday is of jewellery, pictures, paintings and drawings only. The sale of pictures and paintings takes place at 2.00pm, and the sale of jewellery at 3.30pm.

Andover

BUYER'S PREMIUM: *Nil*
SALES: *General: fortnightly on Mon at 10.00am. Jewellery, pictures, paintings and drawings: fortnightly on previous Sat at 2.00pm.*
VIEWING: *Fri prior 9.00am-9.00pm.*
REFRESHMENTS: *Own café.*
PARKING: *Public car park near by.*
STORAGE: *Yes*
TRANSPORTATION: *Yes*
SHIPPING: *Yes*

MAY & SON

Penton Mewsey Village Hall, Penton Mewsey.
Tel: (0264) 323417 and 363331

300-400 lots. Penton Mewsey is just two miles west of Andover, in a wonderful country setting. A visit to the sale makes an ideal day out in an attractive Hampshire village, with country walks near by and excellent local pubs. The refreshments available in the hall during the sale are made in the village, and very good they are too.

The sale includes antique, period, Victorian and Edwardian furniture (English and Continental), silver, silver plate,

Andover

BUYER'S PREMIUM: *Nil*
SALES: *Monthly on third Wed of month at 10.30am.*
VIEWING: *Day prior 8.00am-4.00pm.*
REFRESHMENTS: *Own café.*
PARKING: *Own parking area.*
STORAGE: *Yes*

TRANSPORTATION: *Yes*
SHIPPING: *Yes*

pottery, china, porcelain, pictures, and so on. All the lots are from private sources as a matter of policy, in order to keep the sales 'fresh'. Frank May, who runs the auction with his son John, has been in the business for over 55 years, earning a well-deserved reputation over that period. The sale attracts dealers and private buyers from local towns such as Basingstoke. It also attracts bidders from much further afield, as well as regulars of many years' standing. Specialist sales of antique toys and textiles are also held once or twice a year, if enough lots have been accumulated.

Basingstoke

BASINGSTOKE AUCTION ROOMS

82/84 Sarum Hill. Tel: (0256) 840707

BUYER'S PREMIUM: 10%
(nil at Heckfield).
SALES: *Mon or Wed at 6.00pm (fortnightly general sale); Tue at 10.30am (six to eight-weekly antiques and fine art sale); Sat at 10.30am (monthly sale, Heckfield).*
VIEWING: *Sat prior, 10.00am-3.00pm (fortnightly general sale); Fri prior, 10.00am-8.00pm, Sat prior, 10.00am-3.00pm, and Mon prior, 10.00am-5.00pm and 6.00pm-9.00pm (six or eight-weekly antiques and fine art sale).*
REFRESHMENTS:
Available on the premises at Heckfield, but not at Basingstoke.
PARKING: *Basingstoke: 40 spaces at rear. Heckfield: ample space.*
STORAGE: *Both: yes*
TRANSPORTATION:
Both: yes
SHIPPING: *Both: yes*

200-300 lots. There are country auctions and there are town auctions, and this is one of the latter. The auctioneers occupy an unimposing building in a part of Basingstoke that has not, as yet, been built up with office blocks. There are two small, low-ceilinged salerooms here, one of which is packed full of large items of furniture on sale days. The lots in the fortnightly sale can be rather nondescript, but the sale of antiques and fine art held here every six to eight weeks is usually more interesting. Past sales have included Georgian mahogany bookcases, mahogany grand pianos, rosewood tables and fine paintings.

The Basingstoke Auction Rooms also run a monthly sale of general household furniture and effects (which sometimes includes antiques) at the Village Hall, Church Lane, Heckfield, Hampshire.

Bishop's Waltham

WEST HOE AUCTIONS

The Youth Hall, Malt Lane. Tel: (0329) 664806

BUYER'S PREMIUM: 5%
SALES: *Every six weeks on Sat at 10.00am.*
VIEWING: *Day prior 6.00pm-9.00pm and day of sale from 9.00am.*
REFRESHMENTS: *Own café.*
PARKING: *Own car park.*
STORAGE: *Yes*

300-400 lots. The Youth Hall is on the corner of Malt Lane, opposite the old abbey ruins. These are open to the public and make a pleasant day out when they are combined with a trip to West Hoe Auctions. The company is a family concern, run by Mr and Mrs Longman, who share the large workload arising from their popular sales.

A variety of general household furniture and effects is included among the lots, and there will also be antique and shipping furniture, collectors' items and pictures. There is also a good selection of jewellery, silver and ornaments (of varying value) in what is termed the 'cabinet' part of the sale. All kinds of people attend — from dealers and collectors to browsers and the simply curious. The saleroom is friendly, informal and noisy.

TRANSPORTATION: Yes
SHIPPING: Yes

FORDINGBRIDGE SALE ROOMS

The Saleroom, Roundhill. Tel: (0425) 652121

350-500 lots. Roundhill is a short road close to the town centre's only car park. The saleroom can be found easily, particularly on sale days when it is a hive of activity. The sales are of quality antique, reproduction and modern furniture and effects. Proceedings begin outside, where various garden tools, benches and wheelbarrows are sold off. Inside the saleroom, linen, carpets, electrical goods, books, porcelain, glass and paintings are up for bidding at the same time. After an hour-long lunch break the auction resumes with good quality household furniture and effects.

Fordingbridge

BUYER'S PREMIUM: 10%
SALES: *Monthly on the first Thu of the month at 10.00am.*
VIEWING: *Day prior 9.00am-4.00pm.*
REFRESHMENTS: *None available on the premises.*
PARKING: *Town centre car park (100 yards away).*
STORAGE: *No*
TRANSPORTATION: Yes
SHIPPING: Yes

MEDLAMS

26c Brockhampton Lane. Tel: (0705) 498098

500 lots. Where, other than at a good auction, could you buy a Victorian dresser, various tables and display cabinets, porcelain and pottery, genuine old copper and brass, kettles, ships' lanterns, office furniture and computers, bicycles and police lost property, plus a lorry or van to take it all home in? Not even Harrods could supply all that! It is worth having a good look round, as it is possible to miss some very interesting items otherwise. A bicycle may be offered for sale among lots of furniture, and a Victorian gentleman's wardrobe may be preceded and followed by pine chests of drawers. Outside are lorries, cars, vans and trailers, which are sold at around 6.00pm.

Havant

BUYER'S PREMIUM: 10% *(£20 maximum payable).*
SALES: *Fortnightly on Tue at 5.30pm.*
VIEWING: *Day of sale from 9.30am.*
REFRESHMENTS: *Available.*
PARKING: *Own car park.*
STORAGE: Yes
TRANSPORTATION: Yes
SHIPPING: Yes

BASINGSTOKE AUCTION ROOMS
See BASINGSTOKE AUCTION ROOMS, Basingstoke, Hampshire

Heckfield

ODIHAM AUCTION SALES

North Warnborough Village Hall. Tel: (0784) 39347

600-800 lots. The Village Hall at North Warnborough is easily accessible, making it popular with the dealers and collectors who attend. North Warnborough is only a mile away from

North Warnborough

BUYER'S PREMIUM: 10%
SALES: *Bi-monthly on Wed at 2.00pm.*
VIEWING: *Day prior*

6.00pm-9.00pm and day of
sale from 9.30pm.
REFRESHMENTS: Own
café.
PARKING: Ample parking
near by.
STORAGE: Yes
TRANSPORTATION: Yes
SHIPPING: Yes

Petersfield

BUYER'S PREMIUM: 10%
SALES: Every six to eight
weeks on Fri at 10.00am.
VIEWING: Thu prior
10.00am-6.30pm.
REFRESHMENTS: None
available on the premises, but
available near by.
PARKING: Public car park
near by.
STORAGE: Yes
TRANSPORTATION: Yes
SHIPPING: Yes

Ringwood

BUYER'S PREMIUM: 10%
SALES: Monthly on Fri at
10.00am.
VIEWING: Day prior
10.00am-4.00pm and morning
of sale from 9.00am.
REFRESHMENTS: None
available on the premises.
PARKING: Own car park, or
public car park 200 yards away.
STORAGE: Yes
TRANSPORTATION: Yes
SHIPPING: Yes

Romsey

BUYER'S PREMIUM: 8%
SALES: Antiques: monthly on
Tue at 11.00am. Silver and

Junction 5 of the M3, and about half a mile away from the pretty village of Odiham, with its Georgian houses and interesting old buildings. North Warnborough itself is not so much a village as a few houses with a pub, strung out on either side of the A287.

Despite this, the Village Hall hosts rather up-market sales of antiques, paintings, porcelain, silver and collectors' items, and prices can range from as little as £20 to £20,000 and more. The proceedings are conducted briskly; the auctioneer knows what he is about, and clearly expects the same from his bidders.

JACOBS & HUNT

Lavant Street. Tel: (0730) 262744

500-600 lots. Petersfield is a pleasant Georgian town. An ideal day out for the family would be a picnic at Heath and Lake (where there are rowing boats and canoes for hire, a playground for the children, and ducks for the youngsters to feed), and then a visit to a sale at Jacobs & Hunt, whose premises are close to the railway station. Here there are general sales of high quality antique, modern and reproduction furniture, general household effects, miscellaneous and collectors' items, books, pictures, photographs, toys, porcelain, pottery, bronze, copper and brass, silver and silver plate, glass, and jewellery. Whether you are a recent winner on the pools, or on the dole, there will be something here for you. At one recent auction a Dutch oil painting fetched £60,000, and a wardrobe sold for just £5.

PHILLIPS

54 Southampton Road. Tel: (0425) 473333

400-500 lots. The saleroom is about 200 yards away from Ringwood's main car park, on the outskirts of the town centre. Phillips hold catalogued sales from their Southampton Road premises on a monthly basis. They are popular events, attracting plenty of interested bidders from the surrounding area. Georgian, Victorian and later furniture and effects are sold, together with smaller items: ceramics, glass, metalware, pictures, silver, books, jewellery, collectables and the like. Typically, prices range from as little as £10 to several hundreds.

MICHAEL G BAKER FSVA

Romsey Auction Rooms, 86 The Hundred. Tel: (0794) 513331

300-400 lots. The firm holds one sale of antiques a month, which usually includes Victorian and later furniture, and all manner of curiosities discovered in attics, cellars and garden sheds. The lots are fun, and many provide an excellent way to furnish a house without paying a fortune. Beds, dressers, settees, bureaux, wash-stands, tables, chairs, and other objects are up for bidding. A gas mask, a bag of razors, some brushes and chess pieces, a glass lantern and a set of scales, were all sold in one box of bric-à-brac recently, and there was no difficulty in finding a buyer. Part of the fun of attending a country auction is not only finding a bargain for yourself, but also working out just what a buyer is going to do with some of his more bizarre purchases.

Every other month, there is also a two-day sale of silver and jewellery here. The staff are happy to help if people wish to view lots outside the official viewing times.

jewellery: alternate months on Tue and Wed at 11.00am.
VIEWING: Day prior 12.00 noon-7.30pm.
REFRESHMENTS: None available on the premises.
PARKING: Own small car park.
STORAGE: Yes
TRANSPORTATION: Yes
SHIPPING: Yes

MILLBANK AUCTIONEERS LTD

Southampton

72 Millbank Street, Northam. Tel: (0703) 228179

400-1,000 lots. Almost anything can be bought at a Millbank auction: plant and machinery, vans, cars, office furniture, desks, typewriters, filing cabinets, antique and modern household furniture, china, pictures, paintings, and jewellery. As Southampton is a port, many lots have connections with fishing and boating. Millbank are agents for the Sheriff of Hampshire, the Official Receiver, the county courts and bailiffs, as well as private sources, and they are one of the largest auctioneers in the area. It is not unusual to find as many as 1,000 people attending their sales. The two-day viewing period is a great help to prospective bidders. Like most other auctioneers, Millbank are happy to make bids on your behalf, if you are unable to attend a sale in person.

BUYER'S PREMIUM: Nil
SALES: Monthly on Thu at 10.00am.
VIEWING: Tue and Wed prior 8.30am-5.00pm.
REFRESHMENTS: Own café.
PARKING: Own car park.
STORAGE: Yes
TRANSPORTATION: Yes
SHIPPING: Yes

D M NESBIT

Southsea

7 Clarendon Road. Tel: (0705) 864321

350-600 lots. Southsea is a town with many holiday attractions, but few match the sight of the constant coming and going of ships through the harbour mouth. The saleroom is situated just opposite the main post office, and near the sea front. Sales here have a definite nautical bias, and D M Nesbit have established a reputation both nationally and internationally as one of the leading auction rooms in the country for the sale of marine paintings, both by local and internationally known artists. Porcelain, ceramics and glass, metalware, oil paintings, watercolour drawings, engravings, prints, china and 18th-century and later furniture are some of the main categories, but they do not appear in the same order at each sale.

BUYER'S PREMIUM: 10%
SALES: Monthly on Wed at 10.30am.
VIEWING: Mon and Tue prior 9.30am-5.00pm.
REFRESHMENTS: None available on the premises, but available near by.
PARKING: Public car parks near by.
STORAGE: Yes
TRANSPORTATION: Yes
SHIPPING: Yes

Winchester

BUYER'S PREMIUM: 10%
SALES: General: fortnightly
on Thu at 11.00am. Specialist:
bi-monthly on Tue at 11.00am.
VIEWING: General: day
prior 10.00am-5.00pm and day
of sale from 9.00am. Specialist:
Sat prior 9.00am-12.00 noon
and day prior 10.00am-6.00pm.
REFRESHMENTS: Coffee
machine on the premises.
PARKING: Own car park.
STORAGE: Yes
TRANSPORTATION: Yes
SHIPPING: Yes

PHILLIPS

The Red House, Hyde Street. Tel: (0962) 862515
300-400 lots. The Red House is a pleasant Victorian building
close to the Theatre Royal. Both general and specialist
auctions take place at this excellent saleroom, where there will
be something to suit most pockets and tastes. The fortnightly
Thursday general sale is devoted to Georgian, Victorian and
modern furniture, as well as ceramics, books and pictures.

Two separate bi-monthly auctions are also held at the
saleroom. The first is given over to antique furniture and works
of art, including pictures, metalware, ceramics, rugs and
collectors' items, while the second concentrates on silver and
jewellery.

HEREFORD &
WORCESTER

Great Malvern

BUYER'S PREMIUM: 10%
SALES: Twice monthly on
first and third Thu of the month
at 10.30am (includes antiques
and fine art sale five times a
year).
VIEWING: General: day
prior 2.00pm-4.30pm.
Antiques: 12.00 noon-8.00pm.
REFRESHMENTS: Own
café.
PARKING: Ample parking
near by.
STORAGE: Yes
TRANSPORTATION: No
SHIPPING: No

HAMPTONS FINE ART, POCOCK & LEAR

Malvern Salerooms, Barnards Green Road. Tel: (0684) 892315
300-400 lots. A sale of general household furniture and effects
is held on the first and third Thursday of each month. Among
the lots might be chairs, desks, cabinets, mattresses, sitting
room and bedroom furnishings, such as wardrobes and dressing
tables, and smaller items, such as clocks, mirrors, desk lamps,
copper, china and glass, books, carpets and rugs and a number
of miscellaneous items.

Five times a year a special antiques and fine art sale is held
in place of one of the general sales. These special sales attract
buyers from all over the country and include antique furniture,
paintings and watercolours, drawings, prints and miniatures,
china, porcelain, silver and plate, jewellery, collectables,
ceramics, glass and other items.

Hartlebury, near Kidderminster

BUYER'S PREMIUM: £1
per lot.
SALES: Monthly on third Sat
of month at 11.00am.
VIEWING: Day prior
3.30pm-6.00pm, morning of
sale from 8.30am.
REFRESHMENTS: Own
café.

PHIPPS & PRITCHARD

Hartlebury Village Hall. Tel: (0562) 822244
700-800 lots. Hartlebury is an old village about half a mile off
the A449 and roughly three miles south of Kidderminster. It
has a couple of pleasant pubs where many buyers can be found
waiting for their lots to come under the hammer. The sale is
rather up-market for a country auction, and most of the lots are
antiques, although increasing amounts of better quality 1930s

furniture can be found. There will also be coins, medals, stamps and other collectors' items, plus silver, plate, china, porcelain, pewter, watercolours, oils, drawings, prints and so on. The sale starts with smaller items, but always moves on to furniture at 2.30pm. If there are any 'smalls' still to be sold, they are auctioned once the furniture sale is over.

PARKING: *Own car park.*
STORAGE: *Yes*
TRANSPORTATION: *No*
SHIPPING: *Yes*

KIDDERMINSTER MARKET AUCTIONS

Kidderminster

Comberton Place. Tel: (0562) 741303

800-1000 lots. These auctions make a good day out for the entire family. In the same market area as the sale there are stalls selling local crafts, clothes, antiques and general bric-à-brac. At the sale itself, it is possible to spend a few pounds or a few hundred pounds bidding for anything from a bag of potatoes to a piece of Royal Doulton china.

The auction starts at 10.30am with 20 or 30 bicycles, in an assortment of conditions and styles. These are followed by 'smalls' — bric-à-brac, china and the like. At 11.00am another auctioneer begins the outside sale of lesser-value furniture and outdoor items, such as garden tools and mowers. As might be expected in a town famous for carpet manufacturing, there is a separate sale for carpets, which begins inside at the same time.

In yet another area, 11.00am also sees the start of the sale of shrubs and farm produce, where around 500 lots are offered at the height of the season. The sale of better quality furniture begins at around 1.30pm in the main saleroom, and may include modern, reproduction and antique items.

The auctioneers also hold weekly special sales of spring shrubs from March to June, and weekly autumn special sales in September and October.

BUYER'S PREMIUM: *7% (not furniture).*
SALES: *Weekly on Thu at 10.30am; weekly on Sat at 10.30am (spring and autumn special sales).*
VIEWING: *Day prior 3.00pm-6.00pm; none (spring and autumn special sales).*
REFRESHMENTS: *Café and licensed premises.*
PARKING: *Own car park.*
STORAGE: *Yes*
TRANSPORTATION: *Yes*
SHIPPING: *Yes*

KINGSLAND AUCTION SERVICES LTD

Leominster

Shirl Heath, Kingsland. Tel: (0568) 708564

1,000-1,200 lots. The saleroom is a little off the beaten track: take the A44 out of Leominster towards Kington, then at Shirl Heath take the A4110. The premises are also used for weekly car auctions, however, so most local people will be able to point you in the right direction. The general sale is massive, and for many it makes as much an entertaining night out as a place to pick up bargains. Anything from front doors to the entire contents of a house have been sold at one time or another at these sales.

In order to finish sales at a reasonable time, auctioning takes place simultaneously in different parts of the premises. Articles sold in the large warehouse might include timber, car parts, odd

BUYER'S PREMIUM: *Nil*
SALES: *Weekly on Wed at 6.00pm.*
VIEWING: *Day of sale from 2.00pm.*
REFRESHMENTS: *Own café.*
PARKING: *Own car park.*
STORAGE: *No*
TRANSPORTATION: *Yes*
SHIPPING: *Yes*

pieces of copper piping, earthenware sinks, baths, toilet bowls and the like. Meanwhile, the main sale takes place in the adjoining saleroom. Behind the auctioneer's area there is a small room set out with tables laden with china, ornaments, antiquarian books, silver, bygones, postcards, cigarette cards, toys and other collector's items. Also here is a locked cabinet where the most valuable small articles are kept. Furniture, ranging from antique to the nearly new, is displayed in front of the auctioneer's stand. Everything has to be sold by the end of the evening.

Leominster

BUYER'S PREMIUM: 10%
SALES: *General: weekly on Thu at 10.30am (but not in the week prior to fine art and antiques sales). Fine art and antiques: monthly on first Wed and Thu of the month at 10.00am. Malvern antiques and effects: monthly on the third Tue of the month at 11.00am.*
VIEWING: *General: day prior 12.00 noon-5.00pm. Fine art and antiques: day prior 10.00am-4.00pm. Malvern antiques and effects: day prior 10.00am-4.00pm.*
REFRESHMENTS: *Leominster: own canteen. Malvern: none available on the premises.*
PARKING: *Both: ample near by.*
STORAGE: *Yes*
TRANSPORTATION: *Yes*
SHIPPING: *Yes*

RUSSELL BALDWIN & BRIGHT MARKETS

Ryelands Road. Tel: (0568) 611166

800-1,000 lots. Established in 1846, this is one of the most prestigious auction rooms in the West Midlands, and many bidders also come from Wales. It is privately owned, and members of the founding family are still involved in the business.

Russell Baldwin & Bright Markets hold weekly general sales, as well as monthly two-day sales of fine art and antiques. For fine art and antiques enthusiasts there is also a sale of antiques and effects on the third Tuesday of the month at The Portland Rooms, Portland Road, Malvern, tel: (0684) 893933.

Pershore

BUYER'S PREMIUM: *Nil*
SALES: *Every five to six weeks on Sat at 11.00am.*
VIEWING: *Day of sale from 9.00am.*
REFRESHMENTS: *Own café.*
PARKING: *Large public car park very close.*
STORAGE: *No*
TRANSPORTATION: *Yes*
SHIPPING: *Yes*

RICHARD WILLIAMS

2 High Street. Tel: (0386) 554031

500-600 lots. Pershore is an attractive Georgian town in the heart of fruit-growing country. If you are waiting between lots, you could look at the 14th-century bridge, which crosses the River Avon to the south of the town, or the remains of Pershore Abbey to the west. The sale occurs every five to six weeks, and is very much a social event for many of the locals. It is also a good general auction, with opportunities for bargains in the form of furniture of all ages and conditions — not only everyday chairs, tables and bedroom suites, but also unusual items, such as a Victorian mahogany-cased organ, or an enormous serpentine-fronted sideboard with a back mirror. Most sales have plenty of jewellery and china (domestic and ornamental), and other household effects as well.

ARROW AUCTIONS (REDDITCH)

Redditch

Arrow Road North. Tel: (0527) 66393
400-500 lots. The saleroom is in the Lakeside area of the town, about 50 yards from the lake itself, which is open to the public for boating. This helps to make the sale a pleasant day out, particularly for children. The popular general sale is held once a fortnight on a Wednesday, in the upstairs auction room. This sale may include police lost property, goods sold under instruction from bailiffs, or liquidated stock. These items are sold in addition to general household furniture and effects, including antiques. Also once a fortnight, but on alternate weeks to the general sale, a 'commercial sale' takes place. This is on Thursdays, beginning at 10.00am, and is devoted to a particular category of goods, for example office furniture and equipment, catering or garage equipment, or vehicles, plant and machinery. The commercial sale takes place in two sheds in the saleyard.

BUYER'S PREMIUM: 10%
SALES: *General: fortnightly on Wed at 6.00pm.
Commercial: fortnightly on Thu at 10.00am (alternate weeks to general sale).*
VIEWING: *General: day of sale from 9.00am.
Commercial: day prior 10.00am-4.00pm.*
REFRESHMENTS: *Own café.*
PARKING: *Own car park.*
STORAGE: *Yes*
TRANSPORTATION: *Yes*
SHIPPING: *Yes*

HERTFORDSHIRE

BERKHAMSTED AUCTION ROOMS

Berkhamsted

Middle Road. Tel: (0442) 865169
400-500 lots. The Auction Rooms are just off Cross Oak Road and to the rear of the large Renault showroom and garage in the High Street. If you see something you want to bid for, you must give reception your name and address in return for a numbered card. Whenever you want to bid, hold up the card so the auctioneer can see it. This is a good country-style auction with antique and modern furniture and effects. The lots can vary in price from £1 to £10,000. Lots are sold in the order in which they arrive at the saleroom, so a three-piece suite could be followed by a small china ornament or a set of cutlery. Paintings and prints are displayed at one end of the room on a rack. Outdoor items, such as bicycles and lawn mowers, can be viewed in the yard outside, although they are sold in the saleroom.

BUYER'S PREMIUM: 10%
SALES: *Fortnightly on Wed at 10.00am.*
VIEWING: *Day prior 10.00am-4.00pm and 6.00pm-8.00pm, morning of sale from 8.00am.*
REFRESHMENTS: *Own café.*
PARKING: *None available on the premises.*
STORAGE: *Yes*
TRANSPORTATION: *Yes*
SHIPPING: *Yes*

Bishops Stortford

BUYER'S PREMIUM: 10%
SALES: General: weekly on Thu at 11.00am. Antiques and fine art: monthly on Tue at 10.30am. Specialist: twice yearly in May and Nov.
VIEWING: General: day of sale from 9.00am. Antiques and fine art: Sat prior 9.00am-12.00 noon, Mon prior 10.00am-4.00pm, day of sale from 9.00am. Specialist: day of sale 10.00am-4.00pm.
REFRESHMENTS: None available on the premises, but available near by.
PARKING: Available near by.
STORAGE: Yes
TRANSPORTATION: Yes
SHIPPING: Yes

G E SWORDER & SONS

Bishops Stortford Auction Rooms, 15 Northgate End.
Tel: (0279) 651388

300-400 lots. G E Sworder & Sons are very much part of the Bishops Stortford scene, and they have a reputation which spreads much further afield. Anything can be bought at their weekly sale of general household furniture and effects. This typically includes paintings, porcelain, china, jewellery, furniture, ornaments, carpets and much else. At one sale a cabinet full of dentures and pre-war artificial limbs was sold. The latter were made of wood and had complicated pulleys. A box of bric-à-brac might contain books, teacups, packets of playing cards and a saucepan or two, with the odd article of real interest among the rest. The furniture varies in quality and value, but most sales include Victorian, Edwardian and modern items.

In addition, there are monthly sales of antiques and fine art, and twice-yearly specialist sales of toys and collectors' items, which are also well worth visiting.

Harpenden

BUYER'S PREMIUM: £2 per lot.
SALES: Monthly at 10.30am (no regular day).
VIEWING: Day prior 9.00am-5.30pm, morning of sale from 9.00am.
REFRESHMENTS: Own café.
PARKING: Own car park.
STORAGE: Yes
TRANSPORTATION: Yes
SHIPPING: Yes

HARPENDEN AUCTION ROOMS

The Harpenden Public Hall, Southdown Road. Tel: (0582) 794544

350-400 lots. The Harpenden Public Hall is in the centre of the town, close to the High Street. An auction is held every month, but the day depends on the availability of the hall, which is used for other activities. Sale dates are booked well in advance though, and a list can be obtained by ringing Harpenden Auctions. The sale has been established for over 30 years, and is run by husband and wife Martin and Jean Brunning. Lots include a wide range of general household furniture and effects, but there is an emphasis on antiques.

Hatfield

BUYER'S PREMIUM: £1 per lot.
SALES: Monthly on last Fri of month at 6.30pm.
VIEWING: Day of sale from 2.00pm.
REFRESHMENTS: Available.
PARKING: Own car park.
STORAGE: Yes
TRANSPORTATION: Yes
SHIPPING: No

LION AUCTIONS

The Red Lion, Great North Road. Tel: (0707) 654028 and 327076

400 lots. Vanessa Bennett is the proprietor, auctioneer and general factotum at this sale. She started the auction having become bored with selling on stalls, and recalls that her grandfather was a great auction-goer at a time when most sales were conducted in houses. 'People are fed up with modern furniture that collapses as soon as you get it home', she says, 'and as I love attending auctions, I decided to start one of my own.' The sale is convivial and Mrs Bennett often stops the selling to exchange a friendly word with a buyer. Among the

lots will be general furniture and effects, including antique items, jewellery, china, silver and other 'smalls', pictures, and collectors' items such as stamps and postcards — something for everyone, in fact. This is a pleasant, small auction.

ANDREW PICKFORD

The Hertford Saleroom, Castle Hall. Tel: (0992) 501421

800 lots. Good examples of 18th- and 19th-century furniture, porcelain, glass, silver, jewellery, paintings, dolls and toys, books, guns and wines regularly appear at Andrew Pickford's monthly auction.

Castle Hall is a modern building in the grounds of Hertford Castle. The centrally heated saleroom is spacious, with cloakrooms, a licensed bar and a buffet.

Hertford

BUYER'S PREMIUM: *£1.50 per lot.*
SALES: *Monthly on Thu at 9.30am.*
VIEWING: *Day prior 12.00 noon-7.00pm, and morning of sale.*
REFRESHMENTS: *Good facilities.*
PARKING: *Free parking at Hartham (off Port Hill).*
STORAGE: *Yes*
TRANSPORTATION: *Yes*
SHIPPING: *Yes*

PAMELA & BARRY AUCTIONS

The Village Hall. Tel: (0727) 861180

350-400 lots. This popular fortnightly auction includes mostly antiques, collectables and small items. There are very few items of large furniture here, and certainly no modern or reproduction. A typical sale might include jewellery of all types, silver and silver plate, china (both domestic and ornamental), porcelain, copper, brass, linen, postcards, books, dolls, paintings, prints and all types of collectors' items. In the latter category there are usually a number of 1950s toys, model railway stock, military medals and the like. A catalogue is always available on the sale day. Payment can be made and the goods removed while the sale is in progress.

Sandridge, near St Albans

BUYER'S PREMIUM: *£1 per lot.*
SALES: *Fortnightly on first and third Tue of month at 7.00pm.*
VIEWING: *Day of sale from 3.00pm.*
REFRESHMENTS: *Own café.*
PARKING: *Own car park.*
STORAGE: *No*
TRANSPORTATION: *No*
SHIPPING: *No*

Tring

BUYER'S PREMIUM:
*General sales: 5%. Fine art:
10%.*
SALES: *General: fortnightly
on Sat at 10.00am. Fine art:
monthly on last Fri of month at
11.00am.*
VIEWING: *General:
2.00pm-6.00pm.Fine art: day
prior 2.00pm-8.30pm.*
REFRESHMENTS:
Available.
PARKING: *Own car parks.*
STORAGE: *Yes*
TRANSPORTATION: *Yes*
SHIPPING: *Yes*

BROWN & MERRY

Tring Market Auctions, Brook Street. Tel: (044282) 6446

1,500-1,600 lots. The sale is on a Saturday, so it is often packed with couples searching for bargains, or with people who are 'just looking' and out to enjoy the excitement of an auction. Good quality furniture, paintings, china, porcelain, gardening equipment, garden plants and other items are sold. The general sale begins at 10.00am and offers around 1,000 lots of antique furniture, restoration pieces, modern furniture, gardening equipment, general household effects and miscellaneous items. At 11.30am, while this sale is still going on, the sale of antiques and better quality items begins in another part of the complex. A small part of the premises is used on Mondays for livestock sales, which adds to the atmosphere of this friendly and informal, but efficient, auction house.

On the last Friday of the month there are special fine art sales, with quality furniture, porcelain, pottery, silver and silver plate, paintings and prints.

Watford

BUYER'S PREMIUM: *10%*
SALES: *Fortnightly on Sat at
10.00am.*
VIEWING: *Day prior
10.00am-9.00pm.*
REFRESHMENTS: *Own
café.*
PARKING: *Multi-storey
opposite.*
STORAGE: *Yes*
TRANSPORTATION: *Yes*
SHIPPING: *Yes*

WATFORD AUCTION ROOMS

26/28 Water Lane. Tel: (0923) 212175

500-550 lots. This is a splendid general auction which attracts buyers from a wide area. It is independently owned and run by brothers Derek Mercer and John Williams (John does the auctioneering). The saleroom is close to the town centre and extends over two floors. The top floor is given over to 300-400 lots of better quality items, such as antiques, collectables, domestic and ornamental china and jewellery. The downstairs saleroom concentrates on lesser quality items, including modern furniture and bric-à-brac. Sometimes you can even find the odd boat, car or caravan for sale here.

HUMBERSIDE

A E DOWSE & SON

Foresters Gallery, Falkland Way. Tel: (0652) 32335

500-600 lots. The fortnightly Tuesday sale is of general household furniture and effects, while the monthly Saturday sale includes antique furniture, pictures, jewellery, silver, brass, copper, porcelain, glass and collector's items.

The quarterly Monday antiques and fine art sale includes similar items, but they are usually of higher value and quality. The Tuesday general sales have furniture of all types, including bedroom, dining and lounge suites, electrical goods, china (ornamental and domestic), boxes of bric-à-brac (always worth a rummage for the good items beneath the books, pots and pans), and a variety of other goods. There are usually bargains to be had.

Barton-upon-Humber

BUYER'S PREMIUM: 12%
SALES: *General: fortnightly on Tue at 6.00pm. Antiques: monthly on Sat at 11.00am. Antiques and fine art: quarterly on Mon at 11.00am.*
VIEWING: *General: day of sale from 2.30pm. Monthly antiques: day prior 2.30pm-7.00pm, morning of sale from 9.30am. Quarterly antiques and fine art: day prior from 2.30pm-5.00pm and day of sale from 9.00am-11.00am.*
REFRESHMENTS: *Own café.*
PARKING: *Own car park.*
STORAGE: *Yes*
TRANSPORTATION: *Yes*
SHIPPING: *Yes*

DICKINSON, DAVY & MARKHAM

DDM Auction Rooms, Old Courts Road. Tel: (0652) 653666

700 lots. This is one of the largest auction houses in the East Midlands. The fortnightly Saturday household sale usually includes good quality Victorian, Edwardian and shipping furniture, as well as china, glass, pictures, books, domestic appliances, garden effects and even motor vehicles. There may also be office equipment and machinery, and other items sold on liquidators' instructions. There is also a sale of antiques and fine art every seven weeks, which in the past has included Royal Doulton tea and dinner services, Royal Worcester, Victorian inkwells, wine decanters, silver and gold pocket watches, sapphire and diamond cluster rings, a George III one-third guinea from 1808, a collection of 11 various albums of Wills cigarette cards, a quantity of damask table cloths, teddy bears, Armand Marseille bisque-headed dolls, sporting guns, rugs and carpets, clocks and barometers, and furniture. Specialist sales of porcelain, paintings, books and toys are also held from time to time.

The same firm also holds general auctions at Alford, Lincolnshire.

Brigg

BUYER'S PREMIUM: 5%
SALES: *Household: fortnightly on Sat at 10.00am. Antiques and fine art: every seven weeks on Tue at 10.00am.*
VIEWING: *Day prior 2.00pm-7.00pm, morning of sale from 8.30am.*
REFRESHMENTS: *On-site facilities.*
PARKING: *Own car park.*
STORAGE: *Yes*
TRANSPORTATION: *Yes*
SHIPPING: *Yes*

Great Driffield

BUYER'S PREMIUM: *10%*
SALES: *General: fortnightly on Sat at 9.30am. Antiques: every two months on Fri and Mon at 10.30am.*
VIEWING: *General: Thu prior 10.00am-7.00pm, Fri prior 10.00am-4.00pm. Antiques: Wed prior 10.00am-7.00pm, Thu prior 10.00am-4.00pm.*
REFRESHMENTS: *None available on the premises.*
PARKING: *Ample parking near by.*
STORAGE: *Yes*
TRANSPORTATION: *Yes*
SHIPPING: *Yes*

DEE & ATKINSON

The Exchange, Exchange Street. Tel: (0377) 43151

350-900 lots. Driffield is a busy, attractive town on the edge of the Wolds, with a population of under ten thousand which increases noticeably on sale days. The Exchange is a large old building, close to the town's only set of traffic lights. The saleroom stands apart from the main building across a small courtyard. General household sales are held about twice a month on a Saturday, and include a wide variety of practical furniture, bric-à-brac, shipping lots, electrical and sundry items, averaging about 450 lots.

Every two months on a Friday and Monday Dee & Atkinson hold their widely advertised two-day sale of antiques and fine art, which is interesting for experts and non-experts alike (average 900 lots). On the Friday the lots include furniture, brass, books, albums, ceramics, carpets and rugs, collectors' items, guns, prints, paintings and so on. The Monday sale concentrates mainly on plated items, silver and jewellery.

Grimsby

BUYER'S PREMIUM: *7½%*
SALES: *General: weekly on Wed at 9.15am. Antiques and collector's: occasionally on Sat at 10.30am.*
VIEWING: *General: day prior 2.30pm-7.00pm. Antiques and collector's: day of sale from 9.00am.*
REFRESHMENTS: *None available on the premises.*
PARKING: *Public car park opposite.*
STORAGE: *No*
TRANSPORTATION: *Local deliveries can be arranged.*
SHIPPING: *No*

JACKSON GREEN & PRESTON

Auction Centre, 1a New Cartergate. Tel: (0472) 355195

400-500 lots. Jackson Green & Preston have been auctioneers since 1920. The sales have a relaxed and friendly atmosphere, and some of those attending seem to have come for the entertainment as well as to buy. The weekly general sale of household furniture and effects is divided into morning and afternoon sessions, with 'smalls' sold in the morning and furniture in the afternoon, starting at 2.00pm. Private vendors can bring in goods for the sale on Thursday and Friday. Typical past lots have included superb lounge suites (some apparently unused), 1930s bedroom suites, wardrobes, bureaux, pine chests of drawers, Edwardian plant stands, pedestal brass jardinières, wall plaques, blue-and-white ware, various Victorian and collector's items, and a range of cookers, washing machines and fridges. Light fittings, adaptors, switches and other electrical items have appeared, thanks to loss adjusters, as have a quantity of cuddly toys, toy cars, novelties and fun hats.

In addition to the general sale, there are occasional special antiques and collectors' sales, which contain many lots kept back from the general sale because their quality merits special attention.

SCREETONS

The Victory Hall. Tel: (0430) 431201

400-500 lots. The general sales take place every six to eight weeks, and are much looked forward to. The area around the quiet and picturesque village has plenty of 'Screetons Sale' signposts to direct you to the village hall, which is hired especially for the auction. An excellent array of home-made refreshments is provided, and many people come from nearby villages to meet friends, as well as to bid. There is usually a fine selection of lots crowded into the hall: antiques, Victoriana, silver, brass, general household furniture and effects, including interesting period pieces from private house clearances. Screetons are also known for agricultural sales and on-site auctions, which take place periodically throughout the year. Robin Screeton established the firm over 25 years ago, and his son Ian now takes responsibility for the general sales.

Laxton, near Howden

BUYER'S PREMIUM: *Nil*
SALES: *Every six to eight weeks on Sat at 11.00am.*
VIEWING: *Day of sale from 9.00am.*
REFRESHMENTS: *Own café.*
PARKING: *Ample parking near by.*
STORAGE: *Yes*
TRANSPORTATION: *Yes*
SHIPPING: *Yes*

CANTER & FRANCIS

8 Doncaster Road. Tel: (0724) 858855

300-500 lots. In a good week at Canter & Francis you will find everything needed to set up a home, including beds, bedding, furniture of all sorts and values, cups, mugs and plates, electrical goods, rugs, carpets, and so on — and even DIY equipment. There is a good family feeling at the sale. Jokes are exchanged between the crowd and the auctioneer, and proceedings go forward entertainingly, in an atmosphere that would put the most timid bidder at ease. The sale begins with smaller table items such as jewellery, china, glass, books, lamps and other electrical equipment. The main furniture sale begins at around 2.00pm to 2.30pm and finishes at around 3.30pm.

Twice a year in the spring and autumn, Canter & Francis hold special antiques and fine art sales. These take the place of the normal weekly sale, and the sales and viewing times are the same.

Scunthorpe

BUYER'S PREMIUM: 5%
SALES: *Weekly on Thu at 12.00 noon (includes twice-yearly antiques and fine art sale).*
VIEWING: *Day prior 2.00pm-4.30pm and 7.00pm-9.00pm.*
REFRESHMENTS: *None available on the premises.*
PARKING: *Ample near by.*
STORAGE: *No*
TRANSPORTATION: *Yes*
SHIPPING: *Yes*

ISLE OF MAN

CHRYSTALS AUCTIONS

Bowring Road. Tel: (0624) 815555

350-450 lots. Ramsey is the second largest town on the Isle of Man, and although it is much quieter than Douglas, it is a popular resort. In May and November/December every year

Ramsey

BUYER'S PREMIUM: *Nil*
SALES: *General: alternating weekly between Ramsey on Fri at 10.00am and Douglas on Fri at 10.00am.*

VIEWING: *Day prior 1.00pm-6.00pm.*
REFRESHMENTS: *None available on the premises.*
PARKING: *Own car park.*
STORAGE: *Yes*
TRANSPORTATION: *Yes*
SHIPPING: *Yes*

Chrystals hold special antiques auctions in Ramsey.

Chrystals also hold general auctions, which alternate weekly between the Bowring Road saleroom in Ramsey and the Majestic Hotel in Douglas. The general auctions are popular with the islanders, and many bidders from the mainland are also attracted to them.

ISLE OF WIGHT

Ryde

WAYS

Garfield Road. Tel: (0983) 562255

BUYER'S PREMIUM: *Nil*
SALES: *Every five weeks on Thu at 10.30am.*
VIEWING: *Day prior from 10.00am-6.00pm.*
REFRESHMENTS: *Own café.*
PARKING: *Own car park.*
STORAGE: *Yes*
TRANSPORTATION: *Yes*
SHIPPING: *Yes*

500-700 lots. Established as long ago as 1815, Ways are the oldest auctioneers on the Isle of Wight. Their saleroom, with its sign swinging prominently outside, was once an old Victorian coach house with three stables. The auctions are mainly of antique and modern furnishings, although they also include plenty of smaller lots such as silver and silver plate, jewellery, china and *objets d'art*, all of which make good holiday souvenirs. There may also be some tempting larger items of furniture. These auctions are packed with good-quality items, and they are well attended by buyers who regularly make the journey over from the mainland.

Shanklin

WATSON, BULL & PORTER

79 Regent Street. Tel: (0983) 863441

BUYER'S PREMIUM: *10%*
SALES: *Antiques: monthly on Tue at 11.00am. General: monthly on Wed at 11.00am.*
VIEWING: *Day prior, 10.00am-4.00pm. 5.30pm-7.30pm.*
REFRESHMENTS: *None available on the premises.*
PARKING: *None on the premises.*
STORAGE: *Yes*
TRANSPORTATION: *Yes*
SHIPPING: *Yes*

600-800 lots. Watson, Bull & Porter occupy a saleroom in the town centre, close to the railway station. Their monthly auctions have proved extremely popular, perhaps because the auctioneers are very selective in the quality of the lots that they sell. Here there is also a wide range of items available, from antique to modern. There are salerooms on two floors; the first-floor saleroom is the setting for the Tuesday sale of antiques, while the ground-floor room tends to be used on Wednesdays for the general sale of modern household furniture, china, brass, and electrical goods.

KENT

HOBBS PARKER

Romney House, Ashford Market, Elwick Road. Tel: (0233) 622222
400-500 lots. Hobbs Parker, established in 1850, are based in the Ashford Market complex, which is the largest in the south-east — livestock sales are held every Tuesday and Wednesday, and seasonally on Thursday and Friday. There are 200 sales a year, which means that the auctioneers have a full calendar. In addition to livestock auctions, Hobbs Parker hold a variety of other sales on a regular basis. These may be of furniture, cars and commercial vehicles, farm machinery, or horses and saddlery. Every month there are sales of household furniture and effects, and eight times a year there are auctions of antiques and fine art. The latter take place at Amos Hall, Ashford Market, and include selected furniture, ceramics, glass, silver and jewellery, among other things.

A more unusual note is struck by the sales of horses, ponies, saddlery and boxes, which are well attended. Held in March, May, July, August and November, these sales usually include 50 to 70 horses, as well as trailers, lorries, and about 2,000 lots of saddlery, harnesses and riding outfits.

THE CANTERBURY AUCTION GALLERIES

The Auction Galleries, 40 Station Road West.
Tel: (0227) 763337
400-500 lots. The Auction Galleries are a purpose-built saleroom, conveniently situated only about 100 yards away from Canterbury West railway station. On the first Saturday of each month there are well-supported sales of Victorian, Edwardian and quality modern household furniture and effects. Specialist antiques auctions are held every second month on Tuesday, and include antique furniture, pictures, ceramics, glass, silver, jewellery, books, bygones and collectors' items, longcase and other clocks, carpets and rugs.

PHILLIPS

11 Bayle Parade. Tel: (0303) 245555
350-400 lots. Folkestone is perhaps best known for its cross-channel ferry service. Phillips' saleroom is easy to miss,

Ashford

BUYER'S PREMIUM: 5%
SALES: *General (livestock, farm equipment, etc.): Tue at 10.15am, Wed at 10.30am, other days at 10.00am. Household furniture: monthly on Wed at 12.00 noon. Antiques: eight times per year on Thu at 10.00am (times vary). Horses and saddlery: Mar, May, Jul, Aug and Nov, on Thu at 10.00am.*
VIEWING: *All sales: day of sale only.*
REFRESHMENTS: *Own café.*
PARKING: *Own car park.*
STORAGE: Yes
TRANSPORTATION: Yes
SHIPPING: Yes

Canterbury

BUYER'S PREMIUM: 10%
SALES: *General sales: first Sat of the month at 10.00am. Specialist sales: every second month on Tue at 10.30am.*
VIEWING: *General sales: Fri prior 4.00pm-8.00pm. Specialist sales: Mon prior 10.00am-7.00pm.*
REFRESHMENTS: *Available on view and sale days.*
PARKING: *Public car parks opposite.*
STORAGE: Yes
TRANSPORTATION: Yes
SHIPPING: Yes

Folkestone

BUYER'S PREMIUM: 10%
SALES: *General: monthly on Wed at 11.00am. Antiques: on*

Thu at 11.00am (eight times a year).
VIEWING: General: day prior 10.00am-4.00pm. Antiques: day prior 10.00am-7.30pm and morning of sale.
REFRESHMENTS: None available on the premises.
PARKING: None available on the premises.
STORAGE: Yes
TRANSPORTATION: Yes
SHIPPING: Yes

Hawkhurst

BUYER'S PREMIUM: 10%
SALES: Twice weekly on Mon and Sat at 10.00am.
VIEWING: Both sales: day of sale from 9.00am. Also day prior 2.00pm-5.00pm (Sat sale).
REFRESHMENTS: Own café.
PARKING: Ample free parking near by.
STORAGE: Yes
TRANSPORTATION: Yes
SHIPPING: Yes

Lyminge

BUYER'S PREMIUM: Nil
SALES: General sales: monthly on Sun at 9.30am. Plant sales: monthly on Sun at 10.00am.
VIEWING: General sales: day prior, 1.00pm-6.00pm. Plant sales: morning of sale only.
REFRESHMENTS: Own café at each location.
PARKING: Available on the premises.
STORAGE: Yes
TRANSPORTATION: Yes
SHIPPING: Yes

tucked away above the harbour area. A set of wrought-iron gates leads into the premises, which are opposite The Guildhall pub.

Phillips hold two regular auctions: a monthly sale, best described as a general sale (although it is referred to by the auctioneers as 'Victoriana'), which boasts all manner of ceramics, glass, paintings, prints, collectors' items and works of art, clocks, watches, barometers, silver and plate, jewellery and furniture; and a sale of better-quality items, including antiques, paintings and works of art, which takes place eight times a year.

AUCTION CENTRES

Rye Road. Tel: (0580) 754545

200-250 lots. On average there are two sales per week in this busy auction room, which can be found in an attractive timber-framed building. The principal, Michael Shortall FRICS FSVA, was formerly with Christie's London, and he is happy to give free valuations. The sales include Victoriana and general household effects, as well as fine art and antiques, bankrupt stock, police lost property and miscellaneous items. The sales of police lost property are particularly interesting, as they encompass not only jewellery but also more unusual items, such as the ski-jet motor boat that appeared recently. Sales are also held at country houses at regular intervals.

VALLEY AUCTIONS

Claygate, Brady Road. Tel: (0303) 862134

400-500 lots. 'Have gavel will travel' is the motto of Mr Edwin Hall, who over the past 15 years has regularly conducted auctions at each of three locations in the area. Twelve times a year he holds auctions at Lyminge Village Hall; auctions also take place under his aegis at the village halls in Barham and Denton.

All the sales contain a broad mixture of general household furniture and effects, including antiques and bric-à-brac, and they are held on Sundays. The atmosphere at these auctions is friendly, and they are often attended by entire families. Mr Hall also holds auctions of plants, shrubs, bedding plants and bulbs (depending on the season) at Lyminge Village Hall.

THE AGRICULTURAL HALL

Maidstone Market, Barker Road. Tel: (0622) 758705

1,500-2,000 lots. Every Thursday there are auctions here, held on alternate weeks by two companies, P S Williams & Co and B J Norris. Both companies are alike in that they hold sales of antique and modern furniture and effects, together with china, glass, silver, books, pictures and so on.

PHILLIPS

13 Lime Tree Walk. Tel: (0732) 740310

200-300 lots. Phillips have a purpose-built saleroom about 200 yards away from their office in London Road. This is host to auctions on average every five or six weeks, and the proceedings may last one or two days. The sales are of good-quality items and include ceramics, glass, china, furniture, and miscellaneous lots. Every other sale will include a specialist section for paintings, or silver and jewellery. Once every three months the sale will also include books. Everything is neatly laid out and there are plenty of experts on hand to give advice to would-be vendors and buyers.

LAMBERT & FOSTER

102 High Street. Tel: (05806) 2083

400-500 lots. Tenterden is an attractive town with many old buildings and an unusually wide main street. The saleroom is opposite the war memorial in the High Street. The practice was first established in 1830, and apart from auctions Lambert & Foster also hold livestock sales at Maidstone and Rye, and what are known as 'on farm' dispersal sales of fruit and other goods. The auctions at Tenterden are friendly and comprehensive, and they are supervised by Mrs Pauline Chalk, who has more than 40 years' experience of the antiques market. Fine art, antique furniture, pottery and porcelain, glass, silver, jewellery, and clocks and watches appear in these sales regularly.

BRACKETTS

27 High Street. Tel: (0892) 533733

300-400 lots. This saleroom is situated just behind Tunbridge Wells' famous colonnaded street, the Pantiles, which is a centre

Maidstone

BUYER'S PREMIUM: *Nil*
SALES: *Weekly on Thu at 10.30am.*
VIEWING: *Day of sale from 8.00am.*
REFRESHMENTS: *Café on premises.*
PARKING: *Own car park.*
STORAGE: *Yes*
TRANSPORTATION: *Yes*
SHIPPING: *Yes*

Sevenoaks

BUYER'S PREMIUM: *10%*
SALES: *On average once every five or six weeks on Wed (or Wed and Thu) at 10.00am.*
VIEWING: *Day prior 10.00am-4.30pm.*
REFRESHMENTS: *Own café.*
PARKING: *None available on the premises.*
STORAGE: *Yes*
TRANSPORTATION: *Yes*
SHIPPING: *Yes*

Tenterden

BUYER'S PREMIUM: *10%*
SALES: *Every three weeks on Thu at 9.30am (4.30pm at irregular intervals).*
VIEWING: *Tue prior 9.30am-4.00pm (also 2.30pm on day of sale when sales begin at 4.30pm).*
REFRESHMENTS: *None available on the premises.*
PARKING: *None on the premises.*
STORAGE: *Yes*
TRANSPORTATION: *Yes*
SHIPPING: *Yes*

Tunbridge Wells

BUYER'S PREMIUM: *10%*
SALES: *Weekly on Fri at 10.00am.*

VIEWING: *Day prior 9.00am-4.30pm. Day of sale from 9.00am.*
REFRESHMENTS: *None available on the premises.*
PARKING: *Public car park near by.*
STORAGE: *Yes*
TRANSPORTATION: *Yes*
SHIPPING: *No*

for antiques shops. Bracketts' weekly sales of fine art and general household furniture and effects are in themselves a tourist attraction. The modern, glass-roofed saleroom is often full of foreign tourists who come here to browse. Coachloads of pensioners have been known to unload outside the saleroom on sale days ... and why not? A visit to an auction can make a day trip to this busy old spa town a memorable one. An abundance of china, glass, silver and porcelain, pictures, jewellery, furniture and bric-à-brac is up for bidding, as well as 'outside effects', such as lawn mowers, which are auctioned at the end of the sale. There should be something to interest everyone here, and the auctioneer's gavel comes down on bids ranging from one pound to thousands. Once every two months on average, the auction is arranged into specialist categories of antiques and collectables.

Westgate on Sea

BUYER'S PREMIUM: *10%*
SALES: *Every two or three weeks, on Sat at 10.00am.*
VIEWING: *Day prior 9.30am-5.00pm, and morning of sale.*
REFRESHMENTS: *Own café.*
PARKING: *None available on the premises.*
STORAGE: *Yes*
TRANSPORTATION: *Yes*
SHIPPING: *No*

WESTGATE AUCTIONS

70 St Mildreds Road. Tel: (0843) 31376

300-400 lots. Westgate auctions can be found directly behind the main post office, which is one of Westgate on Sea's best landmarks. The auctions have been established for over 10 years, and they have steadily increased in popularity. The saleroom is divided into two parts and is usually packed with bidders. Bidding usually begins in the part of the room that contains inexpensive items. Here you can often find electrical gadgets, including kitchen equipment such as cookers and fridges. The other part of the saleroom is given over to good quality furniture, antiques, paintings, china, jewellery and general household items.

LANCASHIRE

Accrington

BUYER'S PREMIUM: *Nil*
SALES: *Weekly on Thu at 5.30pm.*
VIEWING: *Day of sale from 10.00am.*
REFRESHMENTS: *Own café.*
PARKING: *Own car park.*
STORAGE: *Yes*
TRANSPORTATION: *Yes*
SHIPPING: *Yes*

ACCRINGTON AUCTIONS

St James House, St James Street. Tel: (0254) 381739

500-600 lots. One of the delights of attending an auction you've never been to before is that you never know what sort of building to expect (or indeed whether there will be any building at all). Accrington Auctions take place in an ex-Salvation Army church. The weekly Thursday evening sale attracts a great deal of attention from all over the area, and includes not only the general run-of-the-mill goods which appear in most sales, but also unexpected items of antique furniture, china, silver and so on. This is an evening sale with plenty of regular visitors. For many of them the sale is a meeting place as much as a place to browse and bid.

FRANK CHARLES & CO

The Salerooms, Islington. Tel: (0254) 54133

600-700 lots. Blackburn used to be the world centre of cotton weaving, and its Lewis Textile Museum traces the development of the spinning and weaving industry. The saleroom, a newish single-storey building, is off Canterbury Street near the centre of the town. The sales are of general household furniture and effects of all ages and periods, and may include antiques. There are two separate sessions. The morning sale, beginning at 10.30am, is for the lesser quality goods. It starts with boxes of miscellaneous bric-à-brac such as china, books, pots and pans, and continues with electrical goods and then furniture. The afternoon auction, beginning at 1.30pm, has similar lots but of higher quality. Items like china are more carefully displayed in this part of the sale, and may be set out on trays or sold as individual pieces.

Blackburn

BUYER'S PREMIUM: *Nil*
SALES: *Weekly on Wed at 10.30am and 1.30pm.*
VIEWING: *Day prior 1.30pm-5.00pm, morning of sale from 9.00am.*
REFRESHMENTS: *None available on the premises.*
PARKING: *Own car park.*
STORAGE: *No*
TRANSPORTATION: *Yes*
SHIPPING: *No*

CHARLES EDWARDS & CO LTD

4/8 Lynwood Road. Tel: (0254) 691748

250-550 lots. Most sales take place at Lynwood Road, where there are quarterly auctions of fine art and antiques, as well as house contents and specialist sales. The auctioneers also hold monthly sales of general household effects and small antiques at West Unit, Bastfield Mill, Beech Street (also in Blackburn).

Every month there is a general sale in Pendleton, a picturesque little village off the A59, less than a mile from Clitheroe. It is an ideal setting for an auction, which takes place in the village hall, next to the pub. This well-attended sale goes under the title of 'Antique and Later Furniture and Effects'. Selling starts with 'smalls' then moves on to pictures, clocks, prints and finally furniture.

Blackburn

BUYER'S PREMIUM: *Nil*
SALES: *Lynwood Road: quarterly fine art sales: Wed at 10.30am. Other Lynwood Road sales: days and times vary. Bastfield Mill: monthly on Mon at 10.30am. Pendleton: monthly on Wed at 10.30am.*
VIEWING: *Lynwood Road: Mon prior 9.30am-4.00pm, Tue prior 9.30am-7.30pm. Bastfield Mill: Fri prior 9.00am-5.00pm. Pendleton: day prior 10.00am-8.00pm and day of sale from 9.00am.*
REFRESHMENTS: *All sales: available.*
PARKING: *Lynwood Road: on-street parking. Bastfield Mill and Pendleton: own car parks.*
STORAGE: *Yes*
TRANSPORTATION: *Yes*
SHIPPING: *Yes*

W CHARLES FORD AUCTIONS

Royal Oak Building, Waterloo Road. Tel: (0253) 45458

200-300 lots. The saleroom is close to the South Shore railway station and during the summer, particularly on wet days, wise

Blackpool

BUYER'S PREMIUM: *Nil*
SALES: *Weekly on Thu at 10.30am.*

holidaymakers can be found sitting in the saleroom, enjoying the proceedings as part of a day out. The informality of the sale often tempts people to bid who might otherwise be too shy. The lots include general household furniture and run-of-the-mill miscellaneous items, but it is always worth having a look for bargains. Attractive pieces of antique furniture can be found, as can good pieces of china — perhaps the odd Royal Doulton cup and saucer or even complete tea and dinner sets. It is always exciting to rummage through the bottom of a box of miscellaneous kitchen utensils and find something of value or interest.

Blackpool

E GORDON ROUND FSVA

4 Bloomfield Road. Tel: (0253) 43588

300-400 lots. The auction was established over 35 years ago by Mr E Gordon Round, who is still actively involved in the sales but is now assisted by his son Stephen. The saleroom is near Blackpool's football ground and within easy walking distance of the Golden Mile, but it never gets too full, even in the peak summer months. There are some excellent buys to be found at most of the sales. The lots are clean and well presented, and there is ample space for viewing. An old-fashioned charm pervades the proceedings, with selling conducted at a not-too-hectic pace.

The sale is held every three or four weeks on average, and is alternately devoted to furniture and small items. The sale of household furniture and effects includes some better quality modern furniture, but on the whole the emphasis is on 'shipping furniture' and antiques, and the better bargains are in these categories. The separate sales for smaller goods include items such as china, pottery, glass, brass, silver and silver plate, crockery, collectables and so on. These sales have a good reputation.

Blackpool

WATERHOUSES

Exchange Auction Rooms, Caunce Street. Tel: (0253) 22919

300-400 lots. This weekly sale is very popular with summer visitors. Some are so pleased with their buys that they regularly spend more in carriage charges to get an article home than it cost to buy, which shows the excellent bargains to be had. This sale is one of the longest-established in the area, and was started over 60 years ago by the father of the present proprietors, Lindsey Adcock and her husband Robert.

The saleroom is near the Winter Gardens, and the public are invited to pop in for viewing any day of the week from

9.00am to 5.30pm. The nearer it is to sale day, the greater the number of lots there will be on show. In among the general household equipment, furniture, electrical goods, gardening equipment and so on, there are often goods which are being auctioned off on the instructions of bailiffs or liquidators.

SMYTHE SON & WALKER

174 Victoria Road West. Tel: (0253) 852184

300-400 lots. This independently run saleroom was established over 70 years ago, and members of the Smythe family are still involved. The saleroom is in the centre of Cleveleys, which is about five miles north of Blackpool and has its own promenade and sandy beach.

This sale offers excellent buys in every conceivable category of furniture, general household effects, kitchen utensils, china, ornaments, jewellery, books, bric-à-brac and so on. Every six weeks on a Wednesday there are special sales of antiques and fine art. These also contain excellent bargains, although the prices will naturally be higher because the lots have been chosen for their quality. They can be viewed during the Tuesday sale in a different room. Periodically throughout the year Smythe Son & Walker also carry out on-site auctions which are worth an enquiry. Past sales have included the entire contents of hotels and amusement arcades.

WARREN & WIGNALL LTD

The Mill, Earnshaw Bridge, Leyland Lane.
Tel: (0772) 451430 and 435252

800-900 lots. The saleroom is about a mile from the town centre, at the junction of Golden Hill and Leyland Lane. It is an old mill which has been pebble-dashed and painted cream. Mr Philip Warren, who started the firm towards the end of the 1960s, now shares the running of this busy and successful weekly auction with his son Peter.

Every third week the sale is devoted to antiques and collectors' items, including silver, china, jewellery, pictures and so on. In other weeks this is a sale of general household furniture and effects. The antiques sales have gained a particularly good reputation, and many regular buyers travel a long way to attend. The sales are conducted at a fast pace, with two auctioneers doing about an hour each at the rostrum. In the general sale lots are sold at roughly 150 per hour. The antiques sale is a little slower, and you can usually count on around 120 lots per hour.

Cleveleys

BUYER'S PREMIUM: *Nil*
SALES: *General: fortnightly on Tue at 10.00am. Antiques: every six weeks on Wed at 10.30am.*
VIEWING: *General: day prior 8.30am-5.00pm. Antiques: Sat, Mon and Tue prior 10.00am-5.00pm, morning of sale.*
REFRESHMENTS: *None available on the premises.*
PARKING: *Ample parking near by.*
STORAGE: *Yes*
TRANSPORTATION: *Yes*
SHIPPING: *Yes*

Leyland, near Preston

BUYER'S PREMIUM: *General: nil. Antiques sale: 5%*
SALES: *Weekly on Wed at 10.00am (includes antiques and collectors' sale every third week).*
VIEWING: *Day prior 9.00am-7.00pm.*
REFRESHMENTS: *Van selling snacks.*
PARKING: *Own car park.*
STORAGE: *No*
TRANSPORTATION: *Yes*
SHIPPING: *No*

Longridge

BUYER'S PREMIUM: *Nil*
SALES: *Fortnightly on Sat at 10.00am.*
VIEWING: *Day prior 10.00am-8.00pm.*
REFRESHMENTS: *None available on the premises.*
PARKING: *Ample parking near by.*
STORAGE: *No*
TRANSPORTATION: *Yes*
SHIPPING: *No*

HENRY HOLDEN & SON

Central Salerooms, Towneley Road. Tel: (0772) 783274

400-500 lots. Henry Holden & Son have recently celebrated their centenary year, and the company is still owned and run by members of the Holden family. The sale is a typical Lancashire rural auction — a fortnightly pilgrimage for people from outlying areas, who use it not only to look for bargains, but also as a meeting place for a chat with old friends. As a consequence the sale is friendly and informal, but often noisy. Among the general household furniture and effects will be pieces of good quality china, jewellery, mirrors, clocks, antiques and very often works of art. There is no break for lunch, but the sale is divided roughly into two parts. The early part is for more run-of-the-mill items such as household utensils, gardening tools and plainer furniture, and the second part (from about 1.00pm onwards) for better quality lots.

Newton

BUYER'S PREMIUM: *Nil*
SALES: *About monthly on Wed at 11.00am, but check with auctioneers.*
VIEWING: *Day of sale from 10.00am.*
REFRESHMENTS: *Own café.*
PARKING: *Ample parking near by.*
STORAGE: *No*
TRANSPORTATION: *Yes*
SHIPPING: *No*

C SILVERWOOD

Newton Village Hall. Tel: (02006) 652

400-450 lots. Newton is within easy reach of the Forest of Bowland, an extensive area of fells and moors which has been designated an Area of Outstanding Natural Beauty. It is wise to check that the sale is taking place before travelling any distance, particularly in winter months when the weather often makes some of the smaller roads impassable. The sale was started by the father-in-law of the proprietor, and it is well advertised in magazines and local newspapers. This is a quaint, often eccentric village auction, which people from nearby villages and towns look forward to with some delight. The range of lots varies considerably, since most items are the product of house clearances, or in many cases outhouse clearances.

Ormskirk

BUYER'S PREMIUM: *10%*
SALES: *Fortnightly on Tue at 10.30am.*
VIEWING: *Day prior 2.00pm-7.00pm.*
REFRESHMENTS: *None available on the premises.*
PARKING: *Derby Street West car park (limited to two hours).*
STORAGE: *Yes*

EDWARD ABBOTT FRICS

The Saleroom, 22 Church Street. Tel: (0695) 579104

400-600 lots. The saleroom has a large yellow board outside and is in the centre of the town, 100 yards or so from the main Derby Street West car park. The sale was established in the 1930s and is now under the proprietorship of Edward Abbott, who describes himself as a 'one-man band' — an accurate description of the way he oversees the goods arriving, values them and conducts the sale.

This is a friendly sale attended regularly by many local people, which helps create an informal atmosphere. Lots range from modern to good quality antiques, and there are usually some surprising items. The selling starts with all types of outside effects, including garden furniture and tools. All types of furniture are sold next, and the sale usually finishes with the better quality small items. Sales are often conducted for the Sheriff's Office, County Courts and liquidators.

TRANSPORTATION: *Yes*
SHIPPING: *Yes*

CHARLES EDWARDS & CO LTD

See *CHARLES EDWARDS & CO LTD, Blackburn, Lancashire*

Pendleton

SMITH HODGKINSON MCGINTY

The Auction Centre, Preston Road. Tel: *(0257) 261055*

1,000 lots. This independently run household sale is famous among the bargain hunters of central Lancashire. It is held once a week on a Thursday. The sale is packed with goods, and it is hard to see how the proprietors cope with so many lots on a weekly basis. The 1.00pm sale is mainly of lesser quality items and bric-à-brac, including as many as 400 to 500 lots of china, ornaments, toys and games, pots and pans, and various pieces of household equipment such as step ladders, rubbish bins and electrical goods. The 3.00pm sale includes better quality pictures, china, silver, brass and jewellery. At 5.00pm there is a sale of antique and modern furniture, together with household electrical goods.

Every four weeks on a Saturday the firm holds a plant, machinery and tool sale, with lots for the commercial user and all types of tools for the DIY enthusiast or gardener.

Once a quarter there are horsedrawn carriage sales, which have a national reputation. Included are carriages, whips, harness, pictures, prints, books — in fact anything connected with horses, except for the horses themselves.

**Whittle-
le-Woods**

BUYER'S PREMIUM: *Nil*
SALES: *Household: weekly on Thu at 1.00pm. Plant, machinery and tools: every four weeks on Sat at 10.30am. Horsedrawn carriages: quarterly on Sat at 10.30am.*
VIEWING: *Household: day of sale from 9.00am. All others: afternoon prior and day of sale from 9.00am.*
REFRESHMENTS: *Own café.*
PARKING: *Own car park.*
STORAGE: *No*
TRANSPORTATION: *Yes*
SHIPPING: *No*

L E I C E S T E R S H I R E

WILLIAM H BROWN

The Warner Auction Rooms, 16/18 Halford Street. Tel: *(0533) 519777*

300-500 lots. Situated in the centre of Leicester (next door to British Home Stores), this sale is part of the Fine Art and Chattels division of the William H Brown Group, who run major auctions in Colchester, Doncaster and Sudbury, in addition to various smaller auctions in this part of the country.

Leicester

BUYER'S PREMIUM: *10%*
SALES: *General: fortnightly on Wed at 10.00am. Better furniture: monthly on first Mon of the month at 10.00am. Antiques and fine art: quarterly on Mon and Wed. Specialist:*

days and times vary.
VIEWING: *General: morning of sale. Better furniture: Fri prior 9.00am-5.00pm, Sat prior 9.00am-12.00 noon. Antiques and fine art: Thu and Fri prior 10.00am-5.00pm, Sat prior 9.00am-12.00 noon. Specialist: days and times vary.*
REFRESHMENTS: *None available on the premises.*
PARKING: *Large public car park within walking distance.*
STORAGE: *No*
TRANSPORTATION: *Yes*
SHIPPING: *Yes*

Leicester

BUYER'S PREMIUM: *10%*
SALES: *Weekly on Tue and Fri at 11.00am.*
VIEWING: *Afternoon prior and morning of sale.*
REFRESHMENTS: *None available on the premises.*
PARKING: *Own car park.*
STORAGE: *Yes*
TRANSPORTATION: *Yes*
SHIPPING: *Yes*

Leicester

BUYER'S PREMIUM: *10%*
SALES: *Antiques and fine art: every four to six weeks on Thu at 10.30am. Antiquarian and other books: once or twice a year.*
VIEWING: *Day prior 9.30am-4.00pm.*
REFRESHMENTS: *Own café.*
PARKING: *NCP car park within 50 yards..*
STORAGE: *No*
TRANSPORTATION: *Yes*
SHIPPING: *Yes*

The fortnightly sale is a good general auction, and includes furniture and household effects, television sets, fridges, cookers, a kitchen sink or so, garden furniture and garden equipment, such as ladders and wheelbarrows. There will also be the inevitable boxes of interesting miscellaneous items to search through in the hope of finding perhaps a silver teaspoon or a copper jelly mould.

The monthly sale is of Victorian, reproduction and better quality modern furniture, mirrors and so on, and there are many bargains to be found here.

The quarterly sale is of specially selected fine furniture, antiques and fine art, including oil paintings, watercolours, prints, engravings, and miniatures. This is a two-day sale, with furniture, paintings and the like on the Monday, and silver and plate, jewellery and *bijouterie*, watches and other smaller items on the Wednesday.

The auctioneers also hold specialist sales of toys, books and collector's items at irregular intervals.

CHURCHGATE AUCTIONS

Churchgate. Tel: (0533) 621416
300-400 lots. Find the centre of the city and the clock tower, and you have found the auction. It is held on the ground floor of a Grade 2 listed Victorian building with pine beams across the ceiling. This is a good general auction, where sales include the complete contents of houses, perhaps from one of the grander properties abounding in nearby villages. There is no set order of sale, and lots are sold mostly in the order in which they arrive. With two auctions a week, the staff are worked very hard, but they are usually willing to offer advice or help when needed.

HEATHCOTE BALL & CO

Castle Auction Rooms, 78 St Nicholas Circle.
Tel: (0533) 536789
700-1,000 lots. In the dozen or so years since their foundation, Heathcote Ball & Co have established themselves as one of the leading provincial auction firms of antiques and fine art. Their antique and fine art sale includes furniture, porcelain, silver, *objets d'art*, pictures, collectors' items such as silhouettes and miniatures, bronzes and statuary, toys and games, antique jewellery, samplers, linen, lace and costumes, musical instruments, postcards and albums, coins and medals, snuff boxes, paperweights, arms and weaponry, tribal art, fans and ephemera, and so on.

Antiquarian and collectors' book sales are held about twice a year — there is no fixed date for these sales, but they are always on a Thursday. 'Outside sales', consisting of the entire contents of houses, are also held periodically throughout the year. These sales are either held in the house itself, or in a marquee in the grounds, and are often worth attending.

FRECKELTONS

1 Leicester Road. Tel: (0509) 214564

250 lots. As might be imagined in a university city, there are usually a great number of bicycles on sale at this friendly and well-organised auction. The saleroom is prominently situated just off the A6 and is in the town centre. The auctions are held on the ground floor of a large Victorian building that was once a house of detention.

This is a family-owned business with two generations of the family now involved. As well as the bicycles there will generally be good furniture of all types and values — modern, reproduction and antique — plus kitchenalia, paintings, silver, jewellery, pottery, porcelain, plenty of china and all sorts of collectors' items and bygones. Prices vary from £5 to five-figure sums.

GILDINGS

64 Roman Way. Tel: (0858) 410414

500-600 lots. The saleroom is a new, purpose-built single-storey building with offices and a cafeteria at the rear. It stands in the centre of the town at the rear of the church of St Dionysius, whose spire is clearly visible from almost anywhere in Market Harborough. The regular weekly sale is of Victoriana, pine and painted pine, with good-quality furniture and effects, including china, glass and metalware, paintings and so on.

About every six weeks, a sale of perhaps 400-500 lots of antiques and fine art takes the place of the regular sale. The two main sales follow roughly the same order, with smaller items at the start, followed by a lunch break at 1.00pm, and then the sale of furniture, carpets and pictures at around 1.30pm.

Roughly every three months, the sale will be devoted to specialist items, such as toys, motor memorabilia, guns and weaponry, sporting equipment, and other collectors' items.

SHOULER & SON

County Auction Rooms, King's Road. Tel: (0664) 60181

700-800 lots. The saleroom is in the town centre, on the corner of the ring road and the main Grantham Road. It has

Loughborough

BUYER'S PREMIUM: *10%*
SALES: *Monthly on Tue at 10.30am.*
VIEWING: *Sat and Mon prior 9.30am-1.00pm and 2.00pm-4.30pm.*
REFRESHMENTS: *None available on the premises.*
PARKING: *Ample off-street parking.*
STORAGE: *Yes*
TRANSPORTATION: *Yes*
SHIPPING: *Yes*

Market Harborough

BUYER'S PREMIUM: *10%*
SALES: *Weekly on Tue at 10.00am (includes antiques and fine art sale about every six weeks, and specialist sale about once every three months).*
VIEWING: *Sat prior 9.30am-12.30pm, Mon prior 10.00am-7.00pm, morning of sale from 9.00am.*
REFRESHMENTS: *Own café.*
PARKING: *Own 30-space car park.*
STORAGE: *Yes*
TRANSPORTATION: *Yes*
SHIPPING: *Yes*

Melton Mowbray

BUYER'S PREMIUM: *10%*
SALES: *Fortnightly on Thu at 9.30am.*

VIEWING: *Tue prior 2.00pm-7.00pm*
REFRESHMENTS: *Own café.*
PARKING: *Large car park in former school playground.*
STORAGE: *Yes*
TRANSPORTATION: *Yes*
SHIPPING: *Yes*

recently been converted from a large Edwardian school house, and is difficult to miss. The sales are generally packed and friendly, and attract potential buyers with all depths of pocket: one lot might be sold for £1 and another for five figures. The first half of the sale is devoted to lesser-quality items, including furniture and effects, bygones, pottery, kitchenalia and various miscellaneous items. In the afternoon the second half of the sale is held, consisting of better furniture and antiques, paintings, silver, brass, bronzes, china, jewellery, collectables, and many other articles, including goods seized by bailiffs and lost property. The sale ends at around 3.00pm.

Oakham

BUYER'S PREMIUM: *10%*
SALES: *Fortnightly on Thu at 10.30am (includes antiques and fine art sale every other fortnight).*
VIEWING: *Tue (antiques sale only) and Wed prior 10.00am-4.00pm and 7.00pm-9.00pm.*
REFRESHMENTS: *Own small café area (antiques sale only).*
PARKING: *Not available on the premises.*
STORAGE: *Yes*
TRANSPORTATION: *Yes*
SHIPPING: *Yes*

NOTONS OAKHAM SALEROOM

South Street. Tel: (0572) 722681

400-500 lots. The saleroom is near the centre of this pleasant, well-kept town. The sales are held every fortnight, and alternate between 'General Household Furniture and Effects', and 'Antiques and Fine Art'. The Tuesday viewing is only available for the antiques sales, as is the café. Both sales run in roughly the same order, starting off with small items of china. At the antiques sale these might include porcelain teapots, decorated vases, cheese dishes and stands, soup tureens, fruit bowls and the like. Silverware comes next, for example hallmarked silver dishes, serving spoons and ladles, followed by carpets, paintings and furniture. Boxes containing an assortment of items appear at both sales, and are always worth a look: a thorough search might reveal the odd Doulton tea cup, assorted cutlery or a quantity of Victorian ceramic door handles.

Seagrave

BUYER'S PREMIUM: *5%*
SALES: *Once every six to eight weeks on Sun at 12.30pm.*
VIEWING: *Day of sale from 11.00am.*
REFRESHMENTS: *Own café.*
PARKING: *Own car park.*
STORAGE: *No*
TRANSPORTATION: *No*
SHIPPING: *Yes*

MILLER AUCTIONS

Seagrave Village Hall. Tel: (0509) 812037

300-400 lots. This auction was recommended to me by a reader, and a very good auction it is too, with a strong local following.

Seagrave is a small village and on Sunday, once every six to eight weeks, almost everyone seems to be involved in the sale at the Village Hall in one way or another. The lots can sell for any amount, from £5 to £500. Good quality collectables, antiques, large quantities of genuine old jewellery, paintings and some smaller items of furniture are usually up for bidding. There is a very welcoming atmosphere and the auctioneer, Mr Bob Miller, does all he can to reassure anyone who is nervous at the thought of bidding.

LINCOLNSHIRE

DICKINSON, DAVY & MARKHAM

111 West Street. Tel: (0507) 607781

400-500 lots. The saleroom was once a cinema, but has been completely refurbished. Selling takes place on the ground floor, with the old cinema balcony put to good use as a storage area. All lots are inside the saleroom for viewing, but the lots placed in the centre of the hall, such as bicycles, garden tools, timber, doors, wheelbarrows, ladders and so on are taken out on the sale day, to be sold in the yard at the rear of the saleroom. The auctioneer moves inside to sell smaller items such as china, ornamental and domestic crockery, cutlery, jewellery, bric-à-brac, electrical goods and other items. Next comes the furniture sale, which starts with the more modern articles, including office furniture and equipment. After these the auctioneer moves across to sell beds and carpets. At around 1.00pm the sale of the higher-value furniture begins, and the entire sale ends at around 3.00 to 4.00pm.

Alford is the home of Britain's last commercially operated windmill, which is well worth a look if you are visiting the area.

Alford

BUYER'S PREMIUM: 5%
SALES: *Monthly on second or third Thu of month at 10.00am.*
VIEWING: *Day prior 12.00 noon-4.00pm, 6.00pm-8.00pm.*
REFRESHMENTS: *None available on the premises.*
PARKING: *None available on the premises.*
STORAGE: *Yes*
TRANSPORTATION: *Yes*
SHIPPING: *Yes*

JAMES ELEY & SON

The Green, Wide Bargate. Tel: (0205) 361687

2,000 lots. A lavatory bowl, two front doors, a quantity of timber, a wheelbarrow, an electric fire, a gas cooker, half-a-dozen tins of paint, two rolls of wire netting, a Victorian dresser, a drop-leaf table, fresh seasonal produce, eggs, caravan trailers and cars: few shops could offer such variety, but all these have been on sale at Eley's auctions. The sale starts with produce at 10.00am. Also at 10.00am, another auctioneer starts the sale of furniture, carpets, televisions, household utensils, gardening equipment and so on, followed at 11.00am by timber, 12.00 noon by bicycles and at 1.30pm by motor vehicles. The entire auction is held in the open and continues even in the rain, finishing at around 3.00pm.

It is a long established and well-known meeting place for locals, who come not only to buy but simply to chat and meet up with friends, although occasionally a cautious finger will be lifted to bid if one lot appears to be going cheaply. Often, if you attend the following week, you will see the same article up for sale again, in the hope that it will fetch a better price.

Boston itself is a small but active port, handling mostly

Boston

BUYER'S PREMIUM: 11%
SALES: *Weekly on Wed at 10.00am.*
VIEWING: *Morning of sale.*
REFRESHMENTS: *Available.*
PARKING: *Own car park.*
STORAGE: *No*
TRANSPORTATION: *Yes*
SHIPPING: *No*

bananas and timber. The Boston stump (the 272ft tower of St Botolph Church) can be seen for miles across the surrounding fenland. The town gave its name to Boston, Massachusetts, when people sailed from here in 1630 in the wake of the Pilgrim Fathers.

Bourne

BUYER'S PREMIUM: 10%
SALES: *General: weekly on Sat at 10.00am. Office, shop and catering equipment: monthly (days and times vary). Antiques and fine art: monthly on Thu at 10.00am.*
VIEWING: *General: Fri prior 2.00pm-5.00pm, day of sale from 9.00am. Office, shop and catering: day prior (times vary) and day of sale from 9.00am. Antiques and fine art: day prior 2.30pm-7.00pm, day of sale from 9.00am.*
REFRESHMENTS: *Own café.*
PARKING: *Own car park.*
STORAGE: *Yes*
TRANSPORTATION: *Yes*
SHIPPING: *Yes*

RICHARDSONS

Bourne Auction Rooms, Spalding Road. Tel: (0778) 422686

500-600 lots. This is one of the largest and busiest auction houses in the county. The weekly Saturday general sale of modern and antique furniture and effects is very well attended, with a wide range of lots: don't be surprised to see halves of Stilton cheese, the surplus from a local dairy. Vendors bring their goods into the auction rooms on Monday and Tuesday, when the busy job of listing the lots begins. The monthly sale of office, shop and catering equipment includes typewriters, desks and chairs, printers, intercom systems and less predictable items such as, in one sale, a pick-up truck, two outboard motors and a Hobby Prestige touring caravan. All the sales are catalogued, and it is worth picking one up, or having one sent to you.

The lots on offer at the monthly antiques and fine art sale have included 18th-century rush-seated oak dining chairs, a carved Continental fire surround, a Victorian walnut glazed bookcase, oak bureaux, a boudoir grand piano, longcase clocks and paintings. The auctioneers also specialise in 'on site' auctions, when the entire contents of a house, shop or factory are sold on the premises. One such sale included all the contents and equipment needed for 285 boarders and 30 day students at a girls' boarding school! There are no regular dates for these sales but they can be interesting to attend: ask the auctioneers for details of any that are coming up.

Butterwick

BUYER'S PREMIUM: 11%
SALES: *Sixteen sales a year on Sat at 10.30am.*
VIEWING: *Fri prior 6.00pm-8.00pm, morning of sale from 9.00am.*
REFRESHMENTS: *Available.*
PARKING: *Own car park.*
STORAGE: *No*
TRANSPORTATION: *Yes*
SHIPPING: *No*

JAMES ELEY & SON

Butterwick Village Hall. Tel: (0205) 361687

400-450 lots. James Eley & Son's auctions at Butterwick Village Hall are well signposted on the A52. The sales include antiques and collectables of all kinds, good general furniture and household effects, silver, brass, china, books, bric-à-brac, and also many items with a shipping or fishing connection, due to the closeness of the port of Boston.

This is the same auction house responsible for weekly Wednesday auctions there.

PLATT & LOBLEY

Rear of 65 Church Street. Tel: (0427) 612885

700-800 lots. The auctions are held in a large, hangar-type saleroom in the centre of the pleasant old market and industrial town, where the bridge over the River Trent forms the boundary with Nottinghamshire. The weekly auction has been a focal point and an integral part of market day since 1929. Mr Lobley runs a noisy, well-attended sale which, despite the number of years it has been going, is still increasing in popularity. It is also a sale with much to interest children. Anyone can bring the goods they wish to sell to the saleroom, either the day before or until 10.30am on the morning of the sale.

The bidding starts with antique furniture and effects and then moves on to timber, doors and window frames, followed by the 40 or 50 bicycles which are usually on offer each week. A half-dozen or so trailers might be next to go under the hammer, followed by game (when in season). Sundry items come next. This is an interesting part of the sale, because it is so unpredictable. Toys, books, china, gardening tools, builder's tools, boxes containing pieces of kitchen equipment — virtually anything might be found. Produce is sold at the end of the day and there is a wide range of fresh fruit, vegetables and plants to choose from. A section of the sale is also reserved each week for stamps and coins.

Not long ago there was an aeroplane in one of Mr Lobley's sales, although the prospective buyers did have to travel to a nearby field to view it.

ESCRITT & BARRELL

Cattle Market, Dysart Road. Tel: (0476) 66991

650-800 lots. Escritt & Barrell are estate agents and their auction department has been built up over the last four years by Ian Ward. The saleroom is an unusual but attractive building which used to shelter horses. The sale starts outside with items such as gardening tools, lawn mowers and other equipment, and any cars or trailers that are up for auction. Then the sale moves inside for pine and modern furniture. In a second room, what is called the 'shipping sale' is held: this refers to better-quality 1930s and 1940s furniture, Victorian and Edwardian items, pictures, prints, small silver, jewellery, coins, glass and porcelain. The term 'shipping sale' has survived in many auction houses because at one time many of these items were bought and then instantly crated and shipped abroad. Two or three times a year a special catalogued fine art

Gainsborough

BUYER'S PREMIUM: 8%
SALES: *Weekly on Tue at 11.00am.*
VIEWING: *Day of sale.*
REFRESHMENTS: *Café near by.*
PARKING: *Own parking area in yard, and ample off-street parking.*
STORAGE: *Yes*
TRANSPORTATION: *Yes*
SHIPPING: *No*

Grantham

BUYERS'S PREMIUM: *7.5%*
SALES: *Every three weeks on Tue at 10.00am (catalogued fine art sale two or three times a year).*
VIEWING: *Day prior 11.00am- 7.00pm, and morning of sale.*
REFRESHMENTS: *Van selling snacks.*
PARKING: *Own 200-space car park.*
STORAGE: *Yes*
TRANSPORTATION: *Yes*
SHIPPING: *No*

sale is held, which consists of better-quality items that have been held back from house clearances. Some goods are also sold on the instructions of executors at this sale.

Grantham

BUYER'S PREMIUM: *10%*
SALES: *Household goods: fortnightly on Wed at 10.00am. Antiques and collector's items: every six weeks on Wed at 10.00am.*
VIEWING: *day prior 1.00pm-5.00pm (antiques day prior, 1.00pm-7.00pm). Both: morning of sale from 9.00am*
REFRESHMENTS: *Own café.*
PARKING: *Own car park.*
STORAGE: *Yes (free before sales).*
TRANSPORTATION: *Yes*
SHIPPING: *Yes*

GOLDINGS

Grantham Auction Rooms, Old Wharf Road. Tel: (0476) 65118

400-600 lots. Sir Isaac Newton was born in Grantham and there is a statue of him outside the Guildhall. Old Wharf Road is off Harlaxton Road, which is the main road through Grantham. The entire auction is conducted under cover and is the largest purpose-built auction saleroom in the area. The general sale of household goods includes a wide range of modern, period and antique furniture. Every six weeks a catalogued sale of better-quality antiques is held. Auctioneers Robin Hall and Colin Young believe in making buying fun and in keeping the 'audience' entertained, so waiting for the lot you have your eye on is never dull.

Grantham

BUYER'S PREMIUM: *10%*
SALES: *Fortnightly (on average) on Wed at 10.00am (includes antiques and fine art sale once every two months).*
VIEWING: *General: day prior 11.00am-4.30pm. Antiques: two days prior, 11.00am-4.30pm.*
REFRESHMENTS: *Not available on the premises.*
PARKING: *Not easy, but public car park in Market Place gives up to two hours' parking.*
STORAGE: *Yes*
TRANSPORTATION: *Yes*
SHIPPING: *Yes*

MARILYN SWAIN

Westgate Hall, Westgate. Tel: (0476) 68861

200-400 lots. Formerly part of the William H Brown group, this saleroom is now run independently by its former director, Marilyn Swain. Westgate Hall is just off the A1 near the town centre. It is an attractive Victorian building which used to be a corn exchange. The general sale usually has a good selection of Victorian and later furniture, plus china, glass and collectables. Large pieces of furniture might include button-back leather and imitation leather lounge seats, corner units and reproduction mahogany bedroom suites. This is always an interesting auction, and a well run one. Marilyn Swain is the Hon. Secretary of the Society of Fine Art Auctioneers (SOFAA). An antiques and fine art auction takes the place of the general sale once every two months.

Note: At the time of going to press, the company was considering moving premises, although its telephone number was expected to remain the same.

Holbeach

BUYER'S PREMIUM: *5%*
SALES: *Usually once a week in spring and autumn on Sat at 1.30pm.*
VIEWING: *Morning of sale.*

HIX & SON

28 Church Street. Tel: (0406) 22777

250-300 lots. Hix & Son is a traditional firm of local auctioneers. A sale is held on most Saturday afternoons in spring and autumn, and will probably be on the vendor's premises rather than at a saleroom. 'To the sale' signs are provided on roads in the area on the day. The sales offer a wide range of goods, from modern farming machinery and implements to bygones.

REFRESHMENTS: *Van selling snacks.*
PARKING: *Usually roadside.*
STORAGE: No
TRANSPORTATION: No
SHIPPING: No

ROBERT BELL & CO

Horncastle

The Town Hall. Tel: (0507) 522222

800-1,000 lots. This auction is run by a firm of independent auctioneers with a history that can be traced back to the early 19th century. Many of the people attending these sales are pleased to tell you about the bargains they have picked up here in the past. 'I don't think I could have furnished my house without this auction,' one old gentleman told me, 'and when my time comes I've made arrangements for all my stuff to be put back into the sale.' The Town Hall is a very large selling area, but the acoustics are good and it is easy to hear the auctioneer. The first two hours of the auction take place outside in the area around the Town Hall. This is the sale of less valuable goods. It is always worth looking through these lots, as there are bargains to be found: perhaps a clutch of step ladders or Victorian cast-iron radiator tops (suitable for use as pot stands), an Edwardian cast-iron fire surround, crockery (of which there is a great deal), or walking sticks. The lots are not numbered and there is usually a crowd following the auctioneer as he walks from lot to lot. If you have a purchase in mind, it is wise to stand by it well before the auctioneer gets there, and to hold your ground until he arrives. At some point between 12.00 noon and 1.00pm the auction moves inside the Town Hall for the sale of better quality furniture and effects. These lots are all numbered. The proceedings usually begin with tied-up bundles of linen, which might include beautiful table cloths, embroidered afternoon tea and tray cloths, napkins and table centres. Next to be sold are silver, brass and other small items, and lastly the furniture.

Twice a year in April and October Robert Bell holds a catalogued antique sale of about 700 lots. This replaces the general sale.

BUYER'S PREMIUM: 5%
SALES: *Monthly on last Wed of month at 10.00am (includes antiques sale twice a year in Apr and Oct).*
VIEWING: *Day prior 3.00pm-6.00pm.*
REFRESHMENTS: *Own café.*
PARKING: *Ample parking near by.*
STORAGE: Yes
TRANSPORTATION: Yes
SHIPPING: Yes

WOODROFFE WALTER, WILLIAM H BROWN

Horncastle

Town Hall, Boston Road. Tel: (0507) 526877

400-600 lots. A long-established, friendly auction which is well used by the locals, not only as a place to pick up a good bargain or to sell unwanted goods, but as a meeting place for

BUYER'S PREMIUM: 5%
SALES: *Approximately every two months on Wed at 10.00am.*

VIEWING: *Day prior 2.00pm-6.00pm.*
REFRESHMENTS: *Own café.*
PARKING: *Available in Town Hall car park and adjoining the cattle market.*
STORAGE: *Yes*
TRANSPORTATION: *Yes*
SHIPPING: *Yes*

old friends. It is noticeable that many people come to the auction chiefly to be entertained by the proceedings, making themselves comfortable by bringing their own sandwiches and flasks of drink, even though there is a good café on the premises. Probably they feel so much at home because the building is used for leisure activities, such as badminton and dancing, in the evenings.

The first part of the sale is devoted to 'deadstock' — step ladders, rolls of wire netting, wheelbarrows, perhaps building equipment, doors and other large, heavy goods. These are sold on the grassy area immediately outside the Town Hall. The auction then moves inside for the sale of beds, and after that smaller table items such as books, mirrors and ornaments are sold. At around 12.00 noon, there are a number of lots of good linen, china and glass. The furniture sale comes last, at about 2.00pm, and includes antique, modern, pine and reproduction items of all types.

Lincoln

BUYER'S PREMIUM:
General: 10%. Antiques and fine art: 5%.
SALES: *General: fortnightly on Wed at 11.00am. Antiques and fine art: monthly on Wed at 11.00am. Sporting guns: annually in Jan or Feb.*
VIEWING: *All sales: day prior until 4.30pm. Antiques and fine art: also Sun and Mon prior, afternoon only.*
REFRESHMENTS: *None available on the premises.*
PARKING: *Public multi-storey car park a few minutes walk away.*
STORAGE: *Yes*
TRANSPORTATION: *Yes*
SHIPPING: *Yes*

THOS. MAWER & SON

63 Monks Road. Tel: (0522) 524984

400-500 lots. Monks Road is close to the magnificent Lincoln Cathedral, which sits high on a limestone ridge overlooking the streets. Another interesting building is the Library, which has books and correspondence from the family of Alfred, Lord Tennyson. He was born near by.

Every other Wednesday, Thos Mawer has a sale of general household furniture and effects, and innumerable miscellaneous items. Once a month, slipping in between the general sales, there are special antiques and fine art auctions. A sale of sporting guns is held once a year at the end of the shooting season in January or February. Anyone wishing to buy a firearm at auction must show the auctioneer a firearms certificate issued in the area in which they live. Otherwise the firearm cannot be removed from the auctioneer's custody.

Thos Mawer has a good reputation for bygones, and often there is such a section in the antiques sales. This could include kitchen, farm and garden bygones, or perhaps a variety of signs — an old roadside 'School' warning sign, an enamel advertisement for Park Drive cigarettes, a poster for PG tea, and assorted cast-iron railway plaques. One sale included over two million items, collectively weighing 50 to 60 tons, including wooden legs, a large number of dentist's extracting tools, a boar's head and a rhino's foot. These had been collected and stored by the vendor for a number of years in two chicken sheds.

WILLIAM H BROWN

34 Market Place. Tel: (0406) 363224

200-400 lots. The Friday market auction at Long Sutton is a weekly pilgrimage for many people from the nearby villages. It is a wonderful example of a country auction, and perhaps a good illustration of how markets were in days gone by. The market was granted a charter by King John, and there has been a Friday market auction as long as anyone can remember. Vendors bring their goods from 8.30am onwards on the Friday, and simply lay them out in the market place. Everything is considered saleable — furniture, tins full of screws and nails, boxes of cutlery or china — indeed quite often the auctioneer, Mr R Scrimshaw, does not know what it is he is selling. 'A sort of press made of wood' was the description of one lot — no one knew or could imagine its use, but it was nevertheless sold. If something does not find a buyer it may well be added to the next lot, so with a single purchase it is possible to end up with a most unusual array of goods, perhaps a doll's pram, a pair of lined curtains, a bucket full of tools, a box of children's books, a couple of china cups and a saucepan or two. Quite often, after the sale, someone will ask the successful bidder if he wants to sell one of the items from such an assorted lot privately. To add to the confusion, the auctioneer has to make himself heard over the noise of traffic from the street.

BROADGATE & THOMPSON

1 Cornmarket. Tel: (0507) 603101

500-1,500 lots. Louth is a mixture of many architectural styles, from Elizabethan in the centre to Georgian at Westgate. It has a splendid 300-foot church spire, visible for miles before the town is reached. The wonderful country auction held here was established over 100 years ago and has probably changed little since. Vendors bring in goods that they wish to sell from 7.30am on the day of the sale. Buyers come for their weekly vegetables, and often leave with a piece of furniture or two as well, or perhaps a piece of jewellery or a bicycle.

The sale is in two main sections, beginning with eggs, dressed poultry and meat at 10.45am and then game (when in season) at 1.00pm. The sale of household furniture and effects is in the afternoon and usually goes on until about 3.00 or 4.00pm. The entire sale is conducted in the open, and all buying is strictly in cash only, unless you are known to the auctioneer.

Long Sutton

BUYER'S PREMIUM: 10%
SALES: *Weekly on Fri at 12.00 noon.*
VIEWING: *Morning of sale: goods arrive from 8.30am.*
REFRESHMENTS: *None available on the premises.*
PARKING: *None available on the premises.*
STORAGE: *No*
TRANSPORTATION: *No*
SHIPPING: *No*

Louth

BUYER'S PREMIUM: 6%
SALES: *Weekly on Wed at 10.45am.*
VIEWING: *Morning of sale: goods arrive from 7.30am.*
REFRESHMENTS: *None available on the premises, but available near by.*
PARKING: *None available on the premises.*
STORAGE: *No*
TRANSPORTATION: *No*
SHIPPING: *No*

Louth

BUYER'S PREMIUM: 5%
SALES: *Monthly on the second Tue of the month at 11.00am.*
VIEWING: *Sun prior 2.00pm-4.00pm, Mon prior 12.00 noon-6.00pm, morning of sale from 8.30am.*
REFRESHMENTS: *None available on the premises.*
PARKING: *None available on the premises.*
STORAGE: *Yes*
TRANSPORTATION: *Yes*
SHIPPING: *Yes*

Skegness

BUYER'S PREMIUM: 5%
SALES: *Monthly on Thu at 10.30am.*
VIEWING: *Day prior 11.00am-3.30pm.*
REFRESHMENTS: *None available on the premises.*
PARKING: *Off-street parking.*
STORAGE: *Yes*
TRANSPORTATION: *Yes*
SHIPPING: *Yes*

Sleaford

BUYER'S PREMIUM: 10%
SALES: *General: weekly on Mon at 10.00am. Better furniture etc: monthly on Thu at 10.00am.*
VIEWING: *General: morning of sale — goods arrive from 7.00am. Better furniture etc: day prior, all day.*
REFRESHMENTS: *Mobile canteen.*
PARKING: *Ample space.*
STORAGE: *Yes*
TRANSPORTATION: *Yes*
SHIPPING: *Yes*

JOHN TAYLORS

Woolmart, Kidgate. Tel: (0507) 603648

400-500 lots. This is a traditional, family-run auction. The sale takes place in a big, three-storey auction house, and staff are always on hand to answer questions. The 'smalls' are sold first, including for example silver, silver plate, jewellery, lamps, paintings, prints, glass, coins, books and photographs. These are sold on the first floor. The sale of furniture and other large items takes place next, on the ground floor, with the auctioneer walking round and selling each item *in situ*. The lots are clean and well presented, and the furniture includes antique, Victorian, modern and reproduction. This is a good auction for those setting up home and looking for quality at an affordable price.

TURNER EVANS

32 Roman Bank. Tel: (0754) 766061

400-500 lots. 'Skeggy', as the resort is affectionately known, is popular for family days out, and this busy auction is one of the attractions. Many a holidaymaker has cut his or her auction-going teeth at this friendly sale. The auctioneer and porters are particularly helpful, and eager to offer advice. The saleroom is a large and comfortable former school building which has undergone extensive alterations. All the lots come from private sources and include a wide range of furniture and effects, for example antique, modern, Victorian and reproduction furniture, silverware, china, porcelain of many types, books and photographs, domestic bygones, paintings, prints and needlepoint.

C J DAYKIN

Northgate Saleroom, 69 Northgate. Tel: (0529) 413954

300-500 lots. The Daykin family, father and son, have been involved in the auction business for over 60 years. The saleroom and yard are just outside the town centre, close to the market (also on a Monday, with some interesting stalls). The weekly sale is a good traditional country auction, and one that children particularly enjoy. Vendors arrive with their goods from 7.00am on the day of the sale, and the lots can include anything from pheasants and rabbits to furniture (in all styles and states of repair), rolls of wire netting, boxes of books, television sets, washing machines, spin-driers, ornaments, building materials, and unwanted new toys or other presents. This is a cash-only auction, and selling is fast — around 500 lots are often sold in less than two-and-a-half hours. A sale of garden produce begins at 11.00am.

Once a month in the saleroom there is a sale of better-quality items, such as antique, Victorian, Edwardian, modern and reproduction furniture, and a variety of other goods.

AP SALES

38 New Road. Tel: (0775) 725300

Hundreds of lots. The very busy Tuesday auction at the Cattle Market, Spalding, includes livestock, eggs, fruit and vegetables, flowers, plants and other produce from local smallholders, as well as furniture, bicycles, television sets, brass and other 'deadstock' (anything which is not produce or livestock, or part of another category). The Saturday auction at the Cattle Market offers the same type of goods, but without the livestock. The 'deadstock' at these sales is quite unpredictable — one recent example was a Second World War bomb case, which fetched £5. Goods are brought in on the morning of the sale; the gates are officially open at 7.00am, but it is not unusual to see vehicles queuing up from 5.30am onwards.

Every month an antiques and fine art sale is held at Spalding Common Hall, Spalding Common, about one mile from the Cattle Market, by AP Sales. They are the official South Lincolnshire auctioneers for the Sheriff's office, the police and the county courts.

Spalding

BUYER'S PREMIUM: 5%
SALES: *General, livestock and produce: weekly on Tue at 10.00am. General only: weekly on Sat at 10.00am. Antiques and fine art: monthly on Fri at 5.00pm.*
VIEWING: *General (both days): day of sale (goods arrive from 7.00am). Antiques and fine art: day of sale from 3.00pm.*
REFRESHMENTS: *Cattle Market: tea bar in saleyard.*
PARKING: *Cattle Market: own car park.*
STORAGE: *Yes*
TRANSPORTATION: *Yes*
SHIPPING: *Yes*

WILLIAM H BROWN

Auction Halls, Swan Street. Tel: (0775) 711711

500-600 lots. William H Brown hold sales in the Auction Halls in Swan Street, which they share with R Longstaff & Co. Richard Stimson and S Kingston, William H Brown's two chief auctioneers, conduct good general auctions here, including a wide variety of furniture and other items. A great many lots on sale are from private vendors, who are becoming increasingly aware that selling at auction is the most satisfactory way of gaining the best possible price for their goods. Other items are sold by William H Brown on behalf of executors and liquidators.

If you are new to auction-going and perhaps feel too shy to bid, it is always possible to ask one of the porters or clerks to make the bid for you. This can also be arranged if you see something you like at a viewing, but are unable to attend the actual auction in person. A telephone call to the auctioneers after the sale will confirm whether your bid has been successful or not. If you attend a sale personally, though, you will find out just how simple, but very exciting, bidding is.

Spalding

BUYER'S PREMIUM: 5%
SALES: *Every two months on Fri or Sat at 10.00am.*
VIEWING: *Day prior 5.00pm-7.00pm.*
REFRESHMENTS: *Tea bar in hall.*
PARKING: *Public car park adjacent.*
STORAGE: *Yes*
TRANSPORTATION: *No*
SHIPPING: *No*

Spalding

BUYER'S PREMIUM: 5%
SALES: *Every six weeks on Fri or Sat at 9.30am.*
VIEWING: *Day prior 5.00pm-7.00pm.*
REFRESHMENTS: *Tea bar in hall.*
PARKING: *Own car park.*
STORAGE: *Yes*
TRANSPORTATION: *Yes*
SHIPPING: *Yes*

R LONGSTAFF & CO

Auction Halls, Swan Street. Tel: (0775) 766766

500-600 lots. The Auction Halls are just off Winfrey Avenue, by the bus station and near the town centre. The sale calendar is always worked out at the start of the year, and buyers can ring R Longstaff & Co. for exact future sale dates. The firm was established in 1770 and conducts interesting sales, which usually include a selection of antique, modern and period furniture. There will also usually be brass, china, silver, ornaments, paintings and other items, plus all sorts of bicycles, from the old-fashioned, sit-up-and-beg ladies' variety and butchers' delivery bicycles (which still seem to crop up in great numbers) to the most modern and up-to-date Emmelle and Dawes models. Television sets and general good-to-root-through bric-à-brac boxes are always to be found as well. Larger pieces of furniture, such as wardrobes, seem to sell for amazingly low prices, possibly because they are too large for most modern houses. Sometimes craftsmen buy these larger pieces of furniture and then make smaller pieces from them, simply because the wood is too good to destroy — the fate of unsold cumbersome items at many auction houses.

MERSEYSIDE

Hoylake

BUYER'S PREMIUM: 9.56%
SALES: *Weekly on Tue at 10.30am.*
VIEWING: *Sat prior 9.00am-12.30pm, day prior 9.00am-5.00pm.*
REFRESHMENTS: *Own café.*
PARKING: *Ample parking near by.*
STORAGE: *Yes*
TRANSPORTATION: *Yes*
SHIPPING: *Yes*

KINGSLEY & CO

3/4 The Quadrant. Tel: (051) 632 5821

350-400 lots. The saleroom is on the main road in Hoylake, adjacent to the roundabout. It has a large shop-type front, in which goods for the forthcoming sale are displayed. A friendly atmosphere prevails, and both trade and private buyers attend the sales. This is a family concern, run by Ian McKellar and his wife Jane. The sale is long established and has all the variation that makes going to auctions so exciting. Goods range from modern pieces to good-quality antiques. Among them are furniture and household effects, jewellery, pottery, paintings, porcelain, bicycles, electrical goods, toys, and many other items. Expect prices to fluctuate widely. For instance, a box of china might sell for just a few pounds, whereas some good quality items of antique furniture may well fetch five-figure sums.

ABRAM & MITCHELL

Liverpool

32 Bedford Road, Walton. Tel: (051) 525 1718

180-200 lots. Walton is an attractive and busy suburb of Liverpool. The saleroom is by Walton Church in the foyer of what was the old Bedford Cinema. Abram & Mitchell is a small, locally well known, independent company, who are also involved in removals and storage. The fortnightly Wednesday sale is a popular meeting place for local people, and has a reputation as a place to buy all types of good quality household furniture. Many of the lots come from house clearances, so televisions, videos, china, electrical goods and a wide variety of other items can be expected. It is worth making a thorough search for the odd good piece of furniture or china hidden among more run-of-the-mill goods. Smaller, pocket-sized items are not put out for show during viewing, but are kept locked in the office and brought out only during the sale.

BUYER'S PREMIUM: *Nil*
SALES: *Fortnightly on Wed at 11.00am.*
VIEWING: *Day prior 9.00am-5.00pm.*
REFRESHMENTS: *Van selling snacks usually outside.*
PARKING: *None available on the premises.*
STORAGE: *Yes*
TRANSPORTATION: *Yes*
SHIPPING: *Yes*

HARTLEY & CO

Liverpool

12/14 Moss Street. Tel: (051) 263 6472 and 263 1865

300-400 lots. The saleroom is a short distance from the new Royal Hospital, which is just out from the centre of Liverpool. Hartley & Co have been established for over 120 years and their weekly Friday sales are almost as much of a landmark to some Liverpudlians as the Liver Building. The sale will include a range of goods, as is usual when many of the lots come from house clearances. Among the furniture there could be antique, reproduction or modern items, and the miscellaneous goods often include strange and unexpected pieces. There are usually plenty of small lots such as silver, china and jewellery. Outside effects will also be sold, including gardening tools, garden furniture and bicycles. The more run-of-the-mill lots are sold before 12.00 noon, when selling stops for lunch. The sale resumes at 1.00pm with antiques and better quality items, including china, silver, jewellery and any fine art.

BUYER'S PREMIUM: *5%*
SALES: *Weekly on Fri at 10.15am.*
VIEWING: *Day prior 9.00am-4.30pm.*
REFRESHMENTS: *None available on the premises.*
PARKING: *Car park facing premises.*
STORAGE: *Yes*
TRANSPORTATION: *Yes*
SHIPPING: *Yes*

OUTHWAITE & LITHERLAND

Liverpool

Kingsway Galleries, Fontenoy Street. Tel: (051) 236 6561

300-600 lots. Outhwaite & Litherland were established in 1907, and are one of the largest independent salerooms in the north-west. The present partners are Michael Litherland and Kevin Whay. The weekly general sale is held in the No 2 saleroom on Tuesdays, and is of good general household effects of all periods, including electrical goods, televisions, beds, dining room and lounge suites, tables, chairs, china and

BUYER'S PREMIUM: *10%*
SALES: *General: weekly on Tue at 10.30am. Fine art and antiques: every four to six weeks on Wed at 10.30am.*
VIEWING: *General: day prior 9.00am-5.00pm, morning of sale from 9.00am. Fine art and antiques: two days prior 9.00am-5.00pm, morning of*

sale from 9.00am.
REFRESHMENTS: *Own café.*
PARKING: *Own car park.*
STORAGE: *Yes*
TRANSPORTATION: *Yes*
SHIPPING: *Yes*

crockery, pictures, jewellery, gardening tools and equipment, toys, lamps and so on. Antiques and shipping goods are sold on alternate Tuesdays.

Every four to six weeks on Wednesdays there is a sale of fine art and antiques in the main gallery (called the Fine Art Saleroom).

Several times during the year, but at no regular intervals, Outhwaite & Litherland also hold specialist sales in various categories. Past examples are antiquarian and other books, musical and scientific instruments, clocks, and marine and boating collectables. These sales are worth enquiring about.

The firm also has a large restoration department, and can provide expert work on furniture, clocks, jewellery, silver, paintings, and other goods. If you see something that interests you during viewing, you can get an estimate for repairs before the sale, and take that into account when bidding. Catalogues are available for all sales.

Liverpool

BUYER'S PREMIUM: *Nil*
SALES: *Weekly on Thu at 11.00am.*
VIEWING: *Day prior 9.00am-5.00pm.*
REFRESHMENTS: *None available on the premises.*
PARKING: *Own car park.*
STORAGE: *No*
TRANSPORTATION: *Yes*
SHIPPING: *Yes*

TURNER & SONS

28/36 Roscoe Street. Tel: (051) 709 4005

200-300 lots. Much of Liverpool seems to be in the midst of being knocked down or renovated and it is not a city where you would expect to find good quality antique furniture. However the Turner & Sons sale includes a wide variety of general household furniture and effects, and the lots range from antique through to modern. The weekly sale may also include fine art. It is the mix of quality and value that makes the sale interesting, and this is probably the reason why it is so well attended, both by local people hoping to furnish a house cheaply, and by dealers. There is plenty of Liverpudlian humour and a good atmosphere in the saleroom, although the selling is brisk — the entire proceedings are often finished by 1.00pm. The sale starts outside at 10.45am with vehicles such as cars, trailers, and perhaps plant and machinery, followed by the general goods at 11.00am. The saleroom is in the centre of Liverpool, near the imposing Anglican Cathedral.

Liverpool

BUYER'S PREMIUM: *10%*
SALES: *About every two weeks on Thu at 11.00am (alternate general and antiques).*
VIEWING: *General: day prior, 10.00am-4.00pm, morning of sale. Antiques: two days prior 10.00am-4.00pm, morning of sale.*

WORRALLS

15 Seel Street. Tel: (051) 709 2950

200-300 lots. The saleroom is centrally placed with easy access to Lime Street railway station. The company's chief concern is with fine art and antiques. An antiques sale is held about once a month. The regular sale of general household furniture and effects also takes place about once a month. Sales are arranged so that there is usually an auction every two weeks. The antiques sale could include collectors' items such as dolls, model trains, cars and other toys, antiquarian and other books, glass, oil paintings and watercolours, ceramics, silver, jewellery, clocks, rugs and carpets, with antique furniture finishing the sale. The general sale often includes the contents from complete house clearances, and so you may find everything from salt and pepper shakers and teapots to coal scuttles, television sets, cookers, and all types of furniture, including antiques. These sales are worthwhile for those interested in the unusual or valuable, or those who simply need to furnish and equip a house on a budget.

REFRESHMENTS: *None available on the premises.*
PARKING: *Own car park.*
STORAGE: *Yes*
TRANSPORTATION: *Yes*
SHIPPING: *Yes*

W FLINN & CO

473/5 New Chester Road. Tel: (051) 645 1280

400-500 lots. The saleroom is a large, impressive building on the corner where Bedford Road and New Chester Road meet. It is just a few minutes' walk from Rock Ferry Station. On sale days the lots are attractively set out, with a busy team making sure that everything is clean and polished. W Flinn & Co was established in 1875 and is now owned by George Gaunt, who oversees all aspects of the sale. Mr Gaunt walks around the saleroom during the sale, stopping at various points to conduct the bidding. This brings him into closer contact with the bidders and helps to make the proceedings more informal. Many of the lots will have come from complete house clearances and may vary enormously in type, age, value and condition. Typical sales have included general household furniture, gardening tools and equipment, jewellery, china, kitchen items, photograph albums, postcards, electrical goods, lamps, cameras, general bric-à-brac, books and so on. Selling starts with the lesser quality goods; the more expensive articles are kept to the end. Something can usually be found to suit every interest and every pocket.

Rock Ferry

BUYER'S PREMIUM: *Nil*
SALES: *Fortnightly on Tue at 11.00am.*
VIEWING: *Sat prior 9.00am-12.30pm, day prior 9.00am-5.00pm.*
REFRESHMENTS: *None available on the premises.*
PARKING: *Ample parking near by.*
STORAGE: *Yes*
TRANSPORTATION: *Yes*
SHIPPING: *Yes*

A J COBERN

The Grosvenor Saleroom, 93b Eastbank Street.
Tel: (0704) 500515

400-800 lots. The saleroom is about 200 yards from Lord Street, the tree-lined boulevard and main thoroughfare of this seaside resort. Sales alternate: one month an auction will be devoted to general household furniture and effects, and the next it will be given over to antiques and fine art. The general sales offer good quality modern and reproduction furniture, crockery, paintings, jewellery, electrical goods, kitchen items, boxes of bric-à-brac and so on. The antique and fine art sales have better quality

Southport

BUYER'S PREMIUM: *10%*
SALES: *Monthly on Wed at 10.00am (alternate general and antique sales).*
VIEWING: *General: Mon and Tue prior 9.00am-4.30pm. Antiques: Sat and Sun prior 11.00am-1.00pm, Mon and Tue prior 9.00am-4.30pm.*
REFRESHMENTS: *None available on the premises.*

Wallasey

goods, including pictures, silver, porcelain and furniture. Both sales are excellent for those wishing to furnish or equip a house on a budget, and they are well attended by local people and visitors. The sales are conducted in a manner which entices even reluctant bidders to take the plunge.

J KENT

2/6 Valkyrie Road. Tel: (051) 638 3107

400-500 lots. Wallasey is at one end of the Mersey Tunnel (the other end being just north of Liverpool's Exchange Station). It has a beach backed by sand dunes. Valkyrie Road is just behind the Liscard Shopping Centre in the heart of the town. J Kent is the only agent for the Official Receiver of the Wirral, and often sells commercial stocks, cars and vehicles. The saleroom is large, and there is plenty of room for each lot to be studied. Small items such as silver and jewellery are displayed on shelves and in cabinets. The weekly sales are of general household furniture and effects, including bedroom, dining room and lounge suites, upholstered furniture, kitchen items, jewellery, crockery, gardening tools and equipment, and linen. Every six to eight weeks the sale is devoted to antiques and collectables instead. A typewritten list giving a brief description of each lot is on view for the general sale. For the antique sales such lists are available for a small charge. There are plenty of good buys to be found at both auctions, and a modern computer system means that you can pay within about 10 minutes of making a successful bid.

N O R F O L K

Aylsham

G A KEY

Aylsham Salerooms, Palmers Lane. Tel: (0263) 733195

1,000 lots. This is one of the largest and busiest auction room complexes in the east of England. There are eight large salerooms, and storage areas. The weekly Monday sale includes some 1,000 lots of modern second-hand furniture, second-hand motor vehicles and miscellaneous items such as garden produce, cycles and 'deadstock' —anything that doesn't count as produce or another special category. The sale starts with the produce and poultry (both at 10.00am) followed by 'deadstock' at 10.30am, and bicycles and motor vehicles at 12.30pm. The furniture is sold separately in two batches. The first furniture sale starts at 11.30am in Auction Room 5, and includes a variety of antiques, collectables and better-quality items. The other furniture sale begins at about 2.00pm in Auction Room 6, and is devoted to cottage furniture.

Every three weeks there is a sale of antiques and fine art, including period, Victorian and Edwardian furniture of English and Continental design, plus porcelain, pottery, silver and plate, glass, jewellery, collectors' items and the like. Picture sales are held every other month, and have about 700 lots of watercolours, oil paintings and prints. Book and collectors' sales are held in the alternate months, with a range of topography, natural history and children's illustrated titles, first editions, and various collectables such as ephemera.

In addition, special sales are held throughout the year — these are usually sales of company assets and stock, but are sometimes devoted to vintage motor vehicles.

CASE & DEWING

The Green. Tel: (0362) 692004

400 lots. This auction is an attraction for the summer visitors who flock to this part of Norfolk. The setting is pleasant for browsing and buying, and gives a taste of country auctions in bygone days. The sale is held entirely in the open on the village green, which is surrounded by Georgian houses and divided by a stream. Furniture, both large and small, silver, pewter, copper and brass can be found, as well as china, ornaments, bygones, old postcards, photo albums and the like. Numerous craftsmen and women have set up workshops in this area, and many of them put their products in for auction as well. The sale continues even in the rain, and bad weather has the possible advantage for the determined bidder of keeping away less hardy rivals. Mr Dewing, the auctioneer, is also responsible for the monthly auction at the Memorial Hall in East Dereham.

THOS WM GAZE & SON

Auction Rooms, Roydon Road. Tel: (0379) 650306

1,500-2,000 lots. Thos Wm Gaze & Son was established in 1857 and has been an auction house of one sort or another ever since. This is a large, busy sale where it is possible to bid for anything from eggs, vegetables and pet rabbits to tin baths, caravans, antique furniture and possibly a piece of fine art. Up to four auctions may be going on at once. Selling starts in the yard with the 'Sale Meadow' auction of items like timber, sheds, caravans, lawn mowers, rolls of wire netting, garden tools and so on. At the same time, pet rabbits, chickens and

2.30pm-8.30pm, day of sale from 9.00am. Pictures/books: day prior 10.00am-8.30pm, day of sale from 9.00am.
REFRESHMENTS: *Own tea rooms.*
PARKING: *Own large car park.*
STORAGE: *Yes*
TRANSPORTATION: *Yes*
SHIPPING: *Yes*

Burnham Market

BUYER'S PREMIUM: *Nil*
SALES: *Fortnightly from Jun to Sep on Mon at 1.00pm.*
VIEWING: *Morning of sale from 10.00am.*
REFRESHMENTS: *Available in village.*
PARKING: *Available in the street.*
STORAGE: *No*
TRANSPORTATION: *Yes*
SHIPPING: *No*

Diss

BUYER'S PREMIUM: *Nil*
SALES: *Weekly on Fri at 10.00am. Antique and cottage furniture: weekly on Fri at 12.00 noon (replaced every two months by antiques and collectors' sale).*
VIEWING: *Day prior 2.00pm-8.00pm. Day of sale from 8.30am.*
REFRESHMENTS: *Own café.*

PARKING: *Own car park, 50p per car.*
STORAGE: *Yes*
TRANSPORTATION: *Yes*
SHIPPING: *Yes*

other livestock are sold in another part of the yard, with eggs, fruit, vegetables and farm produce in yet another area.

Modern furniture and household effects, including pots, pans and all sorts of other kitchenalia, as well as china, paintings, prints and a wide range of miscellaneous items, are sold in Saleroom 3 at 11.00am. At 12.00 noon the sale of antique and cottage furniture begins in Saleroom 1, with better-quality items, brass and so on. Every two months this sale is replaced by a special antique and collectors' sale, which starts at 12.00 noon in Saleroom 2.

Downham Market

BUYER'S PREMIUM: *Nil*
SALES: *Monthly on third Wed of month at 11.00am.*
VIEWING: *Morning of sale.*
REFRESHMENTS: *None available on the premises.*
PARKING: *Free street parking at time of writing.*
STORAGE: *Yes*
TRANSPORTATION: *Yes*
SHIPPING: *Yes*

BARRY L HAWKINS

The Repository, Lynn Road. Tel: (0366) 387180

300-400 lots. The Repository is an attractive building which used to be a 28-stall stable. It is by the traffic lights — the town only has one set of lights, so it is easy to find. The pleasant town has a good selection of shops and a picturesque square with an unusual Victorian iron clock tower. If you have time between bidding, an interesting journey can be made along the Denver Road to Denver Sluice, where part of the drainage of the Fens is controlled. The auction has been going for 30 years, except for a three-year break, and usually has a good array of furniture, such as dining and lounge suites, chairs, desks and cabinets, plus brass ornaments, carpets, china, kitchenalia and a variety of outdoor effects — lathes and steam engines, tools, doors, window frames, bricks, boxes of nails and other handy items for DIY. Lots are sold at an average of about 100 per hour.

East Dereham

BUYER'S PREMIUM: *Nil*
SALES: *About twice a month on Tue at 12.00 noon.*
VIEWING: *Morning of sale from 9.30am.*
REFRESHMENTS: *Splendid homemade refreshments in hall.*
PARKING: *Ample space in nearby streets.*
STORAGE: *Yes*
TRANSPORTATION: *Yes*
SHIPPING: *No*

CASE & DEWING

Memorial Hall, Norwich Street. Tel: (0362) 692004

300-400 lots. The Memorial Hall is off the market place, by the old East Dereham railway station. The sale draws most of its items from executors and private vendors from the many villages in the area, so there is a wide range of goods to suit all pockets and needs. Beautifully cared-for antique and modern furniture, brass, china and ornaments will be found, some of which have clearly been in a family for generations. In addition, there are usually gardening tools and equipment, a great deal of kitchenalia, and interesting miscellaneous items which might include old family photograph albums, or a child's collection of cigarette cards. Case & Dewing are also responsible for the fortnightly auction held in summer on the green at Burnham Market.

HUGH BECK AUCTIONS

The Corn Hall. Tel: (0328) 851557

600-700 lots. When Long & Beck, the previous owners of the sale, were taken over by a large public company, this auction was closed — much to the disappointment of locals and visitors alike, because it had been a focal point of Fakenham for many years. However Hugh Beck — half of the original firm — came to the rescue and started the sale up again in a brand new building on a site very near to the old auction rooms. Mr Beck, who has over 30 years experience in the art of auctioneering, said that he missed the atmosphere and the excitement of the sales. The auctioneers boast that anything from a potty to a piano can be bought here. Also to be found are furniture, washing machines, mirrors, wardrobes, bicycles, pots and pans, china, ornaments, paintings — there will usually be at least one thing you want to bid for, if not several. Also under Mr Beck's management is a flea market of around 100 stalls, immediately outside the auction rooms. More than half of the stalls are run by amateurs, and they offer anything from home-made jams to records and tapes, seeds and bulbs, antique buttons and locally hand-crafted goods.

Thursday is both auction day and market day, so the town centre is very busy then. Hugh Beck Auctions also hold a flea market every Thursday in Fakenham Cattle Market to coincide with their sales in the Corn Hall. To find the saleroom, go down Bridge Street and turn left by Finn's Fish Shop.

TYRONE R ROBERTS

The Village Hall. Tel: (0836) 723510

300-400 lots. Tyrone R Roberts holds two regular sales. The monthly sale at the Village Hall, next to the church in Garboldisham, is of general lots. Another sale of antiques and fine art takes place approximately every six weeks at Lynford Hall, Mundford, tel: (0842) 878252, a large mansion, part of which is a motel. Both sales are very well attended and worth visiting, set as they are amid the beautiful Norfolk countryside. The venues are well signposted and it is difficult to miss either saleroom once you get there, as both villages are rather small. The Village Hall is next to the church in Garboldisham.

Tyrone R Roberts is also responsible for the popular Saturday auctions held in the Saleyard at Swaffham (see separate entry). The sales at Garboldisham and Lynford Hall tend to offer goods of higher quality (and somewhat higher prices) than those at Swaffham. Sales at Lynford Hall typically

Fakenham

BUYER'S PREMIUM: *Nil*
SALES: *Weekly on Thu at 11.00am.*
VIEWING: *Wed prior 2.00pm-5.00pm.*
REFRESHMENTS: *Vans selling snacks.*
PARKING: *Town centre car parks, but very busy.*
STORAGE: *Yes*
TRANSPORTATION: *Yes*
SHIPPING: *Yes*

Garboldisham

BUYER'S PREMIUM: *Nil*
SALES: *Garboldisham: monthly on Sun at 12.00 noon. Lynford Hall, Mundford: on average every six weeks on Sun at 11.00am.*
VIEWING: *Garboldisham: day of sale 10.00am-12.00 noon. Lynford Hall, Mundford: Sat prior, 2.00pm-8.00pm and morning of sale from 9.00am..*
REFRESHMENTS: *Garboldisham: available. Lynford Hall, Mundford: own café.*
PARKING *Garboldisham: ample near by. Lynford Hall, Mundford: own car park.*
STORAGE: *Both: yes*

TRANSPORTATION:
Both: yes
SHIPPING: *Both: yes*

include antique furniture, porcelain, metalware, paintings and jewellery. You might find oak roll-top desks, Grandfather and wall clocks, wash stands and Staffordshire tea sets among the lots. At Garboldisham you are more likely to find modern, reproduction and post-war furniture plus jewellery, china, silver and ornaments.

Great Yarmouth

ALDREDS

Kitchener Road Salerooms. Tel: (0493) 844891

BUYER'S PREMIUM: *Nil*
SALES: *Fortnightly on Wed at 10.30am.*
VIEWING: *Tue prior 2.00pm-8.00pm.*
REFRESHMENTS: *Van selling snacks.*
PARKING: *On street.*
STORAGE: *Small amount available.*
TRANSPORTATION: *Yes*
SHIPPING: *Yes*

300-400 lots. The firm was established in 1857 and the auction is run by Geoffry Duffield, assisted by his son Mark. The saleroom is in the centre of Great Yarmouth, off Northgate Street, by the Parish Church of St Nicholas. Yarmouth is known as the 'Blackpool of the East Coast' and has a large number of amusement arcades: an interesting feature of this auction is that quite often pinballs, various slot machines, juke boxes, snooker tables and the like come up for sale. Yarmouth's fishing industry is also reflected in the sale, which often has seafaring items such as ships' compasses and sextants. These lots will be in addition to the more usual array of antique, period and modern furniture, plus silver, glass, china, paintings and bric-à-brac that you would expect to find at all country sales. Unusually for this type of auction, Aldreds sell a catalogue describing the lots on offer.

Great Yarmouth

HOWLETT & EDRICH

Acle Market, Acle. Tel: (0493) 750225

BUYER'S PREMIUM: *Nil*
SALES: *Weekly on Thu at 9.00am.*
VIEWING: *Wed prior 2.00pm-4.00pm.*
REFRESHMENTS: *Sale day only.*
PARKING: *Own car park for 400-500 cars, but often full on Thu.*
STORAGE: *No*
TRANSPORTATION: *Yes*
SHIPPING: *No*

900-1,000 lots. There are usually some 20 to 30 TV sets in the Thursday sale, and a fine array of antique and modern furniture — tables, chairs, pine dressers, pine chests of drawers and so on. The sale begins with garden produce at 9.00am, and is worth attending for the fun of bidding for five pounds of carrots or a bunch of flowers. Then at 10.00am the auctioneer, Peter Edrich (a cousin of the ex-England cricketer, John Edrich) starts the general sale in building No 2. The sale of outside effects begins at 10.30am, and might include perhaps 300 lots of old and new timber, bicycles, plywood sheets, gardening and other tools, old baths, kitchen sinks and so on. At 12.00 noon in the main saleroom a sale of better-quality furniture and effects begins; this sale usually includes good china, linen and ornaments, and there are usually around 400 lots. As a bonus for the auction-goer, Thursday is also market day in Acle. There will usually be 40 to 50 stalls selling various types of bric-à-brac, books, and market goods.

LANDLES FRICS

Blackfriars Hall, Blackfriars Street. Tel: (0553) 772816

500-600 lots. The sale includes good modern furniture, antiques and effects from local house clearances, including plenty of brass and copperware, pictures, garden tools, dinner services, tea sets and so on. The better-quality items tend to be sold at the latter end of the sale, and usually include Georgian, Victorian and Edwardian furniture. Blackfriars Street is in the centre of Kings Lynn, near the post office, public swimming pool and museum, and a few minutes from the modern shopping precinct. The sale has been in existence since the 1890s. It takes place on two floors in a large Victorian building (formerly the British School). If possible allow time to explore the town, which has one of the finest collections of medieval merchants' combined houses and warehouses. The harbour was used as a location for the film *Revolution*.

King's Lynn

BUYER'S PREMIUM: *Nil*
SALES: *Monthly, usually on second Wed of month at 10.00am.*
VIEWING: *Tue prior 9.00am-8.00pm.*
REFRESHMENTS: *None available on the premises, but available near by.*
PARKING: *Council car park opposite.*
STORAGE: *Yes*
TRANSPORTATION: *Yes*
SHIPPING: *Yes*

METHWOLD AUCTION MART

High Street. Tel: (0842) 827398

700-1,000 lots. This is a family business, run by George and Rosemary Reeve and their son Simon, who shares the auctioneering with his father. It is a country auction of the type that gets people hooked on attending them and wanting more.

Practically the whole village is given over to accommodating the Monday sales, especially on Bank Holiday Mondays when special antiques sales are held as well.

Vendors bring in goods for the weekly sale on Sunday and Monday morning. At 10.30am the auctioning of farm produce, plants, eggs, shrubs and so on starts in the saleyard, while the selling of household furniture and effects begins in the saleroom. The auctioneer who finishes first starts the sale of outside effects, but never before 1.00pm. This section covers lots such as bundles of timber, various building materials, gardening tools and equipment, and bygones. The sale often lasts until 5.00 or 6.00pm.

For the antique sales there is something of a carnival atmosphere in the village. Local halls take advantage of the extra visitors to hold their own jumble and bric-à-brac sales, with home-made tea and cakes. To cope with the extra numbers, St George's Hall, opposite the saleroom, is also used for the antiques auction. Furniture, paintings, china, silver, bygones and craft items may all be found at this sale.

Methwold

BUYER'S PREMIUM: *Nil*
SALES: *General: weekly on Mon at 10.30am. Antiques: Bank Holiday Mondays (never New Year's Day) at 1.00pm.*
VIEWING: *Day of sale.*
REFRESHMENTS: *Not available on the premises.*
PARKING: *Ample car parking space.*
STORAGE: *Yes*
TRANSPORTATION: *Yes*
SHIPPING: *Yes*

Mundford

TYRONE R ROBERTS
See TYRONE R ROBERTS, Garboldisham, Norfolk

North Walsham

NIGEL F HEDGE
Midland Road Saleroom. Tel: (0692) 402881

BUYER'S PREMIUM: *10%*
SALES: *Fortnightly on Fri at 10.00am.*
VIEWING: *Thu prior 3.00pm-5.00pm and 7.00pm-9.00pm.*
REFRESHMENTS: *Van selling snacks.*
PARKING: *Own car park.*
STORAGE: *Yes*
TRANSPORTATION: *Yes*
SHIPPING: *Yes*

700-800 lots. North Walsham is seven miles from Wroxham, one of the main places for boat-hire in the Norfolk Broads. During the summer, many people on boating holidays tie their cruisers up for the morning and come to the sale. Some first came here as children, and are now bringing their own offspring with them. There is often a wide and interesting range of lots of various values: furniture in all sorts of condition, domestic electrical appliances of all types, porcelain, china, brassware, books and boxes of bric-à-brac, which are always worth rummaging through. The main auction takes place in a large, purpose-built saleroom, but there is a yard in front of the saleroom where outside effects such as bicycles, lawn mowers, garden tools and timber are kept. These are sold off at 10.30am.

Norwich

CLOWES, NASH & THURGAR
Cornhall Saleroom, Norwich Livestock Market, Hall Road. Tel: (0603) 627261 and 627262

BUYER'S PREMIUM: *Nil*
SALES: *Weekly on Wed at 10.00am (includes antiques sale about every two months).*
VIEWING: *Tue prior 2.00pm-4.00pm (extended to 7.00pm for antiques sale).*
REFRESHMENTS: *Available.*
PARKING: *Own car park.*
STORAGE: *Yes*
TRANSPORTATION: *Yes*
SHIPPING: *Yes*

400-500 lots. The Cornhall auction and the livestock market moved to the present site, just outside the town, in 1960. The cattle market is one of the most up-to-date in the world, with sale rings looking rather like astronomical laboratories. It is a bonus for children, and they usually find the general sale interesting as well. This includes some antiques as well as modern furniture and effects from local house clearances, plus books, bicycles and collectables — sets of cigarette cards, comics, lead soldiers and working toys of all sorts. About every second month the general sale becomes a special antiques sale. A cannon is one of the more memorable lots sold by auctioneers Barry Martin and Chris Thurgar. In the city centre, Norwich's market is also worth a visit, with its striped awnings and interesting stalls. It is said to date back to Norman times.

Snettisham

CRUSO & WILKINS
Snettisham Auction Centre, Common Road. Tel: (0485) 542656

BUYER'S PREMIUM: *5%*
SALES: *Weekly on Fri at 10.00am.*
VIEWING: *Thu prior, 3.00pm-6.00pm.*

400-500 lots. This is a good general auction selling a wide and varied range of furniture, bicycles, paintings, brass and silverware, bygones, antiques, collectables, and miscellaneous items such as garden tools, electrical appliances, bundles of wood and kitchen sinks. It would be possible to spend a day at a Cruso & Wilkins' sale and buy everything for a house, including a working television.

The saleroom is large and comfortable, and well heated in winter. The lots are laid out with generous room for viewing, and there is also plenty of seating. The sale takes place entirely under cover. It begins with wood, if there is any, then moves on to gardening equipment, electrical goods such as washing machines, cookers, vacuum cleaners, spin driers and so on, and then items of furniture. The 'table' lots come next — ornaments, china, dinner and tea sets, jewellery and other small items of value. Then the larger furniture is sold, for example lounge and bedroom suites, beds and so on, finishing up with carpets and television sets. There are ample sockets around the room for testing electrical goods, so you can plug in a television or a mower to see if it works.

Snettisham is a mile from the coast and three miles from the Queen's Norfolk residence at Sandringham. Cruso & Wilkins are well signposted on the main Kings Lynn-Hunstanton road.

REFRESHMENTS: *Own café.*
PARKING: *Own large car park.*
STORAGE: *Yes*
TRANSPORTATION: *Yes*
SHIPPING: *Yes*

JONATHAN HOWLETT

Upper Staithe Road. Tel: (0692) 580203

900-1,000 lots. The sale begins outside at 10.00am with 'deadstock' — items such as paving stones, timber, tools, roofing felt, doors, window frames, bicycles and so on. In another part of the saleyard, garden produce is auctioned from 10.30am. Inside the large barn, the general auction of an often huge number of lots begins at 11.00am. This sale will include furniture and miscellaneous effects from local house clearances: lounge and bedroom suites, chests of drawers, ornaments, crockery and kitchenalia of all sorts, in all states of repair.

Stalham is on the Broads, and the sale is a good place to look out for boating equipment, including dinghies, which turn up from time to time. The auction was established before the First World War and buyers travel from all over Norfolk to attend. Tuesday is also market day for Stalham, and the market stalls with their clothes, fruit and vegetables and bric-à-brac all help to make a good day out for the family. Stalham also has a large staithe. If you are on a boating holiday, you can approach Stalham by water from Barton Broad.

Stalham

BUYER'S PREMIUM: *Nil*
SALES: *Weekly on Tue at 10.00am.*
VIEWING: *Mon prior 2.00pm-4.00pm.*
REFRESHMENTS: *Available on the premises.*
PARKING: *Own car park.*
STORAGE: *Yes*
TRANSPORTATION: *Yes*
SHIPPING: *Yes*

Swaffham

BUYER'S PREMIUM: *Nil*
SALES: *Weekly on Sat at 11.00am.*
VIEWING: *Day of sale only.*
REFRESHMENTS: *Many cafés and pubs near by.*
PARKING: *Large council car parks, but usually very busy.*
STORAGE: *No*
TRANSPORTATION: *Yes*
SHIPPING: *Yes*

TYRONE R ROBERTS

The Saleyard. Tel: (0362) 691267

400-500 lots. 'Du yew open thaat owd buggar up bor. Du yew du, I du believe yew'll foind thaat'll go' ... auctioneer Tyrone Roberts offering a clock up for sale at his Swaffham Saturday auction. Unfortunately the East Anglian accent is as difficult to write as it is for a 'foreigner' (a non East Anglian) to speak, but Tyrone Roberts is one of the best and most entertaining auctioneers around. Constantly exchanging banter with the crowd, he would make most comedians green with envy. The Swaffham Saturday auction was featured in the BBC television series *In at the Deep End*, when presenter Chris Searle began his education as an auctioneer under the tutorship of Mr Roberts.

The auction is held in the open air in the market square. The lots are laid out in rows, with the auctioneer walking along and selling each lot as he comes to it. Purchases are paid for straight away, and as there is no one to check that the right buyer has the right item, it is best to grab what you have bought without delay. The goods for sale range from furniture to bicycles, and from rabbits to cars. There is always a good selection of televisions, which can be seen working and are sold under cover in the saleyard at the rear of the square, behind the Greyhound pub.

Watton

BUYER'S PREMIUM: *Nil.*
SALES: *Weekly on Tue at 10.30am.*
VIEWING: *Mon prior 4.00pm-8.00pm.*
REFRESHMENTS: *Own café.*
PARKING: *Own car park.*
STORAGE: *Yes*
TRANSPORTATION: *Yes*
SHIPPING: *Yes*

STEPHEN ROBERTS

Breckland House, Norwich Road. Tel: (0953) 885676

700-800 lots. This is an Aladdin's cave for the collector, connoisseur or browser. Stephen Roberts has a contract with the Ministry of Defence, so expect to see, not bombs and guns, but surplus clothing: uniforms, boots, gas masks, ski goggles, ties, socks, shirts and many, many other things, some without any obvious military connections. Carpets, furniture and gardening equipment from military family quarters are also sold. Another contract with the Norwich Union to sell their excess or redundant office furniture and equipment means that Stephen Roberts also usually have a large number of typewriters, office chairs, desks and the like for sale. Indeed, one room is entirely devoted to the sale of office equipment and furniture.

The auction starts outside with 'deadstock' — gardening equipment, mowers, timber, corrugated iron sheets, glass baths and other heavy items — then moves inside to the better quality and antique lots, arriving finally at electrical goods, office equipment, and general furniture and effects.

NORTHAMPTONSHIRE

SPENCERS (AUCTIONEERS)

Corby

Unit 3a, Southfold Road. Tel: (0536) 743755

500-600 lots. This is an independently run auction in the Great Oakley industrial estate, on the edge of the town. It is usually more suitable for those wanting to furnish a house on a budget than for collectors, but occasionally some good items of furniture, china or collectables do appear. The auctioneers offer the guarantee that all electrical goods sold here are 'in working order', which is unusual — most auctions prefer to emphasise that goods are sold 'as seen'. There are plenty of electric points in the saleroom so that buyers can satisfy themselves as to the condition of an article before bidding. The auction starts with 'market trading goods', which at this sale means china, porcelain, ornaments and general bric-à-brac. These are followed by domestic electrical goods, carpets, general furniture such as three-piece suites and tables, televisions, video and audio equipment, and antique and better quality furniture. Last of all come beds, bedding and bedroom furniture. Two auctioneers help to keep up the pace of the sale, which moves rapidly and finishes at around 9.00pm.

BUYER'S PREMIUM: *Nil*
SALES: *Weekly on Wed at 6.00pm.*
VIEWING: *Day of sale from 11.00am.*
REFRESHMENTS: *Own café.*
PARKING: *Own car park.*
STORAGE: *Yes*
TRANSPORTATION: *Yes*
SHIPPING: *Yes*

J M BAYES

Irthlingborough

43B High Street. Tel: (0933) 651015

300-350 lots. Irthlingborough is a small town with a big name. The saleroom is in a former Methodist chapel, about 50 yards from the post office. This is very much a local sale, offering a service to the community both as a place to sell unwanted goods and as somewhere to buy at budget prices.

Anything to furnish and equip a house may be found here, from three-piece suites and beds to cutlery, china, lamps and televisions. As in all auctions, for those who have time to search the lots thoroughly there is always the chance of exciting and unusual finds, such as rare old gramophone records, old cameras, collections of childrens' books, good

BUYER'S PREMIUM: *Nil*
SALES: *Every two or three weeks on Mon at 6.00pm.*
VIEWING: *Day of sale from 1.00pm.*
REFRESHMENTS: *None available on the premises.*
PARKING: *Ample parking near by.*
STORAGE: *Yes*
TRANSPORTATION: *Yes*
SHIPPING: *Yes*

ornaments, jewellery and so on. The better quality items are sold towards the end of the auction.

Kettering

BUYER'S PREMIUM: 10%
SALES: Antiques, objets d'art and superior furniture: monthly on first Thu of month. General: monthly on second Sat after antiques sale at 11.00am. Sporting guns and antique arms: twice a year in Mar and Sep on Thu after general sale at 3.00pm. Sporting memorabilia: twice a year in Apr and Oct on Wed after general sale at 4.00pm.
VIEWING: Antiques: day prior 9.30am-8.00pm. General and others: day of sale.
REFRESHMENTS: None available on the premises.
PARKING: Council car park behind saleroom.
STORAGE: Yes
TRANSPORTATION: Yes
SHIPPING: Yes

SOUTHAM & SONS

Corn Exchange Saleroom, Thrapston. Tel: (0832) 734486

600 lots. The saleroom is centrally located in Thrapston, about eight miles east of Kettering. It is in a large building with a stone sheaf of corn above the main entrance. There are plenty of Southam & Sons' sale direction boards placed around the town.

The Thursday antiques sale is of catalogued lots, and usually includes Georgian, Victorian and Edwardian furniture, silver, silver plate, pottery, porcelain, pictures, prints, jewellery and collectables, such as tea caddies and cameras. The jewellery is kept in a locked cabinet, but the porters will unlock it if there is anything you wish to examine.

The uncatalogued sales, which take place on the second Saturday after the Thursday antiques sales, are of general household furniture and effects. Occasionally antiques will be found too. The furniture is placed around the walls of the saleroom; at the rear are garden chairs and benches, and tools: hammers, mowers, ladders and so on. This sale offers some very good buys. Linen of all types, such as bed linen, tablecloths, napkins and curtains, usually starts the sale. Next come carpets and rugs, then boxes of assorted items, which might include books, kitchen utensils, various pieces of china, and ornaments. Furniture is sold at the end of the day.

A sporting guns and antique arms sale takes place twice a year, and there is also a twice-yearly sale of sporting memorabilia, including fishing equipment, sporting books, prints and so on.

Northampton

BUYER'S PREMIUM: 10%
SALES: General: fortnightly on Sat at 9.30am. Antiques and fine art: about every three months on Thu at 10.30am.
VIEWING: General: day prior 10.30am-4.30pm, morning of sale from 9.00am. Antiques and fine art: day prior 10.00am-4.00pm, morning of sale from 9.00am.
REFRESHMENTS: Own café.

HEATHCOTE BALL & CO (NORTHAMPTON) LTD

Albion Auction Rooms, Commercial Street. Tel: (0604) 22735

600-700 lots. Heathcote Ball & Co hold popular sales of household furniture and effects, in the attractive setting of what used to be an old brewery. It has a cobbled stone courtyard, and is one of the oldest buildings in Northampton.

The saleroom is a large L-shaped room, and the sale tends to fall into two sections; the smaller end of the L holds smaller lots, such as boxes full of kitchenalia, sundry pieces of china and portable electrical goods like personal stereos, while the main part of the hall holds furniture, (which could include bedroom and dining room suites, single armchairs, pianos, tables, washstands and so on), and large electrical goods — photocopying machines, washing machines, dishwashers and so on. Many of these electrical goods will have come from a local warehouse, or are end-of-line or showroom items.

Antique and fine art sales are also held, on average about once every three months.

WILFORDS

76 Midland Road. Tel: (0933) 222760 and 222762

900-1,000 lots. This weekly sale attracts many regulars, and Thursdays in the saleroom are hectic. The firm was established in 1934 and is still owned by the Wilford family. The sale has a reputation for the variety of goods and the friendly, helpful service offered to both buyer and vendor. A typical sale will have electrical goods, kitchen items, modern furniture, and domestic and ornamental china. Selling starts with outside effects such as bicycles, lawn mowers and gardening tools. In among the lots there may be some good antiques. Unlike many other auctioneers, Wilfords do not keep back better quality articles for special sales.

NORTHUMBERLAND

IAN A ROBERTSON

Narrowgate Salerooms, Narrowgate. Tel: (0665) 602725

600-700 lots. Alnwick is a delightful stone market town, set on a hill above the River Aln. The saleroom is part of the old castle — it is at the end of the castle wall, with a beautiful park to wander around during the lunch break in the sale. As might be expected in such surroundings, the selling in the auction is unhurried. The fortnightly sale is very much a local meeting place, with many people from the nearby villages arranging their regular shopping trip to coincide with the sale. The lots generally include an array of well-cared-for household furniture and effects, and interesting items of china, brass, jewellery and other goods. About twice a year, but at no set times, the auctioneers hold a special two-day catalogued sale of antiques and fine art.

PARKING: *NCP 50 yards away.*
STORAGE: *Yes*
TRANSPORTATION: *Yes*
SHIPPING: *Yes*

Wellingborough

BUYER'S PREMIUM: *10%*
SALES: *Weekly on Thu at 10.00am.*
VIEWING: *Day prior 8.00am-6.00pm.*
REFRESHMENTS: *Coffee vending machine.*
PARKING: *None available on the premises.*
STORAGE: *No*
TRANSPORTATION: *Yes*
SHIPPING: *Yes*

Alnwick

BUYER'S PREMIUM: *5%*
SALES: *General: fortnightly on Tue at 10.00am. Special antiques sale: twice yearly on Mon and Tue at 10.00am.*
VIEWING: *General: Fri, Sat and Mon prior 10.00am-4.00pm. Special antiques sale: Thu, Fri and Sat prior, 10.00am-4.00pm.*
REFRESHMENTS: *None available on the premises.*
PARKING: *None available on the premises.*
STORAGE: *Yes*
TRANSPORTATION: *Yes*
SHIPPING: *Yes*

Morpeth

BUYER'S PREMIUM: 10%
SALES: Monthly on Sat at
9.30am (includes sale of
antiques in alternate months).
VIEWING: Wed, Thu and
Fri prior 10.00am-4.00pm
(also Thu 10.00am-7.00pm for
antiques sale).
REFRESHMENTS:
Available.
PARKING: Car park
opposite.
STORAGE: Yes
TRANSPORTATION: Yes
SHIPPING: Yes

LOUIS JOHNSON

Oswald House, 63 Bridge Street. Tel: (0670) 513025

400-500 lots. Morpeth is an old market town in the charming wooded valley of the Wansbeck. The saleroom is part of an attractive three-storey building, which has recently been extended. Louis Johnson's monthly auctions alternate between general sales and sales of better quality antiques, reproduction furniture and fine art. The general sales have a typical range of household furniture and effects, and as a rule some gardening equipment as well. At the rear of the saleroom there is an area where classic cars are auctioned. Around eight to a dozen of these cars may be sold during the antiques sale. There is also a craft centre opposite the saleroom, selling blown glass, dried flowers, tapestry and other locally made items.

NORTH YORKSHIRE

Bedale

BUYER'S PREMIUM: 5%
SALES: Every three weeks on
Sat at 10.30am.
VIEWING: Wed and Fri
9.00am-12.00 noon.
1.00pm-4.30pm, Thu
9.00am-12.00 noon.
REFRESHMENTS: None
available on the premises.
PARKING: Ample parking
near by.
STORAGE: Yes
TRANSPORTATION: Yes
SHIPPING: Yes

M W DARWIN & SONS

The Dales Furniture Hall, Bridge Street. Tel: (0677) 422846

400-500 lots. The saleroom is a converted chapel, and a visit is a must for many people from nearby villages, while local people will often pop in quickly during sale day just to see what is on offer.

The sale is on a Saturday, and it is a popular meeting place for many who turn up, not just to buy, but also to meet old friends and exchange local gossip. A typical sale will have general household furniture and effects, including antiques. There is usually a fair amount of china, glass, pottery, jewellery and so on, with bicycles, mowers and lesser quality items to finish the proceedings.

Within this broad range, the value of the lots varies widely. A glass ornament might be auctioned off for a couple of pounds, while a few lots later a piece of antique furniture could well fetch a three- or four-figure sum.

Escrick

BUYER'S PREMIUM:
General: 7%. Antiques sale:
5%.
SALES: Monthly on Sat at
12.00 noon (includes antiques
sale three times a year).

JOHN SIMPSON

The Saleroom, North Selby Mine Road. Tel: (0904) 424797

300-700 lots. This is an independently run sale under the proprietorship of John Simpson, who has over 20 years' experience in the trade. The saleroom is a massive old farm building which becomes a hive of activity and noise on sale days. Mr Simpson always manages to gather an interesting mix

NORTH YORKSHIRE •

of general household furniture and effects together for his sales. A typical auction will include Victorian, modern, reproduction, cottage and shipping furniture, china, glass, brass, pictures and books, rugs, electrical and hi-fi equipment, bikes and many other goods. Three times a year, in April, July and October, the general sale is replaced by a special sale of antiques.

VIEWING: *Morning of sale from 9.30am.*
REFRESHMENTS: *Own café.*
PARKING: *Ample near by.*
STORAGE: *Yes*
TRANSPORTATION: *Yes*
SHIPPING: *Yes*

MORPHETS

4 & 6 Albert Street. Tel: (0423) 530030
300-400 lots. The saleroom is a short walk from the railway station, behind the company's offices and close to the centre of this busy town. There is a general auction most Thursdays, but the catalogued sales of antiques and fine art are held bi-monthly. Lots in this sale could include period and later furniture, oil paintings and watercolours, pottery, porcelain, silver, jewellery and *objets d'art*, among other items. The other Thursday sales are just as rewarding, but they offer lesser quality goods, such as Victorian and Edwardian household furniture and effects, kitchenalia, domestic and ornamental china, various household items and some collectables.

Harrogate

BUYER'S PREMIUM: 10%
SALES: *General: weekly on Thu at 12.00 noon. Antiques: bi-monthly on Thu at 10.00am and 2.00pm.*
VIEWING: *General: morning of sale from 9.00am. Antiques: day prior 10.00am-4.00pm.*
REFRESHMENTS: *None available on the premises.*
PARKING: *None available on the premises.*
STORAGE: *Yes*
TRANSPORTATION: *Yes*
SHIPPING: *Yes*

G SUMMERSGILL

The Village Hall. Tel: (0904) 791131
300 lots. Huby is a village about five miles from Easingwold. G Summersgill has been holding auctions in this area for over 25 years. These are held every six weeks in the Village Hall, which is hired for the occasion. The majority of the lots are supplied by local people. It is amazing how many interesting bits and pieces farmers and others can find tucked away in their lofts or sheds. General run-of-the-mill goods mix in with well-cared-for antiques, and successful bids can range from a few pounds to thousands. Quite apart from the possibility of picking up an unusual item, the atmosphere is pleasant, and the surrounding countryside is attractive, too.

Huby, near York

BUYER'S PREMIUM: *Nil*
SALES: *Every six weeks on Sat at 1.00pm.*
VIEWING: *Day of sale from 9.00am.*
REFRESHMENTS: *None available on the premises.*
PARKING: *Ample parking near by.*
STORAGE: *Yes*
TRANSPORTATION: *Yes*
SHIPPING: *No*

TENNANTS

The Auction Centre, Harmby Road. Tel: (0969) 23780
700-900 lots. This is a Yorkshire country auction with an increasing national and international reputation. Tennants' custom-built saleroom covers no less than 40,000 sq ft and has excellent amenities, including a library and conference facilities. The Saturday sales are of general household furniture and effects, with an emphasis on antiques. At most sales there will be around 400 lots of small items such as china, glass,

Leyburn

BUYER'S PREMIUM: 10%
SALES: *Weekly on Sat at 9.30am, plus regular catalogued and specialist sales.*
VIEWING: *Day prior 9.30am-7.00pm.*
REFRESHMENTS: *Own restaurant.*

127 •

jewellery, clocks and paintings, with some 300 lots of cottage and shipping furniture, and 200 lots of better-quality furniture and antiques.

Typical lots at past sales have included Georgian dressers, Victorian oak bookcases, chests of drawers, dining tables of all periods, writing desks, bureaux, painted and stained pine, wheelback chairs, dressing tables and pianos. Paintings and prints, ceramics and glass can also be found, as well as a host of silver and plate, jewellery and coins, and collectors' items: cigarette cards, photograph albums, kitchenalia and books.

The box and tray lots of miscellaneous items are always worth looking at, as are the crochet and linen. In addition, you will probably find electrical goods such as washing machines and refrigerators, and outside effects, including stone troughs and garden furniture.

Malton

BUYER'S PREMIUM: *Malton: 5%. Murton: nil.*
SALES: *Malton and Murton: monthly on Wed at 10.30am (location alternates).*
VIEWING: *Malton: day prior 10.00am-8.00pm. Murton: day prior 2.00pm-8.00pm.*
REFRESHMENTS: *Malton: none available on the premises. Murton: own snack bar.*
PARKING: *Both: ample near by.*
STORAGE: *Both: yes*
TRANSPORTATION: *Both: yes*
SHIPPING: *Both: yes*

Murton, near York

BUYER'S PREMIUM: *Nil*
SALES: *Antiques and Victoriana: five times a year in Mar, May, Jul, Oct and Dec at 9.30am. Equipment and machinery: five to six times a year, from Mar to Nov on Wed at 10.00am. Horse and tack: monthly on Tue at 11.00am.*
VIEWING: *Antiques and Victoriana: day prior 2.00pm-8.00pm, day of sale. Equipment and machinery: day prior. Horse and tack: day of sale.*
REFRESHMENTS: *Own café.*

BOULTON & COOPER

Milton Rooms. Tel: (0653) 696151

500-700 lots. Boulton & Cooper hold a one-day catalogued sale here every other month. On alternate months, the firm holds a one-day catalogued sale at the Livestock Centre, Murton, near York, tel: (0904) 625533. Both sales consist of somewhat up-market goods. The sale at Murton usually comprises antiques and general household items.

STEPHENSON & SON

The York Salerooms. Tel: (0904) 489731

800-900 lots. These sales are of antiques and Victoriana, and are held usually in March, May, July, October and December. The sale calendar is arranged well in advance, and exact dates are available from the auctioneers. The lots are carefully selected and gathered over a long period, so they are generally of high quality. The range is very wide, however. Past sales have included an Aeolian pianola, brass and iron bedsteads, antique rocking chairs, antique bureaux, pictures and prints (many of local interest), silver and jewellery (including Georgian teaspoons, plated cutlery, entrée dishes, gold rings and gold watch chains), china and pottery (including Clarice

Cliff, Victorian tea services and various items by Doulton, Coalport, Wedgwood and Staffordshire).

Sales of machinery and equipment are held between March and November on the same site. Among the 3,000 or more lots there will be second-hand timber, lawn mowers and garden tools, workshop machinery, livestock feeding equipment, tractors, combine harvesters and other vehicles.

The same firm holds monthly horse and tack auctions which are open to the public. They take place in stables at Rufforth Park, Rufforth. Saddles, blankets, spurs and other equipment are auctioned off first, followed by about 80 horses.

PARKING: *Ample parking available.*
STORAGE: *Yes*
TRANSPORTATION: *Yes*
SHIPPING: *Yes*

JOPLINGS

Ripon

The Old Saleroom, Coltsgate Hill. Tel: (0765) 602614 or 607968

300-500 lots. Ripon is a quiet and peaceful city, with an ancient centre full of narrow streets and alleyways. The Old Saleroom is just off North Street, the main thoroughfare, and auctions have been held there since the turn of the century. The fortnightly sales take place on two floors, and are very much a local asset: people regularly use them for buying and selling a huge range of goods. The atmosphere is fun and there are usually many interesting lots to browse through. You will find anything from fine antiques to modern household furniture, including domestic electrical goods, gardening tools and equipment, ornaments, china, brass, books, paintings, childrens' toys, collectables and bric-à-brac.

BUYER'S PREMIUM: *7½%*
SALES: *Fortnightly on Fri at 11.00am.*
VIEWING: *Thu prior 11.00am-3.00pm.*
REFRESHMENTS: *Available.*
PARKING: *Ample parking near by.*
STORAGE: *Yes*
TRANSPORTATION: *Yes*
SHIPPING: *Yes*

H C CHAPMAN & SON

Scarborough

The Auction Mart, North Street. Tel: (0723) 372424

200-400 lots. H C Chapman & Son are members of the Society of Fine Art Auctioneers. Their weekly Monday sale was established in 1903 and is still going strong. Lots include

BUYER'S PREMIUM: 10%
SALES: *General: weekly on Mon at 10.00am (except weeks*

with antiques sale). Antiques: every four to six weeks on Tue at 10.00am.
VIEWING: General: Sat prior 10.00am-4.00pm. Antiques: Fri prior 4.00pm-7.00pm, Sat prior 10.00am-4.00pm, Mon prior 9.00am-12.00 noon.
REFRESHMENTS: None available on the premises.
PARKING: Own car park.
STORAGE: Yes
TRANSPORTATION: Yes
SHIPPING: Yes

Scarborough

BUYER'S PREMIUM: 10%
SALES: Fortnightly on Mon (or Tue if this coincides with a Bank Holiday) at 10.00am or 10.30am depending on the number of lots (includes sale of especially good quality items every two months).
VIEWING: Wed prior 6.00pm-8.00pm, Thu and Fri prior 10.30am-4.00pm.
REFRESHMENTS: Own café.
PARKING: Queen Street public car park.
STORAGE: Yes
TRANSPORTATION: Yes
SHIPPING: Yes

Scarthingwell, near Tadcaster

BUYER'S PREMIUM: 10%
SALES: Twice monthly on first and third Mon of month at 6.00pm.
VIEWING: Day prior 12.00 noon-5.00pm, day of sale from 4.00pm.
REFRESHMENTS: Own café.
PARKING: Own car park.
STORAGE: No
TRANSPORTATION: Yes
SHIPPING: No

good quality modern, reproduction and nearly-new household furniture, and a wide range of miscellaneous items, which helps to make the sale one of the most popular in Yorkshire.

Every four to six weeks there is a special sale of antiques and fine art, which is held on a Tuesday. This auction will include Georgian, Victorian and later furniture, ceramics, glass, *objets d'art*, jewellery, silver and plated items, watercolours, oil paintings and prints, and specialist categories of lots where appropriate. Sales are also held on the vendor's premises from time to time.

GA FINE ARTS AND CHATTELS

Scarborough Auction Rooms, 14/15 Queen Street.
Tel: (0723) 353581

400-500 lots. This sale is popular with summer visitors, many of whom may never have attended an auction before. It is held fortnightly on Monday, except when this overlaps with a Bank Holiday, in which case the sale is on the Tuesday. A wide variety of good quality lots can be found: gardening equipment, kitchenalia, domestic and ornamental china, jewellery, boxes of bric-à-brac, bygones, books and comics, while set out around the room will be Georgian, Victorian and later furniture, electro-plate and silver, brass and copper, pictures and so on. Every two months the general sale is replaced by a sale of items of especially good quality.

PAUL HIRST

Scarthingwell Antique & Auction Centre. Tel: (0937) 557742

500 lots. These auctions are held on the first and third Monday of the month and offer an exciting and unusual day out in magnificent countryside.

The saleroom has been converted from an old barn, and stands in a group of old buildings. These house an antiques centre selling collectables and crafts. The centre is open on weekdays and at weekends, when there are also viewings for the auctions. The delicious, home-cooked meals on offer are also worth trying.

The auction itself is of general household goods, including modern, Edwardian and Georgian furniture, domestic and ornamental china, pottery, silver, brass, glass, collectables, jewellery, paintings, prints and other items.

MALCOLM H SKIDMORE

Victoria Hall. Tel: (0535) 275265

700-950 lots. In addition to this Wednesday afternoon sale at Settle, Mr Skidmore conducts Friday evening auctions at the Town Hall, Main Street, Cottingley (about one mile from Bingley). Both sales take place at three-weekly intervals and are similar in content, although Settle is the larger. The sales are ideal for those wishing to furnish a house cheaply, buy high quality antiques, develop a collection of one type or another, or simply browse. A typical sale might include a complete farmhouse dispersal of old furniture and general effects, as well as new and nearly new furniture, carpets and effects from modern houses.

Among the lots in past sales have been oak roll-top desks, Welsh dressers, grandfather clocks, pine, mahogany and oak antique furniture, books, china, silver, brass and jewellery. The selling is relaxed and there is a pleasant informal atmosphere, with a lot of country humour. Mr Skidmore travels as a livestock auctioneer when not conducting these sales; on a Monday you may find him selling at the livestock sale at Otley, and on a Tuesday he can be found at Holmfirth cattle market.

Settle

BUYER'S PREMIUM: 5%
SALES: *Settle: every three weeks on Wed at 2.00pm. Cottingley: every three weeks on Fri at 6.00pm.*
VIEWING: *Settle: day of sale from 10.00am. Cottingley: day of sale from 2.00pm.*
REFRESHMENTS: *Own cafés.*
PARKING: *Own car parks.*
STORAGE: *Yes*
TRANSPORTATION: *Yes*
SHIPPING: *Yes*

MALCOLMS NO 1

The Village Hall. Tel: (0977) 684971 and 685334

300-400 lots. On both the sale day and the viewing day, the Village Hall is surrounded by vehicles belonging to potential buyers, so it is not hard to find. Malcolm Dowson's sales have a reputation for a good selection of antiques and collectables which sell at reasonable prices, and they attract both trade buyers and members of the public from far away. A computerised system is used to avoid long queues.

The hall is centrally heated and has seating for around 150. The sales start at 6.30pm prompt with furniture, followed by top quality antiques and collectables. Likely to be found are good quality items such as lowboys, Victorian dressers, tiled wash stands, tables, display cabinets and farmhouse pine. There is usually a selection of antique, Art Nouveau and Art Deco porcelain and pottery, which might include early Spode, Davenport, Limoges, Charlotte Rhead, Clarice Cliff, Keith Murray, Mason, Shelley, Doulton and Moorcroft. Among the other lots you might find jewellery, glass, old lanterns, paintings and prints, silver and quality plate, and farmhouse items.

Sherburn-in-Elmet

BUYER'S PREMIUM: 10%
SALES: *Monthly on last Thu of month at 6.30pm.*
VIEWING: *Day prior 12.00 noon-8.00pm, day of sale from 9.00am.*
REFRESHMENTS: *Own café.*
PARKING: *Own car park.*
STORAGE: *Yes*
TRANSPORTATION: *Yes*
SHIPPING: *Yes*

Whitby

BUYER'S PREMIUM: 10%
SALES: *General: weekly on Wed at 10.00am. Antiques: monthly on Wed at 10.00am (replaces general sale).*
VIEWING: *General: day prior 9.00am-4.30pm. Antiques: Sat prior 9.00am-4.00pm, Mon prior 9.00am-8.00pm, Tue prior 9.00am-4.30pm.*
REFRESHMENTS: *None available on the premises.*
PARKING: *None available on the premises.*
STORAGE: *Yes*
TRANSPORTATION: *Yes*
SHIPPING: *Yes*

NATIONWIDE FINE ART & FURNITURE

West End Saleroom, The Paddock. Tel: (0947) 603433

300-400 lots. The saleroom is off Skinner Street, on the West Cliff, which is the more modern area of this picturesque town. The sale is a popular meeting place for local people and holidaymakers alike. Unlike many auctions, this one includes a break for lunch, which is welcome after a morning of exciting bidding. Buyers can prepare themselves for an afternoon of hand-raised confrontation in one of the excellent pubs near by. The weekly sale usually offers a comprehensive range of general household furniture and effects, with the morning session devoted to small items and lesser-quality furniture. The afternoon session is devoted to better-quality furniture, beds, linen and so on.

Once a month the general sale is replaced by an antiques and fine art sale. Due to the length of time and work involved in preparing for this catalogued sale, there is no general sale the week before.

Whitby

BUYER'S PREMIUM: *Nil*
SALES: *Fortnightly on Thu at 9.30am (includes antiques and paintings every six weeks). Jewellery: at irregular intervals, usually on Sat at 10.30am.*
VIEWING: *General: Tue and Wed prior 9.30am-4.30pm. Antiques: Sat prior 9.00am-12.00 noon, Mon prior 9.30am-8.00pm, Tue and Wed prior 9.30am-4.30pm. Jewellery: morning of sale, or by appointment.*
REFRESHMENTS: *None available on the premises.*
PARKING: *Ample near by.*
STORAGE: *Yes*
TRANSPORTATION: *Yes*
SHIPPING: *Yes*

RICHARDSON & SMITH (INCORPORATING ROBERT GRAY & SONS)

West Cliff Saleroom, 19 Silver Street. Tel: (0947) 602298

500-600 lots. Whitby is a picturesque town with an ancient abbey. The saleroom is within walking distance of the latter. Most of the locals seem to visit the saleroom at one time or another during the fortnightly auction. This is a sale of good quality modern and reproduction furniture and general household chatttels. Boxes and trays of miscellaneous items such as china and ornaments are the first lots to be sold, followed by electrical goods, including TVs (usually numerous).

The afternoon session starts at 1.30pm sharp, regardless of what time the morning session finished. It begins with a sale of carpets and rugs, and goes on to beds, general furniture, pictures, books, linen and other items.

Every six weeks the sale is of period and later furniture, and will include general antiques plus paintings, a specialist area in which the company is building a reputation.

Frequently, but at no set intervals, there are special jewellery sales. These are very popular, often attracting buyers from far away. They include jewellery of all types and values, from costume jewellery to modern hallmarked gold and silver.

JAMES JOHNSTON

Whixley Village Hall. Tel: (0423) 322382

600-800 lots. Whixley is a small village just off the A59 between Harrogate and York. James Johnston's sales have become rather a local event, and there is plenty of humour during the proceedings. Auctioning begins outside the Village Hall, where around 150-200 lots of garden tools, electrical goods and outside effects are arranged. Inside, there is usually a good selection of antique and modern furniture, china, glass, jewellery, pictures, linen and boxes of bric-à-brac.

Whixley, near York

BUYER'S PREMIUM: 5%
SALES: *Monthly on second Fri of the month at 6.00pm.*
VIEWING: *Day of sale from 3.00pm.*
REFRESHMENTS: *Mobile van.*
PARKING: *Ample near by.*
STORAGE: *Yes*
TRANSPORTATION: *Yes*
SHIPPING: *Yes*

NOTTINGHAMSHIRE

RICHARD WATKINSON & PARTNERS

17 North Gate. Tel: (0636) 77154

400-500 lots. Newark is a picturesque town of considerable antiquity, with many historical associations. It is also a delight for auction-goers, and this Wednesday morning sale is one that children will love. It is held on the Wharf by the side of the River Trent, just before the Trent Bridge. The first part is entirely in the open, and includes the sale of livestock such as pigeons, chickens and rabbits, as well as fruit and vegetables, flowers and other produce. There will also be items of furniture, and boxes containing anything from books and puzzles to pots, pans and building equipment, or perhaps tins of nails or electrical goods. Almost anything can turn up here. The auctioneer walks along selling each lot as it is arrived at, and payment is made in cash at the completion of each sale.

At 2.30pm the auction moves into one of the two salerooms behind the auctioneers' offices. Here 150 or so lots will be sold, mainly boxes of miscellaneous items such as china, general kitchenalia, books and ornaments. There will also be some modern household furniture and general effects. Wednesday is also market day, and the main market stalls are only a few minutes' walk away.

The Thursday sale takes place at 11.00am in the second saleroom, and includes some 300 lots of general household furniture (including Victorian, reproduction and modern), kitchenalia, lawn mowers, electrical equipment, tools of all sorts, brass, china, bric-à-brac and other goods.

On the first Thursday of the month this general sale is replaced by a special antiques and fine art sale, which takes

Newark-on-Trent

BUYER'S PREMIUM:
Antiques and fine art: 5%.
Others: 10%
SALES: *General: weekly on Wed at 10.30am and 2.30pm, and on Thu at 11.00am.*
Antiques and fine art: monthly on first Thu of month at 11.00am (replaces general Thu sale). Poultry: annual on Wed before Christmas at 2.00pm.
VIEWING: *General (Wed): day of sale from 9.30am.*
General (Thu): day prior 9.30am-5.00pm, morning of sale from 9.00am. Antiques and fine art: day prior 9.30am-7.00pm, morning of sale from 9.00am.
REFRESHMENTS: *Vending machine.*
PARKING: *Own car park.*
STORAGE: *Yes*
TRANSPORTATION: *Yes*
SHIPPING: *No*

place in the smaller of the two salerooms and includes Victorian and antique furniture, paintings, oils, watercolours, silver and plate, collectables and so on. There is also a yearly sale of poultry.

Nottingham

ARTHUR JOHNSON & SONS

The Nottingham Auction Centre, Cattle Market, Meadow Lane.
Tel: (0602) 869128

BUYER'S PREMIUM: 4%
SALES: *Weekly on Sat at 9.30am.*
VIEWING: *Fri 2.00pm-6.45pm, and day of sale from 9.00am.*
REFRESHMENTS: *Available.*
PARKING: *Own car park.*
STORAGE: *Yes*
TRANSPORTATION: *Yes*
SHIPPING: *Yes*

2,000 lots. This is possibly the largest weekly auction in the Midlands, if not in the whole country, with six separate sales taking place in different rooms during an extremely busy morning and early afternoon. The auctions are all usually completed by 2.00pm to 2.30pm. Buyers may pay by cash, cheque (by prior arrangement) or credit card.

At 9.30am the proceedings start outside the saleroom with such things as timber, building materials, garden shrubs and produce. Inside the saleroom complex, antique and pre-1940s furniture is to be found in Saleroom 1. The smaller good quality items, for example jewellery, watches, silver, silver plate, porcelain, bronzes and brass, are sold in Saleroom 2. Modern household items such as dining room and kitchen furniture, cookers, beds and televisions, are offered for sale in a separate auction room.

In yet another saleroom, commercial goods go under the hammer. These might include filing cabinets, garden machinery and woodworking tools.

All the lots are numbered (except garden shrubs and timber), so prospective buyers can put in written bids if they are interested in lots at more than one of the sales.

Nottingham

NEALES (INDEPENDENT FINE ART AUCTIONEERS)

The Nottingham Salerooms, 192/4 Mansfield Road.
Tel: (0602) 624141

BUYER'S PREMIUM: 10%
SALES: *General: weekly on Mon at 11.00am. Antiques and fine art: every six weeks on Thu and Fri at 10.30am. Collectables: three times a year (no fixed months) on Tue at 1.00pm.*
VIEWING: *General: Sat prior 9.00am-12.30pm, morning of sale from 9.00am. Antiques and fine art: Tue prior 10.00am-8.00pm and mornings of sales from 9.00am. Collectables: day prior*

1,000-1,500 lots. The four salerooms are in an imposing early 20th-century building, designed in a style which would meet the approval of Prince Charles. It occupies a prominent spot in the centre of the city.

The weekly Monday sale has general household furniture and effects (largely Victorian, Edwardian and modern), together with secondary antique furniture and smaller items, from the 19th century and later. There are bargains to be had in all departments.

Sales of antiques and fine art are held at approximately six-weekly intervals and are spread over two days, encompassing the whole range of antique and fine art categories. The sale is divided into specialist sections, starting on the Thursday morning with silver, silver plate, jewellery, *bijouterie* and watches. These are followed at 1.00pm by European ceramics, glass, Oriental ceramics and works of art. The Friday morning begins with pictures and books, musical instruments, clocks and metalwork, followed in the afternoon by English and Continental furniture and decorative arts.

At irregular intervals three times a year, Neales also hold collectors' sales of autographs, postcards, cigarette cards, toys, dolls, stamps and other small collectables.

HENRY SPENCER & SONS

20 The Square. Tel: (0777) 708633

400-500 lots. Established in 1840, Henry Spencer & Sons is now a part of the Halifax Building Society, but it still has the air of a family firm. It is also very up-to-date, with computerised systems in its modern complex of offices, storage areas and two salerooms. The Wednesday sale is of Victorian and later furniture, or fine furniture and ornamental items, which at some sales might include garden furniture and statuary, light fittings and mirrors. The Monday sales cover six specialist areas, with one area dealt with each week in rotation as follows. Week 1: European and Oriental ceramics and glass. Week 2: silver and plate, jewellery and *bijouterie*. Week 3: European and Oriental works of art, including decorative arts, caddies and dolls and toys. Week 4: clocks and scientific instruments, weapons and militaria. Week 5: oil paintings, watercolour drawings, prints, engravings and miniatures. Week 6: fine furniture, including garden furniture and statuary, light fittings and mirrors.

GASCOINES

1 Church Street. Tel: (0636) 813245

200-300 lots. The saleroom is in the shopping centre, just past the Minster and the Saracen's Head public house. The latter has been an inn since 1396, and Charles I stayed there for a night or two.

Southwell is also notable as the home of the Bramley apple, first raised in the garden at Bramley cottage. The entrance to Gascoines' pleasant, theatre-like auction room is up a flight of stairs. The auction is conducted from a stage at one end. Around the edge of the room are the larger lots of furniture, for example cabinets, wardrobes, dressers, bedroom suites and the like. There is more furniture in the centre, including chairs

10.00am-5.00pm, morning of sale from 9.00am.
REFRESHMENTS: *Vending machine.*
PARKING: *Own car park.*
STORAGE: *Yes*
TRANSPORTATION: *Yes*
SHIPPING: *Yes*

Retford

BUYER'S PREMIUM: *10%*
SALES: *Victorian and later: weekly on Wed at 10.30am. Specialist: weekly on Mon at 10.30am.*
VIEWING: *Weekday prior, 10.00am-3.00pm.*
REFRESHMENTS: *None available on premises.*
PARKING: *Ample parking space.*
STORAGE: *Yes*
TRANSPORTATION: *Yes*
SHIPPING: *Yes*

Southwell

BUYER'S PREMIUM: *5%*
SALES: *Monthly on Fri at 6.00pm.*
VIEWING: *Day of sale 10.00am-5.00pm.*
REFRESHMENTS: *None available on the premises.*
PARKING: *Large public car park two minutes' walk away.*
STORAGE: *No*
TRANSPORTATION: *Yes*
SHIPPING: *No*

and settees, which are usually sat on by the crowd while the auction is in progress. The furniture generally includes some antiques. The paintings, prints, etchings and mirrors in the sale are displayed on the walls of the saleroom, and a wide range of brass, china, glassware, cutlery, linen, bric-à-brac, collectables and other small items is sold.

OXFORDSHIRE

Banbury

BUYER'S PREMIUM: 10%
SALES: Fortnightly on Tue at 10.30am.
VIEWING: Sat prior 9.15am-12.00 noon, Mon prior 10.00am-6.00pm, and morning of sale from 9.30am.
REFRESHMENTS: Available next door.
PARKING: Castle Street multi-storey.
STORAGE: By request.
TRANSPORTATION: Yes
SHIPPING: Yes

Bicester

BUYER'S PREMIUM: 10%
SALES: General: every six weeks (none in Aug) on Thu at 10.30am. Tools and country pursuits: annually in Mar (day varies).
VIEWING: Day prior 8.30am-5.00pm, morning of sale.
REFRESHMENTS: None available on the premises.
PARKING: Manorsfield public car park.
STORAGE: Yes
TRANSPORTATION: Yes
SHIPPING: Yes

Oxford

BUYER'S PREMIUM: 10%
SALES: Oxford: three times a

HOLLOWAYS

49 Parsons Street. Tel: (0295) 253197

400-600 lots. Holloways are busy country auctioneers with an international reputation. They hold two sales per month, which alternate between 'Selected Antiques and Collectors' Items' and 'Victorian and Reproduction Furniture'. There are also specialist sales of silver, jewellery, books, pictures and automobilia at irregular intervals.

The same firm also has an office at Streatley in Berkshire. For details of Streatley sales, tel: (0491) 872318.

MESSENGERS AUCTION ROOMS

27 Sheep Street. Tel: (0869) 252901

400-500 lots. Bicester is an old-fashioned town with an attractive market square. Messengers Auction Rooms are close to Manorsfield Road car park, at the rear of the company's estate agency office. The saleroom is usually full on sale days. The majority of the items in the general sale are sold on behalf of local private vendors and are mostly in a good to fair condition, including Victorian and Edwardian furniture and household effects, decorative china, pictures, silver, jewellery, glass, collector's items and so on.

Every March Messengers hold specialist sales of traditional carpenters' and craftsmen's tools. Collector's sales are also held from time to time, and include all sorts of items, ranging from Victorian clothing and fabrics to kitchenalia.

MALLAMS

Bocardo House, St Michael's Street. Tel: (0865) 241358

150-600 lots. Mallams are an independent auctioneering firm who have been established since 1788. At their Oxford saleroom, close to the Oxford Union Debating Hall, they hold three sales per month of high quality, carefully selected items. Three categories of sale take place on a rotating basis. One week the sale will include ceramics, glass, oil paintings, watercolours, collectors' items and other small lots. The following week the sale will be of Victorian and later furniture, and the sale after that will be of fine antique furniture and works of art, including as a rule a large number of clocks, silver and jewellery.

Mallams also hold a sale in Cheltenham, at the Grosvenor Galleries, 26 Grosvenor Street, tel: (0242) 235712. This is of Georgian, Victorian and antique furniture and effects, ceramics, glass, silver, brass and so on. It takes place about once a month, and sometimes more often.

month on Wed at 11.00am.
Cheltenham: about once a
month on Wed at 11.00am.
VIEWING: *Oxford and*
Cheltenham: Sat prior
9.00am-1.00pm, Mon and
Tue prior 9.00am-5.00pm.
REFRESHMENTS:
Available near by.
PARKING: *Public car parks*
near by.
STORAGE: *Yes*
TRANSPORTATION: *Yes*
SHIPPING: *Yes*

THIMBLEBY & SHORLAND

See THIMBLEBY & SHORLAND, Reading, Berkshire

Shiplake

SIMMONS & SON

Watlington

The Barn, Watcombe Manor, Ingham Lane.
Tel: (049161) 2810

600-700 lots. Simmons & Son hold eight general auctions a year. The Barn is part of a light industrial complex on the Watlington to Henley road. Its entrance looks like the way into a farmyard, which is what the area once was. The well attended auctions usually have a variety of furniture, household effects and bric-à-brac of all periods, from antique right through to modern. Each sale also has special sections for silver, porcelain, glass, ceramics, textiles, paintings, watercolours, prints and collectors' items. Outside effects such as lawn mowers and other machinery are on display outside the saleroom, and the sale finishes with these items.

BUYER'S PREMIUM: *10%*
SALES: *Eight sales a year on*
Fri at 10.30am.
VIEWING: *Day prior*
10.00am-5.30pm.
REFRESHMENTS:
Available.
PARKING: *Own car park.*
STORAGE: *Yes*
TRANSPORTATION: *Yes*
SHIPPING: *Yes*

SHROPSHIRE

Bridgnorth

PERRY & PHILLIPS

New Market Building, Listley Street. Tel: (0746) 762248

400-500 lots. Bridgnorth is split in two, with the High Town perched 200ft up on the right bank of the Severn, and the Low Town on the opposite side of the gorge. There are interesting strolls to be had through the narrow lanes and up and down the steps connecting the two. The Perry & Phillips saleroom is a listed building in the High Town and has been described as the 'largest, ugliest building in Shropshire' and 'a cross between a Victorian Railway Station and a Public Lavatory'. It has been the home of Perry & Phillips' auctions since 1853 however, so most locals are well used to it now.

The weekly auction here is popular and friendly. It offers a typical mix of household furniture and smaller articles, including some attractive and interesting pieces. High value lots are kept back for the special sale of antiques which occurs on the first Tuesday of each month.

BUYER'S PREMIUM: *General: 50p per lot. Antiques: £1 per lot.*
SALES: *General: weekly on Tue at 11.00am. Antiques: monthly on first Tue of month at 11.00am.*
VIEWING: *Day prior 9.00am-8.30pm.*
REFRESHMENTS: *Own café.*
PARKING: *Public car park 200 yards away.*
STORAGE: *Yes*
TRANSPORTATION: *Yes*
SHIPPING: *Yes*

Ludlow

LUDLOW ANTIQUE AUCTIONS LTD

29 Corve Street. Tel: (0584) 875157 and 873496

400-600 lots. The word 'antique' may suggest that this saleroom deals only in pricey items, but in fact it is possible to buy an attractive lot here for as little as £10 — although another lot in the same sale might fetch £25,000. The saleroom is very comfortable, carpeted and well heated. A window display on Corve Street shows articles which are to be sold in forthcoming auctions. Typical past sales have included Victorian and 18th-century furniture, silver plated tea sets, Worcester jugs, Japanese vases, pewter candlesticks and other metalware, and plenty of collectables — an African leather drum, a 19th-century musical box, cases of mounted fish, a magic lantern, clocks, barometers, pictures and many more.

BUYER'S PREMIUM: *10%*
SALES: *Every four weeks on Tue at 10.30am.*
VIEWING: *Sat prior 10.00am-4.00pm, Mon prior 9.30am-5.00pm, morning of sale.*
REFRESHMENTS: *None available on the premises.*
PARKING: *Public car park 500 yards away.*
STORAGE: *Yes*
TRANSPORTATION: *Yes*
SHIPPING: *Yes*

Ludlow

TIMOTHY MEAR & CO

Temeside Salerooms, Ludford Bridge Trading Estate. Tel: (0584) 876081

400-500 lots. A classic country auction will sell some of its lots outside, and there will be at least one old tin bath in the sale. Another requirement is that it contains enough goods to furnish a house completely, down to the cutlery, brooms, buckets and bowls. Timothy Mear's is just such a sale. It starts

BUYER'S PREMIUM: *Nil*
SALES: *Fortnightly on Wed at 11.00am.*
VIEWING: *Apr-Oct: day prior 10.00am-8.00pm. Oct-Apr 10.00am-7.00pm.*
REFRESHMENTS: *Own café.*

with outside effects such as gardening tools and equipment, garden seats and general bric-à-brac. Inside the saleroom, the 'smalls' are sold first, including china (domestic and ornamental), silver, glassware, lamps, cutlery, paintings and innumerable miscellaneous items. The furniture section varies just as much as the others in quality, value and age: one sale might include antique, Victorian, reproduction, modern and nearly new lots, selling for anything between £2 and £2,000. There is something in most sales to suit all pockets and needs. Mr Mear runs the show alone, but brings to it over 20 years' expertise in the antique and auctioneering business, including experience with Sotheby's Fine Art Auctioneers.

PARKING: *Ample car parking space.*
STORAGE: *Yes*
TRANSPORTATION: *Yes*
SHIPPING: *Yes*

TELFORD AUCTIONS

Telford

Rookery Road, St Georges. Tel: (0952) 610033

300-400 lots. The saleroom is in the Oakengates area of Telford, and tends to be full of local people chatting while the sale is in progress, something which may be frowned upon at other auctions. A typical scene is of the auctioneer smilingly soliciting a bid of £40 for a tea set which will be knocked down for £4, while an anxious customer asks the porter for a catalogue, finds there isn't one, but goes home happy with several soup plates, a milk jug and dessert bowl, and two porcelain flower bouquets, all in different designs and from different lots. Down the centre of the room are the tables containing the 'smalls' — china, silver, glass, clocks and watches, books, lamps and so on, which are sold first. Next to come under the hammer are the bicycles, electrical equipment, carpets, blankets and linen, and then at 8.00pm attention is focused on the furniture, which is placed around the room and may be almost new. By the end of the evening virtually everything will have been sold, and two days later many of the crowd will return to watch an auction of motor vehicles which is also held here.

BUYER'S PREMIUM: *Nil*
SALES: *Weekly on Tue at 6.30pm.*
VIEWING: *Day of sale from 9.00am.*
REFRESHMENTS: *Own café.*
PARKING: *Own car park.*
STORAGE: *Yes*
TRANSPORTATION: *Yes*
SHIPPING: *Yes*

SOMERSET

TAMLYN & SON

Bridgwater

The Saleroom, Market Street. Tel: (0278) 458241

900-1,000 lots. The sales take place about once a month on Tuesday, but there is no sale in August or the early part of January. The saleroom is a three-storey brick building, purpose built in 1890. It lies west of the town centre, about 100 yards

BUYER'S PREMIUM: *10%*
SALES: *Monthly on Tue at 10.00am (except Aug and early Jan)*
VIEWING: *Day prior 3.00pm-6.00pm.*

REFRESHMENTS: *Own café.*
PARKING: *Ample parking near by.*
STORAGE: *Yes*
TRANSPORTATION: *Yes*
SHIPPING: *Yes*

from the cinema.

This is an Aladdin's cave of an auction, where almost every type of object imaginable is offered, and buyers are kept on their toes by the hammer coming down on prices ranging from £1 to many thousands. Outside effects are the first to be sold, before attention moves on to modern furniture, such as three-piece suites, dining room furniture, beds and bedroom furniture, upholstered chairs and so on. Antiques and general bric-à-brac are not usually reached until 1.00pm. This is a genuine, independent auction, and lots are sold without a reserve price. Buyers range from local people to dealers from far afield. Many call in regularly in the hope that rare or interesting items will turn up, but they may only bid five or six times a year.

Burnham-on-Sea

BUYER'S PREMIUM: *10%*
SALES: *Monthly on last Thu of month at 6.00pm.*
VIEWING: *Day of sale from 9.00am.*
REFRESHMENTS: *None available on the premises.*
PARKING: *None available on the premises.*
STORAGE: *Yes*
TRANSPORTATION: *Yes*
SHIPPING: *Yes*

J H PALMER & SONS

Bank Chambers, 75 High Street. Tel: (0278) 782326

250-350 lots. The monthly evening sale has become a landmark of this small, attractive seaside town, which also boasts seven miles of flat sandy beaches and fine golf links. Among the lots are general household furniture and effects, including antiques. People have become wise to the value of goods, but auctions such as this are still good places to hunt down oddities, rarities, knick-knacks and memorabilia, or to pick up nearly new items at a fraction of the original price. The smaller 'table' items are sold first, with the better quality items and antiques generally kept until the end of the sale. One-and-a-half miles away at Highbridge, J H Palmer & Sons are also responsible for Monday cattle auctions.

Crewkerne

BUYER'S PREMIUM: *10%*
SALES: *General: on Wed (except the first Wed of the month) at 9.30am. Specialist: fortnightly on Thu at 11.00am.*
VIEWING: *General: day prior 10.00am-7.00pm, morning of sale from 9.00am. Specialist: Sat prior 9.30am-12.30pm, Tue prior 10.00am-7.00pm, Wed prior 10.00am-4.30pm, morning of sale from 9.00am.*
REFRESHMENTS: *Own café.*
PARKING: *Own car park.*
STORAGE: *Yes*
TRANSPORTATION: *Yes*
SHIPPING: *Yes*

LAWRENCE

South Street. Tel: (0460) 73041

800-1,000 lots. The saleroom is about three-quarters of a mile from the railway station. Lawrence is one of the largest provincial companies and provides a comprehensive auction service. In Saleroom 2 there are general sales on Wednesdays (except the first Wednesday of the month) of goods of all types, selling in the £25 or upwards price bracket. As the Lawrence brochure says, goods in this sale range from 'reproduction furniture through to silver pepperpots'.

Separate specialist sales are held on average twice a month on Thursdays, dealing with various categories such as English and Continental furniture, clocks and watches, paintings, silver, jewellery, porcelain, Eastern carpets, mechanical music, toys, books and many others. Some specialist categories occur more frequently than others: check with the auctioneers.

JOHN D FLEMING & CO

The Town Hall, Fore Street. Tel: (0398) 23597

400-500 lots. The Town Hall is next door to John D Fleming's estate agency office, in the centre of this quiet little country town which borders Exmoor. The monthly auction, established over 15 years ago by the present proprietor and auctioneer, is an individual sale taking much of its atmosphere from John Fleming's informal style. The 'Antique and Modern' sale includes china, silver, jewellery, electrical goods (all guaranteed by the auctioneer), general furniture and furnishings. Also here will be collectables, bygones, and miscellanea of all ages, including the odd motor vehicle. The better quality goods are offered for sale in the afternoon session, which begins after the 1.00pm-2.00pm lunch break. The auctions have an excellent reputation and have seen six world-record prices for antiques. It is taken for granted that lots may range in price from pence to many thousands of pounds.

Dulverton

BUYER'S PREMIUM: *Nil*
SALES: *Monthly (except in Aug and Dec) on last Fri of month at 10.30am.*
VIEWING: *Day prior 2.00pm-6.00pm, morning of sale from 9.00am.*
REFRESHMENTS: *Home-made available.*
PARKING: *Ample parking near by.*
STORAGE: *Yes*
TRANSPORTATION: *Yes*
SHIPPING: *Yes*

DORE & REES

The Auction Salerooms, Vicarage Street. Tel: (0373) 462257

400-500 lots. This is a small, privately run, friendly sale, ideal for the dealer, private buyer or earnest collector. Frome is an attractive old market town. The Gothic-style saleroom, which was once a chapel, is at the rear of St John's Church, close to the centre. The fortnightly Wednesday sale is of antique and modern household furniture and effects, with a tremendous variation in the value and quality of the lots. Beautiful pieces of antique furniture, an oil painting, or a piece of valuable china or jewellery will be sold on the same day as a refrigerator, a cooker, a tatty dresser, a box full of children's toys and puzzles, various items of kitchen and garden equipment and other lesser quality goods. Prices reached in one sale can vary from anything from £1 to £4,000.

Frome

BUYER'S PREMIUM: *Nil*
SALES: *Fortnightly on Wed at 11.00am.*
VIEWING: *Mon and Tue prior 9.00am-7.00pm, morning of sale from 9.00am.*
REFRESHMENTS: *Available near by.*
PARKING: *Ample parking near by.*
STORAGE: *Yes*
TRANSPORTATION: *Yes*
SHIPPING: *Yes*

GRIBBLE BOOTH & TAYLOR

Mart Road Saleroom, Mart Road. Tel: (0643) 703646

500-600 lots. Minehead is the most westerly of the county's resorts, with splendid walks, sands and sheltered gardens. Gribble Booth & Taylor are members of Royal Life Estates, and associated companies hold auctions in Avon, Wiltshire, Dorset, Hampshire, with another Somerset auction at Wells. The saleroom is part of an industrial estate in the seafront area. A separate room is used to sell some 200 to 300 lots of 'smalls', and this is a must for anyone interested in ornaments, china,

Minehead

BUYER'S PREMIUM: *10%*
SALES: *Every three weeks on Thu at 10.30am.*
VIEWING: *Day prior 9.00am-5.00pm, day of sale from 9.00am.*
REFRESHMENTS: *Own café.*
PARKING: *Own car park.*
STORAGE: *Yes*
TRANSPORTATION: *Yes*
SHIPPING: *Yes*

glass, porcelain and the like. The main room has a notable stock of modern and reproduction wardrobes, cabinets, dressing tables, cottage pine and genuine antiques. Kitchen and electrical equipment come towards the end of the sale, with gardening tools and equipment last of all.

Standerwick, near Frome

BUYER'S PREMIUM: *Nil*
SALES: *Livestock and chattels: weekly on Wed at 11.00am. Special sales: at irregular intervals on Sat at 10.30am.*
VIEWING: *All: morning of sale.*
REFRESHMENTS: *Own café.*
PARKING: *Own car park.*
STORAGE: *Yes*
TRANSPORTATION: *Yes*
SHIPPING: *No*

COOPER & TANNER (RURAL SURVEYORS)

Frome Market. Tel: (0373) 831010

400-500 lots. The market complex is one of the most up-to-date in the country, and lies on the A36 about three miles north-east of Frome. Within easy driving distance are the Bratton Downs, with a white horse carved into the chalk hillside, and the country seat and safari park of the Marquess of Bath at Longleat.

The weekly Wednesday market sale is of livestock and chattels. Modern furniture and household effects, timber, tools and local farmhouse produce are also sold. Lots can range from £2 to £2,000 or more at the same sale.

Special sales in various categories also take place, at irregular intervals throughout the year. These include farm machinery, garden tools and equipment, trees and shrubs, horse tack and equestrian items.

Taunton

BUYER'S PREMIUM: *10%*
SALES: *General: weekly on Wed at 10.00am. Antiques: monthly on last Thu of month at 10.30am.*
VIEWING: *General: day prior 2.30pm-5.30pm, morning of sale from 9.00am. Antiques: day prior 9.00am-7.00pm, morning of sale from 9.00am.*
REFRESHMENTS: *Within easy walking distance.*
PARKING: *Own car park.*
STORAGE: *Yes*
TRANSPORTATION: *Yes*
SHIPPING: *Yes*

GREENSLADE HUNT FINE ART

Magdalene House, Church Square. Tel: (0823) 332525

700-1,000 lots. Hunts are partly responsible for the local livestock sales, but they also hold three interesting general and antique auctions per month in Taunton.

On Wednesdays there are well-attended sales of general household furniture, effects and Victoriana, at the Market Hall Salerooms, Priory Bridge Road. Here you can bid for anything from a kitchen sink up to a five-piece bedroom suite, through electrical goods, china items, books and so on.

The other sale is held on the last Thursday of the month at the Magdalene House saleroom opposite St Mary's Church, about three-quarters of a mile from Priory Bridge Road. This is an equally large affair, and is concerned with mixed antiques and collectables. The lots in this sale are just as unexpected and wide ranging, but are usually more valuable. Official viewing times are given here, but the saleroom is open from 9.00am-5.30pm every weekday, and you can wander in and look around at any time between those hours.

WELLINGTON SALEROOMS

Clifton House, Mantle Street. Tel: (0823) 664815
400-600 lots. This is a busy, friendly, family-run auction. It was established over 20 years ago by the present proprietors, Ray and Maggie Cooper. The saleroom is an old Methodist chapel, a large, distinctive building on the town's main street.

The fortnightly auctions are looked forward to by local people as social events. Friends cheerfully greet the Coopers and each other before wandering around the hall in small groups, discussing the lots. These range from general modern furniture through to collectables. Many of the local people will tell you proudly they have completely furnished and equipped their houses with articles bought at these sales. Every six weeks the general sale is followed by a special sale of antiques and collectables. For this sale the modern furniture is moved up into the first-floor saleroom. At other times it is sold in the downstairs saleroom.

Wellington

BUYER'S PREMIUM: *10%*
SALES: *General: fortnightly on Tue at 11.00am. Antiques: every six weeks after general sale.*
VIEWING: *Day prior 9.00am-8.00pm.*
REFRESHMENTS: *None available on the premises.*
PARKING: *None available on the premises.*
STORAGE: *Yes*
TRANSPORTATION: *Yes*
SHIPPING: *Yes*

SOUTH YORKSHIRE

WILLIAM H BROWN
See WILLIAM H BROWN, Doncaster, South Yorkshire

Barnsley

TUDOR AUCTION ROOMS
28 High Street. Tel: (0302) 725029
800-1,000 lots. Carcroft is just off the A1, and the saleroom is in the middle of town. George Allen runs the large and busy sale, which has been a popular local focal point for over 10 years. It used to be held on Sundays before falling foul of the Sunday trading laws. A typical sale will offer a large selection of antique furniture, including clocks, pictures, washstands, sideboards and display cabinets. Modern household furniture and goods will also be found, such as cookers, bedroom and lounge suites, televisions and all sorts of bric-à-brac. The selling starts with 'miscellaneous items', which vary a good deal because Tudor Auctions are the official auctioneers for various county courts. Then come general bric-à-brac, pottery, clocks, pictures and prints, electrical goods, and modern household furniture. The auction finishes with the antiques.

Carcroft

BUYER'S PREMIUM: *10%*
SALES: *Weekly on Sat at 11.00am.*
VIEWING: *Fri prior 4.00pm-7.00pm, day of sale from 9.00am.*
REFRESHMENTS: *Own café.*
PARKING: *None available on the premises.*
STORAGE: *Yes*
TRANSPORTATION: *Yes*
SHIPPING: *Yes*

Doncaster

BUYER'S PREMIUM: 10%
SALES: Barnsley: monthly on
Thu at 10.00am (except Aug
and Dec). Doncaster: monthly
on Tue at 10.30am (replaced at
irregular intervals by antiques
sale on Thu).
VIEWING: Barnsley: day
prior 5.30pm-8.00pm.
Doncaster, general: day prior
10.00am-4.00pm. Doncaster,
antiques: Mon prior
2.00pm-7.00pm, Tue prior
10.00am-4.00pm, Wed prior
10.00am-12.00 noon.
REFRESHMENTS: Own
café and van.
PARKING: Ample near by.
STORAGE: Yes
TRANSPORTATION: Yes
SHIPPING: Yes

WILLIAM H BROWN

28 Nether Hall Road. Tel: (0302) 367766

200-500 lots. William H Brown have two separate auctions in South Yorkshire, one in Barnsley and one in Doncaster.

The Barnsley sale is held on a Thursday at the Rockingham Welfare Hall, Hoyland Common, which is within 400 yards of Junction 36 of the M1. This sale is organised from William H Brown's office at 11 Regent Street South, Barnsley, tel: (0226) 299221. It takes place every month except August and December, and is of general household furniture and effects. Typical sales have included Victorian and reproduction furniture, a wide selection of antiques, jewellery, porcelain, pottery, silver, brass, garden equipment and other goods.

William H Brown's Doncaster sale takes place monthly on Tuesday, and has goods of similar quality and variety. This Tuesday sale is replaced at irregular intervals by a special sale of antiques, which is always held on a Thursday.

Doncaster

BUYER'S PREMIUM: 10%
SALES: Weekly on Thu at
6.30pm.
VIEWING: All week
10.00am-4.00pm.
REFRESHMENTS: Own
café.
PARKING: Ample parking
near by.
STORAGE: Yes
TRANSPORTATION: Yes
SHIPPING: Yes

DONCASTER AUCTION ROOMS

Queens Road. Tel: (0302) 328664

500-800 lots. This is a pleasant sale run by a husband-and-wife team. Part of the building housing the saleroom has been sectioned off as an antique centre, with a number of small units selling all kinds of antiques and bygones (open Monday-Saturday 10.00am-4.00pm). It is also possible to wander into the saleroom and look around at these times, but vendors are still bringing in goods for sale late in the week, and so the saleroom does not really fill up until close to the sale day. The auction includes antiques, collectables, crockery, linen and miscellaneous items. The selling starts with smaller items, while modern furniture and antiques bring the sale to a close.

Sheffield

BUYER'S PREMIUM: 10%
SALES: General: fortnightly
on Tue at 11.00am. Antiques:
monthly on Sat at 11.00am.
VIEWING: General:
morning of sale from 9.00am.
Antiques: day prior
2.30pm-7.30pm, morning of
sale from 9.30am.
REFRESHMENTS: Own
café.

A E DOWSE & SON

Cornwall Galleries, Scotland Street. Tel: (0742) 725858

400-500 lots. The large saleroom complex (over 6,000sq ft) is midway along Scotland Street. To get there from the city centre follow signs to Barnsley.

A E Dowse was founded in 1915 by a former mayor of Scunthorpe, and the auction is now run by the second and third generation of the Dowse family.

There are at least four sales per month here, in various categories. A general auction of shipping goods and modern furniture and effects is held every fortnight. In addition, there is a monthly auction of general antiques and collectors' items. Separate monthly specialist auctions are also held; diecast, tinplate and collectors' toys are sold quarterly, and stamps, coins, postcards and cigarette cards twice yearly.

Finally there are quarterly auctions of fine art, antiques and related items.

PARKING: *Ample near by.*
STORAGE: *Yes*
TRANSPORTATION: *Yes*
SHIPPING: *Yes*

EADON LOCKWOOD & RIDDLE

Sheffield

The Sheffield Saleroom, 411 Petre Street. Tel: *(0742) 619518*
400-450 lots. Eadon Lockwood & Riddle were established over 150 years ago. Today they run auctions offering a wide range of good quality general furniture, furnishings and other effects, such as carpets, domestic and ornamental china and glass, silver, jewellery and miscellaneous items. Special antiques sales are held two or three times a year. They are widely advertised and attract buyers from far afield.

BUYER'S PREMIUM: *10%*
SALES: *General: approximately every two weeks on Fri at 10.00am. Antiques: two or three times a year (days and times vary).*
VIEWING: *Day prior 9.00am-4.00pm.*
REFRESHMENTS: *None available on the premises.*
PARKING: *Ample parking near by.*
STORAGE: *Yes*
TRANSPORTATION: *Yes*
SHIPPING: *Yes*

ELLIS, WILLIS & BECKETT

Sheffield

Carlisle Street. Tel: *(0742) 729667*
800-1,000 lots. The auctioneers have recently moved their saleroom to Carlisle Street, on the corner of Hallcar Street (although their offices remain at 54 Campo Lane). Included in their three-weekly Thursday sale is a wide selection of general household furniture and effects, such as pictures and paintings, some excellent china, glassware, pewter, collectables, brass and so on. The firm are official auctioneers for the county courts, so the sales may include stock from bankrupt shops and other businesses. In the past, contents of a hairdressing equipment wholesalers have been sold, as have various bits of DIY equipment and car accessories.

Monthly sales of liquidated stock, such as office furniture and engineering equipment, take place, as well as separate monthly sales of catering equipment. There are also occasional specialist sales of imported furniture and electrical goods.

BUYER'S PREMIUM: *5%*
SALES: *General: every three weeks on Thu at 11.00am. Liquidated stock: monthly on Tue at 10.30am. Catering: monthly on Tue at 11.00am.*
VIEWING: *All: day prior 9.30am-4.30pm and day of sale from 9.30am.*
REFRESHMENTS: *Available at some sales.*
PARKING: *None available on the premises.*
STORAGE: *Yes*
TRANSPORTATION: *Yes*
SHIPPING: *Yes*

Thurcroft

BUYER'S PREMIUM: *10%*
SALES: *Fortnightly on Mon at 11.00am (includes quarterly special antiques sale).*
VIEWING: *Day prior 11.00am-4.00pm.*
REFRESHMENTS: *Own café.*
PARKING: *Own car park.*
STORAGE: *Yes*
TRANSPORTATION: *Yes*
SHIPPING: *Yes*

WILKINSON & BEIGHTON

Woodhouse Green. Tel: (0709) 700005

500-600 lots. Thurcroft is about a two-mile drive from Junction 1 of the M18. The saleroom building is an old cinema on the main road of this quiet little Yorkshire town. Inside there are two separate salerooms — the majority of the auctions take place on the ground floor, but occasionally the second-floor saleroom is used to accommodate an extra large sale. This is one of the fastest-growing and one of the largest auction rooms in South Yorkshire, but it is a friendly place, with experts always available to give advice.

A sale of 'Antiques and Shipping Goods' is held once a fortnight, and includes a variety of furniture, pictures, china, porcelain and so on. Every quarter this sale is replaced by a special sale of fine antique furniture and *objets d'art*, and other goods of higher quality.

STAFFORDSHIRE

Hanley, near Stoke-on-Trent

BUYER'S PREMIUM: *10%*
SALES: *Fortnightly on Tue or Thu at 10.00am or 11.00am, depending on number of lots.*
VIEWING: *Sat prior 10.00am-2.00pm, day prior 10.00am-12.00 noon.*
REFRESHMENTS: *Vending machine.*
PARKING: *Own car park.*
STORAGE: *Yes*
TRANSPORTATION: *Yes*
SHIPPING: *No*

BUTTERS

Warner Street. Tel: (0782) 267752

400-500 lots. Hanley is a small and pleasant town, and its main claim to fame is that it was the birthplace of Arnold Bennett. Butters is an independent family concern established in 1856, and can be found in the centre of the town, just behind the museum and art gallery. The fortnightly sale alternates between general household and electrical goods and liquidated stock. In the past, the latter type of sale has included office equipment (desks, filing cabinets and typewriters), plumbing goods, kitchen units, motor cars and vans, and even a car ramp from a garage. Other sales of liquidated stock often take place on site, and these are worth enquiring about. The general-only sales start with bric-à-brac including china, paintings and silver, and then move on to furniture, finishing with domestic electrical appliances. Antique and better quality furniture are kept for a special section in the middle of the sale.

Hanley, near Stoke-on-Trent

BUYER'S PREMIUM: *10%*
SALES: *General: fortnightly on Mon at 10.00am. Special:*

LOUIS TAYLOR FINE ART AUCTIONEERS AND VALUERS

10 Town Road. Tel: (0782) 214111

800-1,000 lots. The saleroom is opposite the Potteries Centre and has a fortnightly Monday sale of general household goods.

There will usually be brass, china, glass and pictures, in addition to furniture of various types and ages, including antiques.

At three-monthly intervals the general sale is replaced by a special two-day sale which takes place over Monday and Tuesday. The special sales have a good reputation and are well attended by people from far afield. The first day of the sale is for porcelain and china, the second for paintings, silver, jewellery, glass and furniture. Specialist sales of Doulton and Beswick also take place every three months. All the sales here have a comfortable atmosphere which should put at ease those new to bidding.

BURY & HILTON

Heritage Salerooms, Britannia Street. Tel: (0538) 383344

500-600 lots. This is a comprehensive sale in the heart of a beautiful Staffordshire town. The saleroom is a converted school, and is usually surrounded by cars on sale days. The auction starts outside with 50 or 60 lots which could include various types of bicycle, gardening equipment and other outdoor items. After those, selling continues inside with crockery and boxes of miscellaneous items, which are worth searching through. Next to be sold are cookers and other household appliances, followed by smaller items of furniture. The larger pieces of furniture (beds and so on) are sold last.

Twice a year, in April and October, the sale dates are arranged to coincide with school holidays.

Bury & Hilton also hold special fine art and antiques sales at Coronation Hall, Osmaston, near Ashbourne, Derbyshire. The hall is thatched, the village is beautiful, and there are some attractive pubs to visit near by. The sale is also fun because it is something of a social event for the entire village.

WINTERTONS LTD

Lichfield Auction Centre, Wood End Lane, Fradley. Tel: (0543) 263256

1,000-1,500 lots. Wintertons Ltd have been auctioneers since 1864. Their sales are busy and efficient but not intimidating, despite the fact that at the antique and fine art auctions it is possible to buy a painting or piece of furniture worth many thousands of pounds. However, if your pockets do not run to that kind of money, it is also possible to walk away with a piece of silver or furniture after paying no more than £10-£20.

The fortnightly sales are of Victorian and general household furniture and effects, displayed to advantage in three large

---

every three months on Mon and Tue at 10.00 am (replaces general sale).
VIEWING: *General: Fri prior 10.00am-4.00pm, Sat prior 9.00am-12.00 noon. Special: Thu prior 10.00am-7.00pm, Fri prior 10.00am-4.00pm.*
REFRESHMENTS: *None available on the premises.*
PARKING: *Ample near by.*
STORAGE: *Yes*
TRANSPORTATION: *Yes*
SHIPPING: *Yes*

Leek

BUYER'S PREMIUM: *10%*
SALES: *(Leek) general: monthly on first Thu of month at 10.30am (except Jan). (Osmaston) fine art and antiques: twice a year in Apr and Oct on Thu at 11.00am.*
VIEWING: *(Leek) general: Sat prior 10.00am-1.00pm, Wed prior 12.00 noon-3.00pm. (Osmaston) fine art and antiques: Tue prior 10.00am-9.00pm.*
REFRESHMENTS: *Own café.*
PARKING: *Own car park.*
STORAGE: *Yes*
TRANSPORTATION: *Yes*
SHIPPING: *Yes*

Lichfield

BUYER'S PREMIUM: *10%*
SALES: *General: fortnightly on Thu at 11.00am. Antiques and fine art: every two months on Wed and Thu at 11.00am.*
VIEWING: *General: Wed prior 1.00pm-5.00pm. Antiques and fine art: Tue prior 1.00pm-8.00pm.*
REFRESHMENTS: *Own excellent restaurant.*
PARKING: *Own large car park.*

STORAGE: *Yes*
TRANSPORTATION: *Yes*
SHIPPING: *Yes*

salerooms.

On the first day of the two-day antiques and fine art sales (held every two months), there are silver and plated items, jewellery, collectors' items and ceramics. After a 30-minute lunch break there is usually a sale of textiles, which might include Victorian or 1930s dresses, lace and so on, followed by coins, stamps and medals, ceramics and glass. On the second day, pictures are sold in the morning, followed by as many as 400 lots of furniture and furnishings in the afternoon.

Stafford

BUYER'S PREMIUM: *Nil*
SALES: *Fortnightly on Thu at 9.30am.*
VIEWING: *Day prior 2.00pm-6.00pm.*
REFRESHMENTS: *Own café.*
PARKING: *None available on the premises.*
STORAGE: *No*
TRANSPORTATION: *Yes*
SHIPPING: *No*

HALL & LLOYD

South Street Auction Rooms. Tel: (0785) 58176

900-1,000 lots. The saleroom is a massive building situated close to the railway station. On sale day it is necessary for two auctioneers to sell lots simultaneously, because there are so many. Buyers have to check what is being sold when and where. If you have come with a group, it is useful to split up and share the work. It all adds to the excitement of this independent, family-run sale, which has become a landmark in the area. The saleroom is open until 12.00 noon the day before for vendors to bring in goods. On the sale day, one of the two auctioneers starts by selling outside effects such as lawn mowers and gardening tools, while in another area the second auctioneer sells beds and linen, followed by shipping furniture and electrical goods. These may include record players, videos and televisions.

Stone

BUYER'S PREMIUM: *Nil*
SALES: *General: weekly on Thu at 10.30am.*
VIEWING: *Morning of sale.*
REFRESHMENTS: *Available.*
PARKING: *Own car park.*
STORAGE: *No*
TRANSPORTATION: *Yes*
SHIPPING: *No*

C TOMKINSON

The Smithfield, Mill Street. Tel: (0785) 813870

200-300 lots. This is a popular traditional-style country auction which is held every Thursday in the cattle market, in the sheep pens which are used for livestock sales on Mondays. The proceedings start at 10.30am with fresh farm and garden produce, and dressed poultry. At 11.00am the general sale commences. The lots are laid out in rows, and the auctioneer walks along them, followed by the crowd, selling each lot as he comes to it. This is a strictly cash only sale. Among the lots there will usually be household furniture, garden furniture and tools, and odd items such as motor car tyres, tins of nails, boxes of crockery, suitcases (perhaps full of toys) and other items. The sale is carried out with friendly banter, and those with patience and a willingness to search may well pick up something of interest.

The auctioneers also hold a large Monday sale of locally fed prime cattle, sheep and pigs, which are bought by butchers attending from a wide area.

BAGSHAWS AGRICULTURAL

17 High Street. Tel: (0889) 562811

600-800 lots. It is advisable to turn up early for this busy country auction, so as to have a thorough search through the lots before the sale starts. There is no predicting what will be among them, or the whereabouts in the sale of a particular item. This is a sale full of surprises, at which lots go for a few pounds or a few thousand pounds. The sale is held in the Cattle Market, in a yard surrounded by 18th-century stables (now used to store the sale goods). Perhaps 400 lots will be sold outside, and in among the lawn mowers and other outside effects there may well be pieces of high quality furniture. In a recent sale a Regency mahogany desk fetched £1,700, while the next lot, a roll of wire netting, was sold for £5. At another sale a desk brought in by a vendor on the back of a lorry (used normally to convey scrap metal) fetched over £800. Upstairs in the saleroom there will be another 200 lots or so. Some of them will be boxes of assorted items, which could include china and ornaments, and are worth rummaging through. A typical sale will also have jewellery, silver, brass, paintings, collectables, prints and other goods.

Bagshaws also conduct farm and country house sales from time to time, where antiques and bygones may be found.

Uttoxeter

BUYER'S PREMIUM: *Nil (10% on items in upstairs saleroom).*
SALES: *Monthly on second Fri of the month at 11.00am.*
VIEWING: *Thu prior 2.00pm-5.00pm and day of sale from 9.00am.*
REFRESHMENTS: *Available in town centre near by.*
PARKING: *Ample in Cattle Market area (entrance in Carter Street).*
STORAGE: *Yes*
TRANSPORTATION: *Yes*
SHIPPING: *No*

SUFFOLK

DURRANTS

Beccles Auction Mart, Gresham Road. Tel: (0502) 712122

800-1,000 lots. This is perhaps the largest auction in the area, and it is certainly one of the most interesting. At least one object always seems to fetch a four-figure sum, and at the same time a great many lots sell for under £5. The sale starts at 10.30am with good-quality Victorian and other furniture and effects. Items sold in this section of the auction in the past have included Regency mahogany dining chairs, antique oak

Beccles

BUYER'S PREMIUM: *Nil*
SALES: *Weekly on Fri at 10.30am.*
VIEWING: *Thu 9.00am-4.00pm.*
REFRESHMENTS: *Own café.*
PARKING: *Own car park.*
STORAGE: *Yes*

TRANSPORTATION: No
SHIPPING: No

elbow chairs, Victorian dining tables, mahogany and oak side tables, eight-day longcase clocks and flintlock pistols, as well as pottery and porcelain, and a large amount of Victorian bric-à-brac and miscellaneous items. These include things like gold jewellery and silver pocket watches. In contrast to this sale, a second sale starts at 12.30pm in the Old Sale Room, consisting of roughly 300 lots of modern and shipping furniture and miscellaneous effects. Outside at 1.30pm, a sale of outdoor items begins, for example bicycles, timber and other building equipment, gardening tools, motor and hand mowers. This is a good section of the sale for gardeners, as quite often a bundle of gardening tools, perhaps a spade, fork, hoe and rake, will all be included in one lot and sell for a very reasonable price.

Bury St Edmunds

BUYER'S PREMIUM: 10%
SALES: Monthly on first Sun of month at 10.30am.
VIEWING: Sat prior 12.00 noon-5.00pm, morning of sale from 9.00am.
REFRESHMENTS: Light refreshments table in hall.
PARKING: Own car park.
STORAGE: No
TRANSPORTATION: Yes
SHIPPING: No

HERITAGE AUCTIONS

The Village Hall, Great Barton.
Tel: (0953) 884369 and (0760) 440384

500-750 lots. This is a cheerful but well-run Sunday auction. It takes place in the Village Hall, which is next to a playing field with swings and slides — useful for bored children. The three partners who run the auction encourage private buyers and have an excellent arrangement for transport, should a successful bid be made for any item too large to carry home on a roof rack. The sale includes a wide range of furniture, plus china, glass, silver and jewellery, pictures, clocks and other items, which tend to be more antique than modern. There are usually no electrical goods or television sets.

Great Barton is just east of Bury St Edmunds on the main road to Diss. The Village Hall is directly opposite Great Barton's only petrol-filling station. Whilst in the area, antique hunters may be interested in visiting Bury St Edmunds Antiques Centre in Mildenhall Road, or the Risby Barn Antique Centre at Risby, about five miles away on the other side of Bury St Edmunds. Both are open all day.

Bury St Edmunds

BUYER'S PREMIUM:
10%. Toy sale: nil.
SALES: General: every two to three weeks on Sat at 9.30am.
Fine art: four or five times a year, usually on Sat at 10.30am. Toys: held at intervals in spring, summer and autumn, on Sat at 10.30am (time depends on lots).

LACY SCOTT

10 Risbygate Street. Tel: (0284) 763531

700-800 lots. Lacy Scott have been auctioneers since 1869. At their general Saturday auction you can expect to find a wide array of modern and antique furniture, porcelain, silver, metalware, books and general bric-à-brac.

Fine art sales are held four or five times a year on Saturdays at 10.30am, beginning with textiles, dolls, collectors' items, ceramics, glass, metalware, oriental works of art, jewellery, silver and plate. There are up to 300 lots. After a break for lunch, the second session begins at 2.30pm. It consists of up to 200 lots of oil paintings, watercolours and prints. These are followed by 200 to 300 lots of English and Continental furniture, mirrors, clocks, carpets and rugs.

There are also specialist toy sales, generally held on a Saturday in spring, summer and autumn. The starting time varies according to the number of lots, but is usually 10.30am, with simultaneous auctions of Dinky toys in one part of the building and railway models in another.

Lacy Scott are also responsible for weekly Wednesday sales of cattle, pigs and poultry at Bury St Edmunds market, followed by motor vehicles at 12.30pm. Sheep sales are held in the nearby village of Ingham in July, August and September.

Bury St Edmunds is a small town with expanding industries, but as these sales suggest, it still has the character of a country market town. There are many fine old buildings, for example the Town Hall (designed as a theatre by Robert Adam) and the Manor House Museum on Honey Hill, which now houses a collection of clocks.

VIEWING: *All: day prior 4.00pm-8.00pm, and morning of sale from 8.30am.*
REFRESHMENTS: *Provided by local WI for fine art sales.*
PARKING: *Own car park*
STORAGE: *Yes*
TRANSPORTATION: *Yes*
SHIPPING: *By arrangement.*

PHILLIPS EAST ANGLIA
See PHILLIPS EAST ANGLIA, Ipswich, Suffolk

Bury St Edmunds

BOARDMAN
The Town Hall. Tel: (0440) 730414

300-400 lots. When Boardman hold a sale at the Town Hall in Clare, a general air of excitement prevails in this small Suffolk town. Past auctions have seen some world-record prices. Needless to say, the lots are very much at the top end of the market, and consist mainly of selected pieces of high-quality furniture and pictures.

Boardman was established in 1825, and today it is very well run by Neil and Hazel Lanham, whose office is at Station Road Corner, Haverhill.

Clare

BUYER'S PREMIUM: *10%*
SALES: *Quarterly (at no fixed intervals but always on Wed at 10.30am).*
VIEWING: *Day prior 2.00pm-7.00pm and day of sale from 8.00pm.*
REFRESHMENTS: *None available on the premises.*
PARKING: *Available near by.*
STORAGE: *Yes*
TRANSPORTATION: *Yes*
SHIPPING: *Yes*

SUFFOLK SALES
The Saleroom, Church Street. Tel: (0787) 277993

500 lots. Before finding his forte as an auctioneer, Michael Dyson kept a smallholding in the nearby village of Poslingford. Over the 15 years since the auction was started, it has become something of an institution and its reputation has spread through East Anglia. It is a fine country auction in the centre of a beautiful small Suffolk town. Opposite the saleroom is an adventure playground, a bonus for children. A typical sale will

Clare

BUYER'S PREMIUM: *Nil*
SALES: *Every three weeks on Sat at 11.00am.*
VIEWING: *Fri prior 5.00pm-9.00pm, day of sale from 9.00am.*
REFRESHMENTS: *Excellent homemade refreshments sold to raise money for local charities.*

PARKING: *Council car park 500 yards away.*
STORAGE: *Yes*
TRANSPORTATION: *Yes*
SHIPPING: *No*

have good-quality general furniture, a wide selection of antiques, silver and silver plate, jewellery, china, bygones, collectables, old records and so on. A lot of pine and soft furnishings are sold, but there is very little electrical equipment, although the odd cooker may turn up now and then. Mr Dyson notes that many young people setting up home come to buy their furniture at his sales, and items like armchairs for re-upholstering are always popular.

Felixstowe

BANNISTER & CO

Felixstowe Auction Rooms, 89 St Andrew Road.
Tel (0394) 282828

BUYER'S PREMIUM: *Nil*
SALES: *Monthly on Wed at 10.00am.*
VIEWING: *Tue prior all day.*
REFRESHMENTS: *None available on the premises.*
PARKING: *Own car park.*
STORAGE: *Yes*
TRANSPORTATION: *Yes*
SHIPPING: *Yes*

300-400 lots. Wednesdays are busy for the auction-goer in Suffolk: there are two monthly sales in Felixstowe, monthly sales at Woodbridge and Ipswich, and a fortnightly sale in Saxmundham. Care is taken so that the two Wednesday auctions in Felixstowe do not clash. Bannister & Co's sale is a good general auction with a wide mix of antique and modern household furniture and effects, plus china and crockery, silver, jewellery, glass, paintings and collectables. The saleroom is within easy walking distance of the railway station, and is also visited by overseas buyers who arrive at the ferry port. The town is an attractive Edwardian resort and an important container port.

Felixstowe

DIAMOND MILLS & CO

Orwell Hall, Orwell Road. Tel: (0394) 282281

BUYER'S PREMIUM: *10%*
SALES: *Monthly on Wed at 10.00am (includes antiques and fine art sale every three months).*
VIEWING: *Day prior 10.00am-4.00pm (and 6.00pm-7.30pm for antiques and fine art).*
REFRESHMENTS: *Own café.*
PARKING: *Own car park.*
STORAGE: *Yes*
TRANSPORTATION: *Yes*
SHIPPING: *Yes*

300-400 lots. A lacquered press chest embossed with Oriental figures, a Victorian bow-front five-drawer chest, a marble-top washstand, a period wardrobe, five dining chairs, 112 pieces of Noritake china, mahogany boxes, porcelain, copper and brass, bedroom effects, double and single divans, mirror-backed sideboards, pine chests, collectables and a box of costume jewellery . . . these are a few examples of typical lots at this sale. Diamond Mills & Co run efficient catalogued sales with computerised paying systems to cut down waiting. The auction is generally divided into Victorian, Edwardian, modern and general sections. Every three months or so the auction becomes an antiques and fine art sale.

Ipswich

PHILLIPS EAST ANGLIA

Dover House, Wolsey Street. Tel: (0473) 255137

BUYER'S PREMIUM: *10%*
SALES: *Ipswich: monthly on Tue at 11.00am. Bury St*

600-800 lots. Dover House is close to Ipswich town centre, the crown courts and the football ground. Every month, sales are held of good-quality lots, including furniture, collectors' items, china, works of art, carpets, clocks and pictures.

Phillips East Anglia also organise a good quarterly two-day sale of fine furniture, works of art, glass, silver, jewellery, clocks, rugs, ceramics and pictures at The Athenaeum, Angel Hill, Bury St Edmunds. This is a popular event in beautiful surroundings. Further information is available from the Ipswich saleroom.

Edmunds: Mar, Jun, Sep and Dec on Wed and Thu at 11.00am.
VIEWING: *Ipswich: Sat prior, 9.00am-12.00 noon, Mon prior 9.00am-7.30pm, and day of sale 9.00am-11.00am. Bury St Edmunds: check times with Ipswich saleroom.*
REFRESHMENTS: *Both: none available on the premises.*
PARKING: *Ipswich: own car park. Bury St Edmunds: none available on the premises*
STORAGE: *Both: yes*
TRANSPORTATION: *Both: yes*
SHIPPING: *Both: yes*

WEBSTERS AUCTIONEERS & VALUERS

Ipswich

Central Auction Rooms, 13 Great Colman Street.
Tel: (0473) 257491

800-1,000 lots. This is a good general auction in the centre of the town. A typical sale will include a selection of period and modern household furniture, but Websters specialise mainly in the sale of trade stocks, plant, machinery and vehicles, both commercial and private. Trade stocks range from groceries and jewellery, to engineering equipment and computers. So you can expect to find a mixture of goods catalogued — perhaps a rococo-style three-seater sofa, a dumper truck, industrial cleaning fluids, restaurant seating or a BMW. Selling ends at about 3.00pm.

Great Colman Street is in easy walking distance of Christchurch Park Museum and the Buttermarket, where the old dwelling called the Ancient House is now a wonderful bookshop, with low ceilings and many steps and stairs.

BUYER'S PREMIUM: 10%
SALES: *Monthly on the first Thu of month at 10.00am.*
VIEWING: *Wed prior until 8.00pm.*
REFRESHMENTS: *Light refreshments sold.*
PARKING: *None available on the premises.*
STORAGE: *Yes*
TRANSPORTATION: *Yes*
SHIPPING: *No*

LOWESTOFT AUCTION ROOMS

Lowestoft

Pinbush Road, South Lowestoft Industrial Estate.
Tel: (0502) 531532

400-600 lots. Lowestoft Auction Rooms have a varied programme of sales, and according to Bob Hayton, the auctioneer, prices range 'from £1 to several thousands'. Regular sales of antiques and general effects are held on the first Saturday of each month, and there are sometimes sales of office furniture (sold on behalf of liquidators), as well as sales of shrubs, saddlery and tack. Browsers are welcome at any time of the month.

If you have time, take a walk around Lowestoft harbour to see the fleet of trawlers, the kipper-curing houses and

BUYER'S PREMIUM: *Nil*
SALES: *Antiques and general: monthly on first Sat of the month at 10.00am. Others: days vary, but sales always start at 10.00am.*
VIEWING: *Day prior 8.00am-6.00pm and morning of sale from 8.00am.*
REFRESHMENTS: *Own café.*
PARKING: *Own car park.*
STORAGE: *Yes*

TRANSPORTATION: By arrangement.
SHIPPING: By arrangement.

net-drying frames. Lowestoft kippers were once famous, and it is still possible to buy proper oak-smoked kippers here.

Saxmundham

BUYER'S PREMIUM: Nil
SALES: Fortnightly on Wed at 10.30am.
VIEWING: Tue prior 9.00am-4.00pm, morning of sale from 9.00am-11.30am.
REFRESHMENTS: None available on the premises.
PARKING: Limited free parking with additional paying parking.
STORAGE: No
TRANSPORTATION: Yes
SHIPPING: No

WILLIAM H BROWN

Flick's Auction Room. Tel: (0728) 603232

400 lots. Wednesday is market day in Saxmundham and is always busy, but the crowds double when William H Brown hold their fortnightly sale. On auction days there is also a small antiques and crafts fair in the market hall, with some 15 or 16 stalls selling an interesting range of goods. The auction takes place in what used to be a bakery, and old ovens can still be seen at the rear of the hall.

The auction starts at 10.30am. The main auction inside the saleroom is usually of furniture, brass, copperware, china, paintings, kitchenalia, books, jewellery, bric-à-brac and other items of all types and values. When this sale is over the auctioneer moves outside for the sale of outside effects, including for example bicycles, mowers, wire netting and carpenters' tools. The entire proceedings finish at around 3.00 to 3.30pm.

Southwold

BUYER'S PREMIUM: Nil
SALES: Quarterly on Thu at 10.30am.
VIEWING: Wed prior 10.30am-4.00pm.
REFRESHMENTS: Own café.
PARKING: Plenty of parking near by.
STORAGE: Yes
TRANSPORTATION: Yes
SHIPPING: Yes

H A ADNAMS

The Auction Room, St Edmund's Road. Tel: (0502) 723292

400-500 lots. This sale generally has a wide variety of lots, ranging in price from £1 for, box of bric-à-brac, the odd cup or two, or perhaps a child's puzzle, up to a five-figure sum for a piece of furniture or silverware. A typical sale will have antique and modern furniture, soft furnishings, bedroom effects, paintings, ceramics, copper and brass, dinner and tea services, clocks, books and plenty of miscellaneous items. The auction is a good adjunct to a near-perfect seaside town with fine cliffs, a long sandy beach, a little harbour and a wealth of handsome houses, many of them Georgian. St Edmund's Road is in the town centre, just off Pier Avenue, and the sale usually ends around 3.30 to 4.00pm.

Sudbury

BUYER'S PREMIUM: 10%
SALES: General: weekly on Thu at 1.30pm. Antiques and fine art: every two months on Wed at 10.30am.

WILLIAM H BROWN

Olivers Rooms, Burkitts Lane. Tel: (0787) 880305

200-300 lots. The saleroom's name comes from the 200-year-old firm of Olivers, which is now part of the William H Brown group. This is the fine art auction centre for W H Brown's South East region. Specialist sales of fine furniture, pictures, ceramics, glass, silver and plate, jewellery and *objets de vertu*, clocks, rugs and metalware are held regularly, and an annual programme of sales is available on request. Weekly sales of antique and household furniture and effects include china, brass, bric-à-brac, and outside effects.

This is one of the few smaller weekly auctions that produce a catalogue, or rather a sheet identifying the lots on offer. As vendors bring in articles right up to the day before the sale, this is no small feat. The auction takes place in a large, purpose-built saleroom about 200 yards from the market square. Thursday is also market day in Sudbury, so the town will be crowded. An antiques and fine art sale is also held here every two months. Close to the saleroom is the Thomas Gainsborough House Museum, the birthplace of the artist.

VIEWING: *General: morning of sale from 9.00am. Antiques and fine art: day prior 2.00pm-7.00pm, morning of sale from 9.00am.*
REFRESHMENTS: *None available on the premises.*
PARKING: *Free public car parks.*
STORAGE: *No*
TRANSPORTATION: *Yes*
SHIPPING: *Yes*

ABBOTTS

Woodbridge

Abbotts Auction Rooms, Campsea Ashe. Tel: (0728) 746323
700-800 lots. This is one of the largest old-fashioned market auctions left in East Anglia, with the sale of cattle, sheep, pigs, produce, eggs and furniture. It is a treat to attend, and the population of this small, attractive village is easily trebled on sale days. There are three large salerooms in addition to the offices and store room on the premises. The sale of livestock begins at 10.00am. Meanwhile, garden produce, poultry and eggs are also sold. The general sale begins in Saleroom Two at 11.00am, and will usually include furniture in all states of repair, household effects, kitchenalia, brasses, collectors' items, boxes of bric-à-brac, china, ornaments and so on. All the selling is completed by around 4.30pm.

There are also well-attended monthly antique sales, with a wide range of antique furniture, silver, pottery, pictures, jewellery and *objets de vertu*.

BUYER'S PREMIUM: *7%*
SALES: *General: weekly on Mon at 11.00am. Antiques and fine art: monthly on Wed at 10.00am.*
VIEWING: *General: Sat prior 9.00am-11.00am, morning of sale from 8.30am. Antiques and fine art: Mon prior 2.00pm-8.00pm, morning of sale from 8.30am.*
REFRESHMENTS: *Tea shop on site.*
PARKING: *Own very large car park.*
STORAGE: *Pre-sale short term.*
TRANSPORTATION: *Yes*
SHIPPING: *Yes*

NEAL SONS & FLETCHER

Woodbridge

Theatre Street Saleroom, Theatre Street. Tel: (0394) 382263
400-450 lots. Woodbridge is an attractive small town on the Deben Estuary, with small narrow streets and a long river front. The saleroom building was a theatre in the Napoleonic period, and became a school in Victorian times. It is worth a visit in its own right. The monthly general sale is a good-humoured, well-run catalogue auction, attended by some fine Suffolk characters. It usually has a good array of antique and modern furniture, soft furnishings, paintings, ceramics and collectables. The sale finishes around 2.30 to 3.30pm. There are also

BUYER'S PREMIUM: *Nil*
SALES: *General: monthly on Wed at 10.30am. Special antiques and fine art: quarterly (no fixed months) on Wed and Thu at 10.30am.*
VIEWING: *General: day prior 2.30pm-4.30pm, 6.30pm-8.00pm. Antiques and fine art: 11.15am-4.30pm and 6.30pm-8.00pm.*
REFRESHMENTS: *None*

available on the premises.
PARKING: *Own car park.*
STORAGE: *Yes*
TRANSPORTATION: *Yes*
SHIPPING: *Yes*

quarterly two-day special sales of antiques and fine art, which attract private buyers and dealers from all over the country and from the Continent. These sales are not held in a regular month, but there is usually one in each season.

SURREY

Bletchingley

BUYER'S PREMIUM: 10%
SALES: *On average every six weeks on Tue, Wed and Thu usually at 10.00am.*
VIEWING: *Fri and Sat prior 10.00am-5.00pm.*
REFRESHMENTS: *Own café (sale days only).*
PARKING: *Own car park.*
STORAGE: *Yes*
TRANSPORTATION: *Yes*
SHIPPING: *Yes*

LAWRENCE'S

Norfolk House, High Street. Tel: (0883) 743323

2,000-3,000 lots. This is a large, busy, rather up-market auction, yet it is also friendly enough not to intimidate the new auction-goer. Sales take place roughly every six weeks, on a Tuesday, Wednesday and Thursday. Go along on Tuesday morning if you are interested in modern furniture and miscellaneous items (which could include anything from fans to medals) — or if you would like to bid for rugs, carpets and textiles. The afternoon is given over to ceramics and glass. If you are keen on silver and silver plate, jewellery, copper, brass, pewter and other goods made from metal, you will find that the Wednesday morning sale has much to offer. Oil paintings, watercolours and prints are auctioned on Wednesday afternoons, and on Thursday the whole day is taken up with antique and reproduction furniture.

Cheam

BUYER'S PREMIUM: 10%
SALES: *Antiques: first Mon of the month at 10.00am. General: second, third and fourth Mon of the month at 10.00am. Small antiques: monthly on Fri at 7.00pm.*
VIEWING: *All Mon sales: Fri prior 2.00pm-4.00pm and Sat 10.00am-4.00pm. Small antiques: day of sale from 2.00pm.*
REFRESHMENTS: *Hot drinks only.*
PARKING: *None available on the premises.*
STORAGE: *Yes*
TRANSPORTATION: *Yes*
SHIPPING: *Yes*

PARKINS

18 Malden Road. Tel: (081) 644 6127

250-350 lots. Cheam is a suburban area with a quiet atmosphere. If you have time between bids, take a look at 'Whitehall' — one of the earliest two-storey buildings in England, which can be found not far from the saleroom. It has recently been restored and is now open to visitors.

Parkins is a long-established company, whose auctions have been run for the past 20 years by the Zenthon family. Mary Zenthon, the owner, is helped by a small staff with the day-to-day running of the business; her son is the chief auctioneer. Five sales are held every month, and they are attended by locals and dealers from London and beyond. The first Monday of the month is given over to a sale of antiques, collectables and Georgian, Victorian and Edwardian items. The second, third and fourth Mondays of the month are devoted to general household furniture and effects. There is also an evening sale of small antiques — china, glass, jewellery and pictures — once a month on a Friday.

CROWS AUCTION GALLERY

The Car Park, Dorking Halls, Reigate Road. Tel: (0306) 740382
200-500 lots. Crows Auction Gallery offers two kinds of sales. On Monday there is a popular weekly auction of household effects, bric-à-brac and miscellaneous items, and once a month on a Wednesday there is a catalogued sale of better-quality items, including antiques. When this sale takes place, the usual weekly sale is cancelled.

HAMPTONS FINE ART (incorporating MESSENGER MAY BAVERSTOCK)

93 High Street. Tel: (0483) 423567
400-500 lots. Hamptons hold sales at three different auction rooms in Godalming. The High Street auction room holds specialist sales on Wednesdays and Thursdays at monthly intervals. These are given over to furniture, glass, china, collectables, jewellery, silver and so on one week, followed by pictures the following week and books the week after that. There are, however, gaps of four to five weeks between each cycle of specialist sales.

An interesting setting is provided by Hamptons' Bridge Street saleroom, which is situated in a converted Victorian church. Here there are sales of Victoriana and 20th-century effects on the first and third Saturday of the month.

Hamptons also have a monthly sale of general items at their Queen Street saleroom, which includes anything from good Victorian furniture to washing machines and lawn mowers. It is possible to spend a wonderful day at one of these sales, and yet spend no more than a few pounds. Children are welcome.

CLARKE GAMMON

Auction Rooms, Bedford Road. Tel: (0483) 572266
500-600 lots. Clarke Gammon describe themselves as 'a private independent partnership of chartered surveyors and auctioneers'. Their sales, held once every six to eight weeks, are certainly rather up-market affairs, including antique and reproduction furniture, antique and modern silver, watercolour

Dorking

BUYER'S PREMIUM: 10%
SALES: *General: weekly on Mon at 12.00 noon. Catalogued: monthly on the last Wed of the month at 10.00am.*
VIEWING: *General: morning of sale from 9.00am. Catalogued: Sat and Mon prior 10.00am-4.00pm.*
REFRESHMENTS: *Coffee only.*
PARKING: *Ample near by.*
STORAGE: *Yes*
TRANSPORTATION: *Yes*
SHIPPING: *Yes*

Godalming

BUYER'S PREMIUM: *10%*
SALES: *High Street: approximately once a month on Wed at 11.00am and Thu at 10.30am; Bridge Street: 9.30am (first and third Sat of the month); Queen Street: Tue at 10.30am (monthly).*
VIEWING: *High Street: Sat prior, 9.00am-12.00 noon, Mon prior, 9.00am-7.00pm, Tue 9.00am-3.00pm; Bridge Street: day prior, 9.00am-7.00pm; Queen Street: Sat prior, 9.00am-12.00 noon, and day prior, 9.00am-5.00pm.*
REFRESHMENTS: *At High Street and Bridge Street only.*
PARKING: *All: ample parking near by.*
STORAGE: *All: yes*
TRANSPORTATION: *All: yes*
SHIPPING: *All: yes*

Guildford

BUYER'S PREMIUM: *10%*
SALES: *On Tue at 10.30am, once every six to eight weeks.*
VIEWING: *Sat prior, 9.00am-12.00 noon. Day prior, 9.00am-5.00pm.*

REFRESHMENTS: *None available on the premises.*
PARKING: *Multi-storey opposite.*
STORAGE: *Yes*
TRANSPORTATION: *Yes*
SHIPPING: *Yes*

drawings, oil paintings, books and prints, metalware, ornamental items, clocks and watches, English, Oriental and Continental ceramics, Oriental carpets, jewellery and coins. A host of unusual and interesting items may be found among the lots described as 'bygones', which include toys, photographic and optical equipment and other collectables. Past sales have offered carved African elephant book-ends, Victorian needlework boxes, coachmen's whips and wooden rocking horses, to name but a few.

Guildford

BUYER'S PREMIUM: *10%*
SALES: *Every six weeks on Tue at 10.30am.*
VIEWING: *Sat prior, 9.00am-12.00 noon, Sun prior, 2.00pm-4.00pm and day prior, 10.00am-7.00pm.*
REFRESHMENTS: *None available on the premises.*
PARKING: *Millbrook public car park.*
STORAGE: *No*
TRANSPORTATION: *Yes*
SHIPPING: *No*

PHILLIPS

Millmead. Tel: (0483) 504030

300-400 lots. Phillips' saleroom is across the River Wey from the Yvonne Arnaud Theatre, and is part of a period, white-fronted building. Sales of antiques, later furniture and works of art are held here every six weeks on average, and specialist sales of silver and jewellery take place throughout the year.

The lots in these rather up-market sales are described in more detail in the sales catalogues, which are sold at the reception desk to the left of the entrance and are also available by post.

Guildford

BUYER'S PREMIUM:
Guildford: nil. Haywards Heath: 10%
SALES: *Guildford, bric-à-brac: weekly on Tue at 10.30am. Guildford, general: twice monthly on second and fourth Sat of month at 9.30am. Haywards Heath: every six weeks on Wed at 10.30am.*

SOUTH EAST MARTS

Guildford Market, Slyfield Green. Tel: (0483) 573386

500-1,500 lots. Slyfield Green is an industrial complex on the Woking Road, about two miles out of Guildford. There are good old-fashioned, country-style auctions here once a week on Tuesdays. These take place in the open and are of general bric-à-brac, collectables, miscellaneous items and nursery stock. On the second and fourth Saturday of each month, under cover in the Market Barn, there are sales of antique and general household furniture and effects.

The same company is also responsible for the six-weekly Wednesday auction at the Sussex Auction Galleries, 59 Perrymount Road, Haywards Heath, West Sussex, tel: (0444) 414935. This Wednesday sale at Haywards Heath is of more valuable items: lots include antiques, fine art and collectables.

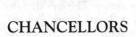

CHANCELLORS

74 London Road. Tel: (081) 541 4139

400-600 lots. Chancellors' large complex is close to the Cattle Market, a short distance away from Kingston's main shopping precinct. Every week an auction takes place in one of the two salerooms here. The general sale of 20th-century items is held three times a month, and the sale of antiques and fine art once a month. The sale of 20th-century items has no categories; goods are allocated lot numbers and are sold in the order in which they arrive at the saleroom, rather than according to what they are.

In contrast, the monthly antiques sale has a formal pattern, and goods are sold by category. Furniture usually starts the bidding, followed by carpets, clocks, pictures, books, miscellaneous items, jewellery, silver, china and glass. Catalogues are available for both sales.

WENTWORTH AUCTION GALLERIES

21 Station Approach. Tel: (0344) 843711

600-700 lots. This saleroom is only a few minutes' walk away from the railway station, and is situated to the rear of some offices. Golfers may be more interested to know that it is only just over a mile from here to the famous Wentworth golf course. The proprietor of Wentworth's, Mr Richardson, takes part in the onerous task of auctioning lots on sale days. Since sales began here more than 25 years ago they have become more than just a place where people buy; many people come now just to talk and enjoy the atmosphere of general banter and friendship that exists here. The lots are usually of high quality and are varied, including jewellery, china, brass, silver, paintings, prints, and modern, antique and general household

VIEWING: *Guildford, bric-à-brac: during sale. Guildford, general: day prior 1.30pm-7.30pm, morning of sale from 8.30am. Haywards Heath: Mon and Tue prior 9.30am-4.30pm.*
REFRESHMENTS: *Guildford: own café. Haywards Heath: none available on the premises.*
PARKING: *Guildford: own car park. Haywards Heath: none available on the premises.*
STORAGE: *Both: yes*
TRANSPORTATION: *Both: yes*
SHIPPING: *Both: yes*

Kingston upon Thames

BUYER'S PREMIUM: 10%
SALES: *Weekly on Thu (general sales of 20th-century items at 11.00am, antiques sales at 10.00am.)*
VIEWING: *General: Day prior, 2.00pm-8.00pm and morning of sale from 9.00am; antiques: Tue prior, 2.00pm-8.00pm, Wed prior, 9.00am-5.00pm, and morning of sale from 9.00am.*
REFRESHMENTS: *Not available on the premises.*
PARKING: *Large public car park near by.*
STORAGE: *No*
TRANSPORTATION: *Yes*
SHIPPING: *Yes*

Virginia Water

BUYER'S PREMIUM: 10%
SALES: *Wed at 9.30am, once every five or six weeks.*
VIEWING: *Day prior, 9.00am-8.00pm.*
REFRESHMENTS: *None available on the premises.*
PARKING: *Large car park near by.*
STORAGE: *Yes*
TRANSPORTATION: *Yes*
SHIPPING: *Yes*

furniture. One important point to note if you wish to contact the auctioneers is that their telephone is manned only during the mornings, unless you call on a sale or viewing day.

TYNE & WEAR

Boldon

BOLDON AUCTION GALLERIES

24a Front Street. Tel: (091) 537 2630

500-600 lots. The saleroom is on the main road in Boldon and is difficult to miss, particularly on sale days when a great number of people will be heading towards it. The weekly sale attracts buyers from Sunderland, Newcastle and South Shields. Over the ten years they have been established, the sales have gained a good reputation in Tyne & Wear both for the friendly way in which they are conducted, and for the variety of interesting lots. The sales have a wide variety of goods: general household furniture and effects, including reproduction and modern items; ornaments, kitchen and garden goods, bric-à-brac, toys, collectables, bygones and others. The cheaper miscellaneous items start the sale, and are followed by linen and furniture. About once in every two months the sale is devoted to better-quality articles, including antiques, paintings and collector's items. The pub opposite the saleroom is a pleasant place in which to wait for your lot to come up.

BUYER'S PREMIUM: *10%*
SALES: *Weekly on Wed at 10.00am (includes antiques sale about every two months).*
VIEWING: *Day prior 2.00pm-6.00pm.*
REFRESHMENTS: *None available on the premises.*
PARKING: *Ample near by.*
STORAGE: *Yes*
TRANSPORTATION: *Yes*
SHIPPING: *Yes*

Crawcrook

ANDERSON & GARLAND
See ANDERSON & GARLAND, Newcastle upon Tyne, Tyne and Wear

Newcastle upon Tyne

ANDERSON & GARLAND

Marlborough House, Marlborough Crescent. Tel: (091) 232 6278

1,200-1,800 lots. Anderson & Garland have been fine art auctioneers in the north of England since 1840. Their fine art sales take place every two months in the Marlborough House Saleroom, which is about 200 yards from the central railway station. Sales last four days, with each day concentrating on different categories. The first day will include about 300 lots of paintings, while on the second day there will be about 300 lots each of silver and jewellery. The third day is for collectors' items such as photographic equipment, bronzes, ivories, toys, models, needlework, coins, stamps and so on, with glass and porcelain in the afternoon. Finally, on the fourth day, around

BUYER'S PREMIUM: *10%*
SALES: *Newcastle: every two months on Tue, Wed, Thu and Fri at 10.30am. Crawcrook: fortnightly on Thu at 9.30am.*
VIEWING: *Newcastle: Thu and Fri prior 10.00am-4.30pm, Sat prior 9.30am-12.30pm. Crawcrook: Tue prior 2.00pm-7.00pm, Wed prior 10.00am-4.00pm.*
REFRESHMENTS: *Newcastle: none available on the premises. Crawcrook: own café.*

250 to 300 lots of furniture and some 20 to 30 lots of Oriental rugs and carpets are sold. The firm has a second saleroom at Pattinsons Rooms, Kepier Chare, Crawcrook, tel: (091) 413 8348, where there are fortnightly sales of Victorian and general furnishings and effects.

THOMAS N MILLER

18/26 Gallowgate. Tel: (091) 232 5617

400-600 lots. The spacious saleroom complex is in the city centre opposite St James's Park (Newcastle United's football stadium). This popular auction was established in 1902 and proudly boasts that it has furnished and equipped many a local household. Almost everything you might need is on sale, from lounge and bedroom suites and televisions to cutlery, cut-glass bowls and jewellery. Two sales are held every week, in a large room which is divided for the sales. On Tuesday the auction is of smaller lots such as domestic and ornamental china, kitchen items, cutlery, small electrical goods, glass, brass and so on. The Wednesday sale includes furniture of all periods and better quality small items, usually of a higher value than the lots available at the Tuesday sale. In addition, a special catalogued sale of antiques and fine art is held every 12 weeks on a Thursday.

J C FEATONBY

234/236 Park View. Tel: (091) 252 2601

400-500 lots. Whitley Bay is one of the most popular seaside resorts on the north-east coast, with a sandy beach and a long and breezy promenade. A trip to J C Featonby's weekly Thursday sale is a pleasant way to pass time here.

The large, purpose-built saleroom is full of 'good-to-browse-through' items, from knick-knacks to English wooden furniture dating from the first half of the century. A wide range of tables and chairs, 1930s dressing tables, period wardrobes and cabinets can usually be found.

In the morning the smaller items are auctioned off, including curtains and gardening tools and equipment. This part of the sale usually goes on until 1.00pm, when there is a break for lunch. At 2.00pm the auctioning begins again with the sale of the furniture. About every two months J C Featonby hold a special auction of antiques, paintings and fine art.

PARKING: *Ample parking near by.*
STORAGE: *Yes*
TRANSPORTATION: *Yes*
SHIPPING: *Yes*

Newcastle upon Tyne

BUYER'S PREMIUM: *10%*
SALES: *General: weekly on Tue and Wed at 9.30am. Antiques: every 12 weeks on Thu at 10.00am.*
VIEWING: *General: Mon 10.00am-5.00pm, Tue (for Wed sale) 9.00am-4.00pm. Antiques: day prior 9.00am-2.30pm.*
REFRESHMENTS: *Vending machine.*
PARKING: *Ample parking near by.*
STORAGE: *Yes*
TRANSPORTATION: *Yes*
SHIPPING: *Yes*

Whitley Bay

BUYER'S PREMIUM: *10%*
SALES: *General: weekly on Thu at 10.15am. Antiques: about every two months on Mon at 1.00pm.*
VIEWING: *General: day prior 10.30am-4.30pm. Antiques: Fri prior 2.00pm-5.00pm, Sat prior 9.00am-12.00 noon.*
REFRESHMENTS: *None available on the premises.*
PARKING: *None available on the premises.*
STORAGE: *Yes*
TRANSPORTATION: *Yes*
SHIPPING: *Yes*

WARWICKSHIRE

Bidford-on-Avon

BUYER'S PREMIUM: 10%
SALES: Weekly on Tue and Thu at 7.00pm.
VIEWING: Day of sale from 9.30am.
REFRESHMENTS: Vending machine in saleroom.
PARKING: Public car park near by.
STORAGE: Yes
TRANSPORTATION: Yes
SHIPPING: Yes

BELLCOURT AUCTIONS LTD

69 High Street. Tel: (0789) 772611

250-500 lots. Bidford is an attractive, traditional village with a lovely fifteenth-century bridge over the river, and an unusual church with wonderful stained glass. Both are well worth a visit should you have time between making bids at Bellcourt's very busy and friendly family-run auctions. The Tuesday sales are of antique furniture, silver, plated ware, jewellery, oil paintings, watercolours, prints, pottery, glass, Oriental ceramics and works of art, including rugs, dolls and clocks. The Thursday sales concentrate on more general household furniture and effects such as electrical goods, kitchenalia, bedroom suites and lounge suites, as well as smaller items: ornaments, lamps, silver plate, carpets and rugs. Now and then, larger outdoor items are sold under the cover of a lean-to outside the main saleroom, and when these are being sold, they are usually at the start of the sale. The saleroom used to be a billiard room in the early Victorian house. Nowadays the areas of the house which are not used either for storage or as offices are occupied by John Homer and his family, who organise the sales.

Rugby

BUYER'S PREMIUM:
50p (lots up to £5), 10% (lots over £5).
SALES: General (Railway Club): fortnightly on Thu at 7.00pm. Antiques and fine art (Lubenham Village Hall): weekly on Wed at 7.00pm.
VIEWING: General (Railway Club): day of sale from 3.00pm. Antiques and fine art (Lubenham Village Hall): day of sale from 2.30pm.
REFRESHMENTS: Not available.
PARKING: Both: on-street only.
STORAGE: Both: yes
TRANSPORTATION: Both: yes
SHIPPING: Both: no

COUNTRY AUCTIONS

141/153 Cambridge Street. Tel: (0788) 536362

300-400 lots. Unprepossessing though it may seem at first sight, the town of Rugby (best known for its public school, immortalised by Thomas Hughes in *Tom Brown's Schooldays*) is surrounded by many beautiful villages.

Country Auctions has a rich variety of goods on sale, and a friendly atmosphere prevails on sale days. It is usually not long before someone comes up to ask your opinion about one lot or another. The fortnightly Thursday evening sale takes place at the Railway Club in Hillmorton Road. It comprises modern household furniture and effects, including lounge and bedroom suites, pine, wall units, carpets, mirrors, automatic washing machines, ornaments, lamps, brass items, copper and bric-à-brac. There are also some outside effects, such as garden ornaments and tools, mowers and bicycles. Outside effects usually begin the auction. The Wednesday evening sale at Lubenham Village Hall comprises antiques and fine art.

BIGWOOD AUCTIONEERS LTD

The Old School, Tiddington. Tel: (0789) 269415

500-700 lots. As well as weekly sales of antique and reproduction furniture and effects, a range of specialist auctions is held here. A sale of oils, watercolours and drawings takes place once a month. There are also special sales of fine quality items every six to eight weeks, quarterly sales of fine and inexpensive wines and spirits, and three sales a year of books, prints and maps.

The antique and reproduction sale has a wide variety of items. This makes Bigwood Auctioneers particularly interesting, as there are always some surprises. For instance, a Regency mahogany bow-fronted chest and a 1920s wind-up gramophone might well stand next to a stripped pine table or a grand piano. On a small table you might find a Chinese rectangular 18th-century teapot standing next to one in the form of a 1950s sports car.

The premises used to be a school in Victorian times, and depending on the size of the sale, one or both salerooms will be used. Situated in the main street of Tiddington, a quiet village two miles from Stratford-upon-Avon, the building has a distinctive clock tower and is difficult to miss.

Stratford-upon-Avon

BUYER'S PREMIUM: *10%*
SALES: *Antiques: weekly on Sat at 11.00am. Others: days and times vary.*
VIEWING: *All: Wed and Thu prior, 9.00am-4.00pm, morning of sale from 9.00am.*
REFRESHMENTS: *Coffee only.*
PARKING: *To front and rear of saleroom.*
STORAGE: *Yes*
TRANSPORTATION: *Yes*
SHIPPING: *Yes*

PHILLIPS BROTHERS

The Saleroom, Bearley Road, Snitterfield. Tel: (0789) 731114

600-700 lots. Snitterfield is a charming village four miles north of Stratford-upon-Avon, and has associations with both Shakespeare and Charles II. If time allows, drag yourself away from the auction to see the font and carved scroll work in the church, which is only a few steps from the saleroom.

Phillips Brothers hold a large and interesting general sale of household furniture and effects, which covers a huge range of items. Every two months or so the sale will include perhaps 100 lots from the police — these will be unclaimed lost property or 'detained property', whose owner cannot be determined. Anything can turn up in this part of the sale: tyres, tools and tarpaulins from lorries, jewellery, rings, watches and household items.

Twice a year, in no regular month, the general sale is taken over completely by police lost property. Once a quarter, again not at regular intervals, the general sale is run simultaneously with a horse tackle sale. For those buying large and heavy objects, the saleroom has large double doors at the back, and cars and vans can drive right in to load up.

Stratford-upon-Avon

BUYER'S PREMIUM: *10%*
SALES: *Fortnightly on Sat at 10.00am.*
VIEWING: *Day prior 2.00pm-5.00pm*
REFRESHMENTS: *Own café.*
PARKING: *Own car park.*
STORAGE: *Yes*
TRANSPORTATION: *Yes*
SHIPPING: *Yes*

WEST MIDLANDS

Birmingham

BIDDLE & WEBB

Ladywood Middleway. Tel: (021) 455 8042

300-400 lots. Biddle & Webb have been holding auctions in Birmingham for almost as long as anyone can remember. The saleroom is a tall, prominent brick building bearing Biddle & Webb signs, on the same road as the Birmingham Children's Hospital. Two weekly sales and three monthly sales are held here. Every Tuesday there are auctions of 'semi antiques', which means Edwardian and Victorian furniture and collectables. Every Wednesday there is an auction of general modern furniture and effects, including electrical goods and kitchen items, china, bric-à-brac, gardening tools and equipment, and other items, usually on the inexpensive side.

The monthly sales are devoted to (1) fine art; (2) antique furniture, china, metalware and so on; (3) silver, gold, jewellery and coins. Every two months there are also sales of toys, dolls, model railways and juvenalia. Periodical sales of lost and unclaimed property are also held on behalf of Gatwick Airport.

BUYER'S PREMIUM: *Nil*
SALES: *Semi antiques: weekly on Tue at 10.30am. General: weekly on Wed at 10.30am. Fine art: monthly on first Fri of month. Antique furniture etc: monthly on second Fri of month. Silver, gold, etc: monthly on fourth Fri of month. All monthly sales start at 11.00am.*
VIEWING: *General and semi antiques: Sat prior 9.00am-12.00 noon, Mon and Tue prior 9.00am-5.00pm. Fine art and antiques: Mon-Thu 10.00am-4.00pm. Silver, gold, etc: Tue-Thu prior 10.00am-4.00pm.*
REFRESHMENTS: *Own café.*
PARKING: *Ample parking near by.*
STORAGE: *Yes*
TRANSPORTATION: *Yes*
SHIPPING: *Yes*

Birmingham

RONALD E CLARE

70 Park Street, Digbeth. Tel: (021) 643 0226

400-500 lots. The salerooms are part of a modern building extending to over 15,000 square feet on two levels, which are used alternately. It stands behind the company offices, and has a loading bay. All the items you might expect can be found here — antique, reproduction and modern furniture, electrical items, bric-à-brac, ceramics, glass, paintings and carpets — but the sale also includes the occasional car or commercial vehicle, pieces of machinery, office furniture and shop stock. Stamps, coins and books can also be found. During one auction it was possible to bid for lots as varied as a Royal Doulton teacup and saucer, and a forklift truck. The prices vary too, from as little as a couple of pounds to thousands.

On most Mondays there are sales of unclaimed goods from national carriers, running to some 300-400 lots. Periodical sales are also held of collectors' items, diecast models and fashion.

BUYER'S PREMIUM: *Nil*
SALES: *General: weekly on Tue at 10.30am. Unclaimed goods: usually weekly on Mon at 10.00am.*
VIEWING: *General: Sat prior 8.30am-12.00 noon, Mon prior 8.30am-5.00pm. Unclaimed goods: during sale.*
REFRESHMENTS: *Van selling snacks.*
PARKING: *Ample parking near by.*
STORAGE: *Yes*
TRANSPORTATION: *Yes*
SHIPPING: *Yes*

HORIZON AUCTIONS

Rear of 80 Broad Street. Tel: (0203) 637154

1,000-1,200 lots. These are good general sales with a friendly atmosphere. There are usually many regular buyers in attendance, as well as people who are there just for curiosity's sake. All types of goods are on offer: Victorian, Edwardian, modern and reproduction furniture, ceramics, glass, metalware, ornaments, jewellery and electrical goods among other things.

Coventry

BUYER'S PREMIUM: *10%*
SALES: *Weekly on Mon at 11.00am.*
VIEWING: *Sat prior 9.30am-5.00pm.*
REFRESHMENTS: *Own café.*
PARKING: *Large car park.*
STORAGE: *Yes*
TRANSPORTATION: *Yes*
SHIPPING: *Yes*

WARWICK AUCTIONS

3 Queen Victoria Road. Tel: (0203) 223377

300-400 lots. Coventry is one of England's most ancient cities, but the old city centre was almost completely destroyed in a fierce air raid in November 1940. Coventry Auction centre is on the opposite side of the city to the cathedral, and has been established over 40 years. Smaller items start the weekly sale. These may include brass fire dogs, ebony clocks, antique telescopes, or crockery. The sale usually continues with an assortment of bicycles, toys, books, colour television sets, electrical goods of all types, and arts and crafts. At the end there is usually furniture of all types.

Sales of antiques and collectables are held on the second Wednesday of the month, and there are other sales at irregular intervals, on behalf of liquidators and the local courts.

Coventry

BUYER'S PREMIUM: *10%*
SALES: *Weekly on Wed at 10.00am.*
VIEWING: *Day prior 9.00am-4.30pm, day of sale from 9.00am.*
REFRESHMENTS: *Hot drinks only.*
PARKING: *Public car parks adjoining.*
STORAGE: *Yes*
TRANSPORTATION: *Yes*
SHIPPING: *Yes*

PHILLIPS

The Old House, Station Road. Tel: (0564) 776151

250-400 lots. This is a branch of Phillips London, who have salerooms spread over Britain and branches in Europe and North America. However, one need not be intimidated by their reputation: often provincial branches of big firms like this have simply absorbed long-established local companies without spoiling the old friendly atmosphere. The prices range from £30 to £30,000-£40,000. The Old House is on the Dorridge turn-off from the A41 Solihull to Warwick road, and is an attractive brick and timber building which was originally a 17th-century farmhouse. The sales cover a wide range of items, from fine furniture, Victoriana and silver, to paintings, collector's items, ceramics and books.

Knowle, near Solihull

BUYER'S PREMIUM: *10%*
SALES: *Weekly on Wed at 11.00am (occasionally also 2.00pm).*
VIEWING: *Sat 9.30am-12.30pm, Mon 9.00am-5.00pm, Tue 9.00am-7.00pm.*
REFRESHMENTS: *On sale day.*
PARKING: *Limited, but three public car parks near by.*
STORAGE: *No*
TRANSPORTATION: *Yes*
SHIPPING: *Yes*

Wolverhampton

WALKER, BARNETT & HILL

Waterloo Road Salerooms, Clarence Street. Tel: (0902) 773531

400-500 lots. The saleroom is close to Beatties, the locally famous department store, and also near the Wolverhampton Wanderers football ground. The fortnightly sales are of Victorian and general household effects and furniture, miscellaneous items, bric-à-brac, kitchen goods, domestic and ornamental china and so on. Every six to eight weeks there is a fine art and antiques auction at the Park House Hotel at Shifnal, with around 500 lots. Past sales have included 19th-century French longcase clocks, pieces by Lalique such as a clock, vase and reading lamp, glazed pottery by John Piper, candlesticks, bisque dolls, William IV tea and coffee services, 18th-century mahogany side tables and Queen Anne walnut writing tables.

BUYER'S PREMIUM: 10%
SALES: Victorian and general: fortnightly on Thu at 11.00am. Antiques: every six to eight weeks on Wed at 10.00am.
VIEWING: Victorian and general: day prior 10.00am-4.00pm. Antiques: day prior 10.00am-8.00pm.
REFRESHMENTS: Availale.
PARKING: None available on the premises; car park at Park House Hotel.
STORAGE: Yes
TRANSPORTATION: Yes
SHIPPING: Yes

WEST SUSSEX

Billingshurst

JOHN BELLMAN AUCTIONEERS

New Pound, Wisborough Green. Tel: (0403) 700858

1,200-1,500 lots. John Bellman's saleroom is about a mile from Wisborough Green Common. It can be found in a large, new building that looks rather like a warehouse, beside a garage and car showroom. On the other side of Loxwood Road is The Bat and Ball public house and a caravan park. The countryside near by is very pleasant and makes a good day out when combined with a trip to an auction.

These monthly two-day sales include antique furniture and collectors' items, clocks, barometers and scientific instruments, silver and jewellery, paintings and prints, ceramics and glass, ephemera... in short, something to suit almost everybody. Smaller items such as porcelain, glass and silver are sold off on the first day of the sale, while furniture, paintings and metalware are auctioned on the second.

BUYER'S PREMIUM: 10%
SALES: Monthly on Thu and Fri at 10.00am and 2.00pm.
VIEWING: Mon and Wed prior 10.00am-4.00pm and Tue prior 10.00am-8.00pm.
REFRESHMENTS: None available on the premises.
PARKING: Own car park.
STORAGE: Yes
TRANSPORTATION: Yes
SHIPPING: Yes

Billingshurst

SOTHEBY'S

Summers Place. Tel: (0403) 783933

700-1,000 lots. Summers Place is Britain's largest provincial saleroom, and with an average of two sales a day three days a week it must also be one of the busiest. The setting is 37 acres of gardens and fields. Morning and afternoon sales are usually held from Tuesday to Thursday, and the valuation counters and

BUYER'S PREMIUM:
15% (items up to £30,000); 10% (items above £30,000).
SALES: On average two per day Tue to Thu, at 10.30am and again at 2.00pm.

salerooms are open from Monday to Friday all day, plus Saturday morning. The specialist sale categories include furniture, silver, jewellery, paintings and prints, porcelain, glass, Oriental items, bronzes, old pewter, copper and brass, dolls, toys, teddy bears, garden statuary, Oriental carpets and rugs, sporting guns and militaria.

Note: Do not be put off by the imposing entrance to the saleroom. As the Sotheby's sign clearly states, visitors are welcome. Verbal valuations are given free of charge.

VIEWING: *Mon to Fri 10.00am-4.00pm, Sat 9.30am-12.30pm. Lots are on view two days prior to sale.*
REFRESHMENTS: *Own restaurant.*
PARKING: *Own car park.*
STORAGE: *Yes*
TRANSPORTATION: *Yes*
SHIPPING: *Yes*

PHILLIPS

Chichester

Baffins Hall, Baffins Lane. Tel: (0243) 787548

300-400 lots. Chichester was one of the earliest sites in Britain to be occupied by the Romans, who called it *Regnum*. Phillips' saleroom is just off East Street, which has some fine old houses and is in the town centre. The regular monthly sales could include antique and reproduction furniture, pictures, ceramics, Oriental and European works of art, jewellery, silver and plate, and other categories. The day of the sale can vary, but is usually Thursday. Periodically, perhaps five times a year, this sale is replaced by a special fine art and antiques sale which may occasionally spread over Wednesday and Thursday.

BUYER'S PREMIUM: *10%*
SALES: *Monthly on Thu (day can vary) at 10.00am (includes fine art and antiques sale about five times a year).*
VIEWING: *Sat prior 9.00am-12.00 noon, day prior 10.00am-4.30pm.*
REFRESHMENTS: *None available on the premises.*
PARKING: *Pay and display car park.*
STORAGE: *Yes*
TRANSPORTATION: *Yes*
SHIPPING: *Yes*

STRIDE & SON AUCTIONEERS

Chichester

Southdown House, St John's Street. Tel: (0243) 780207

800-1,000 lots. This family-run firm was started over 100 years ago by the great-grandfather of the present proprietor, Mr N J Stride. The saleroom is a large, flint building opposite the cattle market. On Wednesday, and on Saturday, too, there is a general market with stalls selling antiques, bric-à-brac and local crafts. Stride & Son's sale is held on the last Friday of the month, and is of antique furniture and effects, including paintings, silver, china and jewellery of all values. The lots could sell for anything from £5 up to £14,000, so it is always interesting. For the first half-hour or so, various items of furniture are sold outside. At around 11.00am the auction moves into the main saleroom. It is organised so that the better quality lots appear as the sale progresses.

BUYER'S PREMIUM: *10%*
SALES: *Monthly on last Fri of month at 10.30am.*
VIEWING: *Day prior 10.00am-4.00pm, morning of sale from 9.00am.*
REFRESHMENTS: *None available on the premises.*
PARKING: *Own car park.*
STORAGE: *Yes*
TRANSPORTATION: *Yes*
SHIPPING: *No*

SUMMERLEY AUCTION ROOM

Felpham, near Bognor Regis

96 Limmer Lane. Tel: (0243) 821212

400-500 lots. The saleroom is a converted flint barn in the heart of this beautiful Saxon village. The barn is easy to find

BUYER'S PREMIUM: *10%*
SALES: *Twice monthly on*

second and last Sat of month at 10.30am.
VIEWING: *Fri prior 9.30am-8.00pm.*
REFRESHMENTS: *Own café.*
PARKING: *Ample parking near by.*
STORAGE: *Yes*
TRANSPORTATION: *Yes*
SHIPPING: *Yes*

once you have found the village, and on sale days all the traffic seems to be heading in that direction. Sale day is rather like a social event, and there will be plenty of cars and trailers parked outside. The proprietors employ an auctioneer to conduct the selling, which is run in a friendly, unhurried manner. All sorts of things may be in the sale, but you can usually expect three-piece suites, upholstered furniture, garden furniture, beds, tables, desks, ornaments, mirrors, plenty of china, silver, photograph albums, interesting bric-à-brac and miscellaneous items. Among it all there will usually be a sprinkling of good antiques and pictures, and it is the latter — oils, watercolours, and prints — that finish the sale. This is a sale to suit most needs and pockets, and the lovely countryside makes a visit a wonderful day out.

Haywards Heath

SOUTH EAST MARTS
See SOUTH EAST MARTS, Guildford, Surrey

Littlehampton

PETER CHENEY
Western Road Auction Rooms, Western Road.
Tel: (0903) 722264 and 713418

BUYER'S PREMIUM: *Nil*
SALES: *Every three weeks on Wed at 9.30am.*
VIEWING: *Sat prior 9.00am-12.00 noon, Mon and Tue prior 9.00am-1.00pm and 2.00pm-4.00pm.*
REFRESHMENTS: *Available near by.*
PARKING: *On-street parking only.*
STORAGE: *Yes*
TRANSPORTATION: *Yes*
SHIPPING: *Yes*

450-500 lots. Peter Cheney is an independent company, and the son of the founder is the present proprietor. The sale here every three weeks is a well-attended affair, with antique and modern furniture, ceramics, silver, pictures and collectors' items. There is a wide variety of lots, and prices can vary from as little as £1 to many thousands. Well-cared-for furniture can be seen on display around the saleroom, while paintings and prints can be studied on walls. Jewellery, books, linen, collectors items, pottery, glass, brass, pewter and porcelain are just some of the things to be found. Peter Cheney's auctions capture something of the sedate atmosphere of the town, which has a charming combination of sea, river and downland to offer visitors.

Midhurst

NATIONWIDE FINE ART & FURNITURE
Bepton Road. Tel: (0730) 812456

BUYER'S PREMIUM: *10%*
SALES: *On average every six weeks on Thu at 11.00am.*
VIEWING: *Tue and Wed prior 10.00am-12.00noon, 2.00pm-4.00pm.*
REFRESHMENTS: *None available on the premises.*
PARKING: *Grange Road*

300-350 lots. Midhurst is an attractive town, close to Cowdray House and its polo ground. Bepton Road is a continuation of the town's main road, and the saleroom is easy to spot — it has been converted from the old Ebenezer Chapel. The sales are called fine art and antiques sales, and on the whole live up to their name. The lots are usually of high quality and they tend not to sell for less than £20. The average is around £100, and prices go as far as £10,000. The atmosphere remains informal though, thanks to the exuberant personality of Mr E Lintott, who conducts most of the bidding.

GIBSON GAMMON

Rake Village Hall. Tel: (0730) 894225
400-600 lots. The Village Hall is situated at the centre of this pleasant village and is hired especially for the sale. The quality of lots, lovely surroundings and easy access from London (Rake is on the A3) bring many buyers from the capital to see what there is on offer. Local people also eagerly anticipate these sales, and can be seen searching excitedly through the lots on viewing days. They are also much in evidence on the day of the sale. A whole range of items may come up, from antique and modern furniture to silver, paintings, rugs, brass and pewter. The proceedings begin with kitchenalia and end with furniture.

DENHAMS

Horsham Auction Galleries, Warnham. Tel: (0403) 255699
600-900 lots. The Horsham Auction Galleries are on the A24, two miles north of Horsham, just outside the tiny picturesque village of Warnham. The galleries are a huge building, next to a large conference centre and hotel but in a rural setting. The most important sale is that of antiques and fine art, held monthly on Wednesdays, which usually includes antique furniture, silver, jewellery, European and Oriental ceramics, pictures, prints, clocks, Persian rugs and various collectors' items. The firm also holds a secondary general sale of lower value goods, including general household furniture and household effects.

R H ELLIS & SONS

44 High Street. Tel: (0903) 38999
400-500 lots. This independent, family-owned and run company was established over 50 years ago and is very much a local landmark. The saleroom is next to the company's office in a converted cottage, close to the centre of the popular seaside resort. There are three sales per month, one of antiques and two of general modern household furniture and effects. The general sales typically include a mixture of lounge and dining room suites, domestic and other electrical equipment, and kitchen and gardening items. The antiques sales include good quality Victorian and Edwardian furniture, porcelain,

public car park.
STORAGE: *No*
TRANSPORTATION: *Yes*
SHIPPING: *Yes*

Rake

BUYER'S PREMIUM: *10%*
SALES: *Quarterly on Fri at 10.30am.*
VIEWING: *Day prior, 10.00am-7.00pm.*
REFRESHMENTS: *Van selling snacks.*
PARKING: *Own car park.*
STORAGE: *Yes*
TRANSPORTATION: *Yes*
SHIPPING: *Yes*

Warnham, near Horsham

BUYER'S PREMIUM: *10%*
SALES: *Antiques and fine art: monthly on Wed at 10.00am. General: monthly on Wed at 10.00am.*
VIEWING: *Sat prior 9.00am-12.00 noon, Tue prior 10.00am-4.00pm (antiques until 7.00pm).*
REFRESHMENTS: *Own café and bar.*
PARKING: *Own car park.*
STORAGE: *Yes*
TRANSPORTATION: *Yes*
SHIPPING: *Yes*

Worthing

BUYER'S PREMIUM: *8%*
SALES: *General: twice a month on Mon at 10.00am. Antiques: once a month on Mon at 10.00am. Special: once a quarter on Mon at 10.00am.*
VIEWING: *Fri prior 9.00am-1.00pm, 2.15pm-5.00pm, Sat prior 9.00am-1.00pm, 2.00pm-4.00pm.*
REFRESHMENTS: *None available on the premises.*

PARKING: *Public car park opposite.*
STORAGE: *Yes*
TRANSPORTATION: *Yes*
SHIPPING: *Yes*

domestic and ornamental china and so on, as well as earlier antiques.

Special sales are held once a quarter, usually in addition to the three regular monthly sales, and offer silver, jewellery, paintings, Oriental rugs and other good quality items.

WEST YORKSHIRE

Bingley

OTLEY CATTLE MARKET AUCTIONS LTD

Bingley Auction Market, Keighley Road. Tel: (0943) 462265

BUYER'S PREMIUM: *Nil*
SALES: *Bingley: monthly on first Wed of month at 6.00pm (second Wed of month in September and October).*
Otley: quarterly (no fixed months) on Wed at 10.30am.
VIEWING: *Bingley: day of sale from 4.30pm. Otley: day prior 4.00pm-7.00pm.*
REFRESHMENTS: *Both: own café.*
PARKING: *Both: own car park.*
STORAGE: *Both: yes*
TRANSPORTATION: *Both: yes*
SHIPPING: *Both: yes*

800-900 lots. The same buildings are used for both general and livestock sales, but do not fear, they are well cleaned prior to the general sales. It is perfectly possible to wear smart clothes as you walk from pen to pen to view the lots, or to follow the auctioneers around the sale. Everything and anything is sold at this magnificent auction: motor vehicles, agricultural implements, sundry plant and equipment, memorabilia such as governess horsecarts, expensive jewellery, rare pottery, horse brasses, ornamental brass, books, paintings, antiques, farmhouse furniture and many other goods. Smaller items are placed on tables in the centre of the main ring, which is surrounded by seats. The auctioneer goes from pen to pen, selling the lots as he comes to them. They are spaciously set out, so there is plenty of room to have a good look. Two auctioneers sell in different areas at the same time, so the proceedings are split.

The same firm holds another sale at Bridge End, Otley (the market used in the television series Emmerdale). This is a catalogued sale of antique, period and general household furniture and effects, china, jewellery, paintings, books and so on, arguably of better quality. It takes place quarterly.

Bradford

DE ROME AUCTIONEERS AND VALUERS

12 New John Street. Tel: (0274) 734116

BUYER'S PREMIUM: *5%*
SALES: *Weekly on Wed at 10.00am.*
VIEWING: *Day prior 10.30am-4.00pm.*
REFRESHMENTS: *None available on the premises.*
PARKING: *None available on the premises.*

300-400 lots. The saleroom is in the north-west corner of the city, opposite the head office of the Yorkshire Building Society. The weekly sales include general furnishings and personal effects, and liquidated stock which varies from week to week. Items sold in the past have included stock from builders' merchants, kitchen manufacturers and a print and picture-framing business, which have comprised such things as angle cutters, mouldings and stretchers. In the general part of the sale there is usually a superb range of furnishings, VHS video recorders, Sony stereo and other colour televisions, various hi-fi equipment, lounge suites, wall units, glass-topped tables, sets of chairs, exercise bicycles, sofabeds and beds, crystal and coloured glass, cutlery, video cassettes, kitchen equipment — and numerous other things. There is usually at least one motor vehicle on sale every week.

Every six weeks the general sale is replaced by a sale of better quality items, which usually includes antiques, Victorian and Edwardian furniture, collectables and fine art.

STORAGE: *No*
TRANSPORTATION: *Yes*
SHIPPING: *Yes*

JOHN H RABY & SON

Bradford

21 St Mary's Road. Tel: (0274) 491121

300-400 lots. There are two St Mary's Roads in Bradford. This one is about two miles north of the city centre and close to the great Lister Mill (postal district Bradford 8). The saleroom is a converted Sunday School. It has been the setting for the weekly sale for the past 20 years, although the company responsible was established well before that, in 1914. The weekly sales are of general household furniture and effects, and miscellanea. There is often a large amount of 'shipping furniture', which can be particularly good value. Once a month the general sale is replaced by a sale of antiques. Both sales have a wide range of articles, both in type and value, with possibilities for both the fleamarket-goer and the international dealer.

BUYER'S PREMIUM: *Nil*
SALES: *Weekly on Thu at 10.30am (includes antiques sale once a month).*
VIEWING: *Day prior 10.00am-4.00pm.*
REFRESHMENTS: *Own café.*
PARKING: *Own car park.*
STORAGE: *Short duration only.*
TRANSPORTATION: *Yes*
SHIPPING: *No*

THRIPPLETON & BISHOP

Bradford

Southend Hall, Tickhill Street. Tel: (0274) 734963

200-400 lots. This is the place to come for antique or pre-1930s furniture, collectables, small silver items or jewellery. The fortnightly sales take place in the evening, in what was once a church hall, about half a mile from the city centre and just off the A647 Leeds Road. There are two types of sale, held alternately: the first type is for antique and pre-1930s furniture only, and the second type has furniture, plus a full range of collectables, small silver items, jewellery, bric-à-brac, porcelain, paintings and so on. Because of the extra number of lots, this sale begins half-an-hour earlier, with smaller items taking up the first hour of the auction. All the lots are well laid out and easy to view, and browsing is good fun. The furniture could include mahogany, oak and walnut, bedroom, dining and occasional pieces; and there could be desks, bureaux and chairs, or pine furniture for stripping.

BUYER'S PREMIUM: *5%*
SALES: *Fortnightly on Thu. Antique and pre-1930s furniture: 6.30pm. Antique and pre-1930s furniture plus other items: 6.00pm. Sales alternate.*
VIEWING: *Day prior 9.30am-5.00pm, day of sale from 9.30am.*
REFRESHMENTS: *Own café.*
PARKING: *Own car park.*
STORAGE: *Yes*
TRANSPORTATION: *Yes*
SHIPPING: *Yes*

Castleford

BUYER'S PREMIUM: 10%
SALES: Weekly on Thu at
6.00pm.
VIEWING: Mon-Thu
10.00am-6.00pm.
REFRESHMENTS: Own
café.
PARKING: Own car park.
STORAGE: No
TRANSPORTATION: Yes
SHIPPING: Yes

CASTLEFORD AUCTIONS

Wellington Street. Tel: (0977) 603106

300-400 lots. The saleroom is converted from an old chapel off the Methley Road (just outside the centre of Castleford heading towards Leeds). This is an independently run evening sale, and it is usually packed with private buyers. Some of them attend week after week, waiting for that special piece of furniture to turn up. The sale is informal and the public is invited to pop in any day of the week between 10.00am and 6.00pm for viewing. The lots often include the contents of a complete house, and a wide range of general household furniture can be expected, including antiques, kitchen bygones, and so on. There are usually good bargains to be had among the china and ornaments. The electrical goods may include televisions, washing machines and refrigerators, and there will probably be outside effects, such as bicycles and gardening tools.

Cottingley

MALCOLM H SKIDMORE

See MALCOLM H SKIDMORE, Settle, North Yorkshire

Hebden Bridge

EDDISONS AUCTIONS

See EDDISONS AUCTIONS, Huddersfield, West Yorkshire

Huddersfield

BUYER'S PREMIUM: Nil
SALES: General: every two to
three weeks on Wed at
10.30am (replaced quarterly by
antiques sale starting at
11.00am). Hebden Bridge:
fortnightly on Tue at 1.00pm.
VIEWING: Huddersfield: day
prior 9.30am-4.30pm. Hebden
Bridge: Sat prior
10.00am-4.00pm, Mon
10.00am-1.00pm.
REFRESHMENTS: cafés
and sandwich bars near by.
PARKING: Pay and display
car parks 100 yards away.
STORAGE: No
TRANSPORTATION: Yes
SHIPPING: Yes

EDDISONS AUCTIONS

4/6 High Street. Tel: (0484) 533151

450-500 lots. The saleroom is a large, interesting building with plenty of gargoyles outside and a big saleroom with a lofty ceiling inside. It is prominent in the town centre and is only five doors away from the town hall. The building has been an auction house since 1844 but was designed for horse auctions, which explains the wide passages and corridors. About every two to three weeks, depending on how quickly the lots come in, there is a sale of general household furniture and effects, which can be very rewarding. This sale is replaced every quarter by a special catalogued sale of antiques, which starts at 11.00am.

Another branch of the firm is responsible for regular Tuesday fortnightly sales which take place at 35 West End, Hebden Bridge, Yorkshire, tel: (0422) 842007. These are of Victorian and later furniture, china and miscellanea.

Eddisons are also involved in on-site auctions, very often of liquidated stock.

HUDDERSFIELD AUCTIONS

Miln Road, Bay Hall, Birkby. Tel: (0484) 451057
250-350 lots. The saleroom is on the ground floor of a former mill, about a quarter of a mile from the town centre. Here there are busy, interesting auctions. Local people often pop in after work to view the proceedings, and there are often quite a few surprises. There is usually a good mixture of antique and modern items among the lots. Furniture is sold at around 7.00pm, while china, glass, porcelain and collectables are up for bidding from about 8.00pm. Much of the furniture, though not antique, is from local homes and has been well cared for.

Huddersfield

BUYER'S PREMIUM: 5%
SALES: *Weekly on Tue at 6.30pm.*
VIEWING: *Day of sale from 10.00am.*
REFRESHMENTS: *Own café.*
PARKING: *Own car park.*
STORAGE: Yes
TRANSPORTATION: Yes
SHIPPING: Yes

WHITWORTHS

32/34 Wood Street. Tel: (0484) 427467
300-350 lots. The saleroom is a 19th-century building in the centre of town, close to the Classical-style railway station. This is a typical independently run local sale, which has gained a loyal following with both buyers and vendors over the years. Sales are held about every four to six weeks, and are looked forward to by local people, many of whom will pop in at least briefly during their lunch time. A typical sale will have a comprehensive range of high-class household furnishings and antiques. There will often be bankruptcy or liquidated stock, with some police lost property and jewellery.

Huddersfield

BUYER'S PREMIUM: 10%
SALES: *About every four to six weeks on Fri at 12.00 noon.*
VIEWING: *Wed and Thu prior 10.00am-4.00pm.*
REFRESHMENTS: *Available near by.*
PARKING: *None available on the premises.*
STORAGE: Yes
TRANSPORTATION: Yes
SHIPPING: Yes

ANDREW HARTLEY FINE ARTS

Victoria Hall Salerooms, Little Lane. Tel: (0943) 816363
600-900 lots. The saleroom is a building of character, which was once a theatre with baths underneath (the baths are still there, but covered over). It is close to the town's only set of traffic lights. The busy and entertaining weekly sale is packed with Victorian, Edwardian, and later furniture, plus a wide range of other goods. Every two months, this general sale is replaced by one of antiques and fine art, which may last two days depending on the number of lots. The firm also holds special sales of toys and games, twice a year in March and October; and other specialist sales are held at irregular intervals. Past categories have included wine and paintings.

Ilkley

BUYER'S PREMIUM: 5%
SALES: *General: weekly on Wed at 10.00am (replaced by antiques sale every two months). Toys: twice a year in Mar and Oct on Sat at 1.30pm. Other specialist: at irregular intervals.*
VIEWING: *General: day prior 10.00am-7.00pm. Antiques: Sat prior 9.30am-12.30pm, Mon and Tue prior 9.30am-4.30pm. All sales: morning of sale from 9.15am.*
REFRESHMENTS: *None available on the premises.*
PARKING: *Ample parking near by.*
STORAGE: Yes
TRANSPORTATION: Yes
SHIPPING: Yes

Leeds

BUYER'S PREMIUM: £1 per lot.
SALES: Monthly on Sat at 3.00pm.
VIEWING: Three weeks prior at Imperial's office, Mon-Fri 10.00am-5.00pm, day of sale at church hall from 10.00am.
REFRESHMENTS: Available on sale day.
PARKING: Own car park.
STORAGE: Yes
TRANSPORTATION: Yes
SHIPPING: Yes

IMPERIAL

3/5 Cross Chapel Street, Headingly. Tel: (0532) 752664

1,500 lots. Imperial holds specialist sales of stamps, postcards, coins, medals, ephemera, cigarette cards and similar collectables at the Methodist church hall, Chapel Street, Leeds 6. They have a well-deserved reputation for these sales and receive postal bids from all over the world — sometimes as much as 95 per cent of the bidding will be by post. The lots are on view for three weeks before the sale. Viewers can just walk in during normal office hours. On the day of the sale lots are on view at the church hall.

Leeds

BUYER'S PREMIUM: 5%
SALES: Twice weekly on Wed and Fri at 10.30am.
VIEWING: Morning of sale from 9.00am.
REFRESHMENTS: Own café.
PARKING: Quarry Hill car park.
STORAGE: Yes
TRANSPORTATION: Yes
SHIPPING: Yes

HARRY WARD & SON

41 Bowman Lane. Tel: (0532) 455425

800-900 lots. This independent family-run business has been established in Leeds for over 100 years. The saleroom can be chaotic at times, because goods to be auctioned are being delivered all the time, sometimes even during a sale. The goods in the Wednesday sale are sold on behalf of loss adjusters and trustees, 'under county court instructions' and in similar circumstances, so the range and type of lots is enormous. There are smaller items such as cameras, jewellery, ornaments and so on, and also brand-new larger articles, such as linen baskets, sofabeds, bathroom suites and garden furniture. A typical sale might have food mixers and vacuum cleaners, office stationery, desks and typewriters, or perhaps new sheepskin coats.

The Friday sale is of general household furniture and effects, and is usually divided into morning and afternoon sessions. This sale often includes the complete contents of a house, which means everything from the cruet set to the bedroom suite, television and garden mower. In the morning smaller items are sold, such as china, glass, silver, paintings, and bric-à-brac. The afternoon is given over to furniture, followed by carpets and rugs at 3.00pm.

WHARF SALEROOM

Canal Wharf, Water Lane. Tel: (0532) 434464

300-400 lots. The saleroom has been converted from an old grain warehouse, and stands on the canal bank. It has a loading bay (unused) directly on to the canal, so people with children need to be cautious. Any auction house which conducts two large sales per week must at times look a little chaotic, and this one is no exception. The company was established in 1923, in a building half a minute away from the present saleroom, and the sale has been a landmark in Leeds ever since. Many elderly people at the present sales proudly boast of having furnished and equipped an entire house from purchases made here.

The Wharf auctions are a wonderful mix of cheap and expensive goods. Valuable lots and antiques are put into the same sale as the rest, so there is never any telling what the value of the next lot will be. An old chest of drawers could be sold for £2 while the very next item could bring a hush over the saleroom as the bids quickly rise to a couple of thousand pounds. The Tuesday evening sale is for smaller goods such as china, glass, silver, jewellery and collector's items. The Wednesday evening sale is for larger items, including electrical goods and furniture, from antique to modern.

Leeds

BUYER'S PREMIUM: *Nil*
SALES: *Twice weekly on Tue (small items) and Wed (large items) at 7.00pm.*
VIEWING: *Day of sale from 4.00pm.*
REFRESHMENTS: *None available on the premises.*
PARKING: *Own car park.*
STORAGE: *No*
TRANSPORTATION: *Yes*
SHIPPING: *Yes*

BASIL KENNY

Thornes Farm, Knotty Lane. Tel: (0484) 603933

300-400 lots. Those looking for an unusual item of furniture or an original present will have fun browsing and bidding here. The auction is four miles out of Huddersfield, about 400 yards off the main road to Wakefield. The saleroom is a marvellous 15th-century cruck barn, which is still part of a farm. Typically the lots will include clocks, pictures, embroidered linen and antiquities of all sorts, and there is usually a large amount of porcelain and good quality Victorian furniture. Vendors are paid in cash on sale day, which adds to the excitement and bustle and gives successful bidders a chance to meet the previous owners of their purchases. Ideally this means that buyers can find out the history of the piece and any little quirks it might have. One buyer, for instance, was told that his newly acquired longcase clock would only work if it was wound up slowly at 4.00am.

Lepton, near Huddersfield

BUYER'S PREMIUM: *Nil*
SALES: *Weekly on Tue at 6.30pm.*
VIEWING: *Day of sale from 4.00pm.*
REFRESHMENTS: *Own café.*
PARKING: *Own car park.*
STORAGE: *Yes*
TRANSPORTATION: *Yes*
SHIPPING: *Yes*

WM SYKES & SON

Old School Room, Sude Hill. Tel: (0484) 683543

500-550 lots. This pleasant little village is about two miles from Holmfirth, and tucked away inside it is an Aladdin's cave

New Mill

BUYER'S PREMIUM: *Nil*
SALES: *Every three weeks on Fri at 2.00pm.*

VIEWING: *Wed prior
7.00pm-9.00pm, Thu prior
2.00pm-9.00pm, day of sale
from 12.00 noon.*
REFRESHMENTS: *None
available on the premises.*
PARKING: *None available
on the premises.*
STORAGE: *Yes*
TRANSPORTATION: *Yes*
SHIPPING: *Yes*

of treasure. Anyone engaged in furnishing or restoring an old house, or looking for an unusual gift, will find plenty to interest them among the doors, old brass taps, jewellery, bygones, cameras, lamps, silver and brass which regularly appear at the sales. In the centre of the old school hall and crammed on to tables, you will find a large selection of ornamental china, glass, brass, kitchen china, cutlery, collectables, toys, and so on, plus jewellery in cabinets. The auctioning starts with linens and then moves on to the large items of second-hand furniture, which are set around the edge of the hall. These range from new self-assembly kits to Victorian, cottage pine, and antique.

Ossett

CHAS W HARRISON & SON

Ashfield House, Illingworth Street. Tel: (0924) 279005

BUYER'S PREMIUM:
2½%
SALES: *Fortnightly on Mon at
10.00am.*
VIEWING: *Sat prior
9.30am-1.30pm.*
REFRESHMENTS: *None
available on the premises.*
PARKING: *Free public car
park adjacent.*
STORAGE: *No*
TRANSPORTATION: *Yes*
SHIPPING: *No*

500-600 lots. It is easy to find the saleroom in Ossett, because of the number of people heading in that direction. Lots are put into the fortnightly Monday sales on instructions from liquidators, the county courts, the Sheriff's office and others, and they can include almost anything. Examples from past sales are the entire contents of a mini supermarket (including the stocks of tinned and packet foods), computer equipment and car accessories, the entire contents of a carpet shop, hi-fi and electrical components, light and sound equipment, sewing machinery, garage accessories and office furniture, and the more usual antiques and general household furniture. Motor vehicles, caravanettes and caravans are always sold at 1.00pm prompt, and can be inspected in the yard.

The company is also responsible for many on-site auctions. These sales occur throughout the year and are sometimes very interesting.

Otley

OTLEY CATTLE MARKET AUCTIONS LTD
See OTLEY CATTLE MARKET AUCTIONS, Bingley, West Yorkshire

Otley

WHARFEDALE FARMERS' AUCTION MART

Leeds Road. Tel: (0943) 462172

BUYER'S PREMIUM: *Nil*
SALES: *Every four weeks on
Thu at 6.00pm.*
VIEWING: *Day of sale from
4.00pm.*

800-1,000 lots. During the sale it is enjoyable to wander around the buildings and hear the talk of old friends meeting — many people attend the auction for an entertaining night out as well as for the bidding. Lots are set out on tables or placed around the shed. Goods of various ages and conditions can be found here: you might find a piece of furniture suffering from woodworm (and, judging by its appearance, only recently removed from the coal shed), well-preserved antiques, pieces of Royal Doulton, or cracked mugs and teapots. There are boxes of assorted cutlery, crockery, milk jugs, tin openers, books, and children's toys and games to sort through. There can also be jewellery, ornaments, silver, beds and bedding, electrical goods and bicycles or parts of bicycles, from just the wheels and frame to the most up-to-date models. In fact the auction is just as its advertisement says: '800 to 1,000 lots of almost everything'. On Mondays the premises are used for busy livestock sales.

REFRESHMENTS: *Own café.*
PARKING: *Own car park.*
STORAGE: *No*
TRANSPORTATION: *Yes*
SHIPPING: *Yes*

DEWSBURY AUCTIONS

629 Huddersfield Road. Tel: (0924) 461210

600-700 lots. The proprietors of the sale are Mr and Mrs William Crow, who also own the retail furniture shop in front of the saleroom. The twice-weekly sales make an entertaining day out, with lots ranging from furniture to police lost property. Children are not encouraged however — they are allowed to attend the yard sales but not the general indoor auctions. The premises are said to be haunted, and a ghost can often be heard walking the full length of the first floor.

The Saturday sale starts with 'deadstock', which means bundles of wood, DIY equipment, lawn mowers, tackle and bicycles. It is followed at 2.30pm by the general sale.

The Tuesday afternoon sale begins at 1.30pm and has a range of general goods. On the last Tuesday of the month the auction is moved to 6.30pm, and becomes a catalogued sale for antiques, good bric-à-brac and quality goods.

Ravensthorpe, near Dewsbury

BUYER'S PREMIUM: *Nil*
SALES: *Twice weekly on Sat at 11.00am and Tue at 1.30pm (6.30pm on last Tue of month for better quality items).*
VIEWING: *Day of sale from 8.30am (12.00 noon for evening sale).*
REFRESHMENTS: *Café across road.*
PARKING: *Queen Street public car park.*
STORAGE: *No*
TRANSPORTATION: *No*
SHIPPING: *No*

Wakefield

BUYER'S PREMIUM: *Nil*
SALES: *Monthly on Wed and Thu at 6.30pm.*
VIEWING: *Day prior 9.00am-5.00pm, day of sale from 9.00am.*
REFRESHMENTS: *None available on the premises.*
PARKING: *Ample near by.*
STORAGE: *Yes*
TRANSPORTATION: *Yes*
SHIPPING: *Yes*

D K TUCKWELL

45 Regent Street, Dellview. Tel: (0924) 377467

300-400 lots. These are evening sales, so many people come along after work, not always to buy, but often to browse. Many just pop in to see what is here each week, so the atmosphere is friendly and noisy. Among the lots there will usually be some antiques, Victorian, Edwardian and modern household furniture, silver, brass, all kinds of kitchen items, and paintings. There may also be period pieces from private house clearances, such as old photograph albums, postcards and cigarette cards. This is a family-run sale and an ideal one for those who are nervous at the thought of bidding. If the auctioneer doesn't at first notice your timidly raised hand, there will be someone in the crowd who will draw his attention to your bid.

Wetherby

BUYER'S PREMIUM: *Nil*
SALES: *On first and third Wed of the month at 5.00pm.*
VIEWING: *Day of sale from 2.30pm.*
REFRESHMENTS: *Own café.*
STORAGE: *Yes*
TRANSPORTATION: *Yes*
SHIPPING: *Yes*

THOMLINSONS

Wetherby Furniture Sale, Victoria Street. Tel: (0937) 582748

700-800 lots. The Wednesday auction is held in the cattle market, which is used on Mondays for livestock sales. This is a busy and popular auction of antique and modern furniture and bric-à-brac. The major part of it is conducted outside,where the general furniture will be — wardrobes, chests of drawers, chairs, dining room and bedroom suites, occasional tables, cookers, refrigerators, carpets and so on. One of the salerooms is used for the auctioning of smaller 'table items' such as china, silver, glass, jewellery, paintings, books, bric-à-brac and collectables. Antiques and better quality items are found in a separate saleroom, and are auctioned in the middle of the sale.

WILTSHIRE

Salisbury

BUYER'S PREMIUM: *10%*
SALES: *Shutter sale: fortnightly on Fri at 9.30am. Antiques: monthly on Thu at 10.00am.*
VIEWING: *Shutter sale: day prior, 10.00am-4.30pm. Antiques: Tue and Wed prior, 10.00am-4.30pm.*
REFRESHMENTS: *None available on the premises.*
PARKING: *Public car park*

WOOLLEY & WALLIS

Salisbury Salerooms, Castle Street. Tel: (0722) 411422

500-700 lots. The fortnightly Friday sales go under the title of 'Shutter sales'. These are sales of all types of household furniture and effects: items such as beds, tables, chairs, various boxes containing bric-à-brac, and sundries. A pine door with leaded panels was offered at one recent sale, together with, among other things, a Victorian oak and brass letterbox, a Chesterfield settee, eight Chippendale design dining chairs, two pairs of skis, a skateboard and a shopping trolley! (The last three items were sold on behalf of the Wiltshire Constabulary.)

Lists with a description of the sale goods are placed strategically around the saleroom.

The monthly Thursday sales are of antique furniture, but there are also specialist categories for Eastern rugs and carpets; English and European ceramics, studio pottery and glass; and textiles, toys and Oriental ceramics and works of art. In addition, there are specialist sales of paintings and watercolours, silver and jewellery, wines, and books and prints.

Established for more than 100 years, these sales have real atmosphere. The auctioneers produce an attractive newspaper on a monthly basis, giving future sale dates, past sale prices and some business gossip.

ALLEN & HARRIS WITH OSMOND TRICKS

The Planks, Old Town. Tel: (0793) 615915

500-600 lots. Swindon became a boom town when the Great Western Railway was built, and today its railway museum and railway village are interesting to visit. Allen & Harris with Osmond Tricks is a member of Royal Life Estates, and there are associated sales in Avon, Somerset, Dorset and Hampshire. The weekly sales at Swindon are of general household items and effects, including some interesting lots. In addition, an 'Antiques and Decorative' sale is held every three months on a Wednesday, and includes good-quality antiques, china and so on.

on other side of the river.
STORAGE: *Yes*
TRANSPORTATION: *Yes*
SHIPPING: *Yes*

Swindon

BUYER'S PREMIUM: *10%*
SALES: *General: weekly on Sat at 10.00am. Antiques and Decorative: every three months on Wed at 10.30am.*
VIEWING: *Both: day prior 10.00am-6.00pm, morning of sale from 9.00am.*
REFRESHMENTS: *Own café.*
PARKING: *The Planks public car park.*
STORAGE: *Yes*
TRANSPORTATION: *Yes*
SHIPPING: *Yes*

· LONDON ·

London is unrivalled for sheer number of auction rooms, and in Sotheby's, Christie's, Phillips and Bonhams it has some of the most famous auctioneers in the world. In these salerooms, auctions take place most days of the week, with a staggering variety of objects coming under the hammer: from sculpture to egg cups, arms and armour, books, works of art, jewellery, silver, costumes and textiles, stamps and many other goods, which may be sold for a few pounds or for millions. Entrance to all auctions is free, and the reputation of the salerooms should not put anyone off visiting them. The sales are exciting, and viewing the lots can be as informative as visiting a museum, because the goods are often of high quality, and may be famous examples of their kind.

As with all the auctions in this book, always check with the saleroom before making any journey, as sale days and viewing times can vary.

BONHAMS

Montpelier Street, SW7.
Tel: (071) 584 9161

Ring the telephone number above for up-to-the-minute sale listings, with dates and times.

BUYER'S PREMIUM: *10%*
SALES: *Most weekdays.*
VIEWING: *Mon 8.45am-7.00pm, Tue to Fri 8.45am-6.00pm, Sun 11.00am-4.00pm.*
UNDERGROUND: *Knightsbridge*
BUSES: *9, 14, 52, 73, 74*

CHRISTIE'S

8 King Street, St James's, SW1.
Tel: (071) 839 9060

BUYER'S PREMIUM: *10%*
SALES: *Most weekdays.*
VIEWING: *Mon to Fri 9.00am-4.00pm, sometimes also on Sun 2.00pm-5.00pm.*
UNDERGROUND: *Green Park*
BUSES: *8, 9, 11, 14, 19, 22, 38*

PHILLIPS

101 New Bond Street, W1.
Tel: (071) 629 6602

For details of all the week's sales, telephone the 24-hour recorded information service on (071) 495 6912. Affiliated to Phillips is Glendining's, tel: (071) 493 2445, which specialises exclusively in sales of coins and medals, usually on Wednesdays.

BUYER'S PREMIUM: *10%*
SALES: *Most weekdays.*
VIEWING: *Tue, Wed and Fri 8.30am-5.00pm, Mon 8.30am-7.30pm, Sun 2.00pm-5.00pm.*
UNDERGROUND: *Bond Street*
BUSES: *7, 8, 10, 12, 25, 73, 88*

SOTHEBY'S

34/35 New Bond Street, W1.
Tel: (071) 493 8080

For details of forthcoming auctions, ring the 24-hour recorded information line on (071) 409 2686.

BUYER'S PREMIUM: *15% (items up to £30,000); 10% (items above £30,000).*
SALES: *Most weekdays.*
VIEWING: *Mon to Fri 9.00am-4.30pm.*
UNDERGROUND: *Bond Street/Green Park.*
BUSES: *7, 8, 10, 25, 73, 503*

OTHER LONDON AUCTIONS

In addition to the four famous auction houses, there are many others with regular general and specialist sales. A selection is given here, with details of other London salerooms that are owned by Bonham's, Christie's and Phillips.

Contrary to what you might expect, prices in London auctions are not necessarily higher than those in country sales. The tradition of shopping at a local auction has rather been lost in London, and fewer private buyers attend the sales. Settings may not always be as attractive as those of sales held regionally, but London auctions have their own atmosphere and can be just as rewarding for buyers and browsers alike. All the following London auctions offer advice on storage, transportation and shipping.

ACADEMY AUCTIONEERS & VALUERS

Northcote House, Northcote Avenue, Ealing.
Tel: (081) 579 7466

1,000-1,500 lots. This is a good local auction with a high standard of lots. People who buy at West End auctions can often be found searching around these salerooms. The monthly auction is held over two days, and is devoted to works of art, miscellaneous items, Oriental and European ceramics and glass, jewellery, silver and silver plate, pictures and clocks. Furniture, carpets and rugs are also sold.

W5

BUYER'S PREMIUM: *10%*
SALES: *Monthly on Tue at 12.00 noon and Wed at 4.00pm.*
VIEWING: *Mon 2.00pm-8.00pm, morning of sale from 9.30am.*
UNDERGROUND/BR: *Ealing Broadway*
BUSES: *65, 207*

BLOOMSBURY BOOK AUCTIONS

3/4 Hardwick Street (off Rosebery Avenue).
Tel: (071) 833 2636 and (071) 636 1945

400-500 lots. These are specialist fortnightly sales of printed books, including antiquarian books, manuscripts, prints and drawings, first and limited editions, periodicals, autograph letters, music, maps and atlases. Two specialist sales of Hebrew books are also held each year.

EC1

BUYER'S PREMIUM: *10%*
SALES: *Fortnightly on Thu at 1.00pm, 11.00am and 2.00pm.*
VIEWING: *Tue prior 9.30am- 5.30pm, Wed prior 9.30am-8.00pm, morning of sale from 9.30am.*
UNDERGROUND: *Angel*
BUSES: *19, 38, 153, 171, 171A*

BONHAMS CHELSEA

65/69 Lots Road. Tel: (071) 351 7111

200-400 lots. The wide variety of auctions held here includes an excellent weekly Tuesday sale of general household furniture and furnishings. Other categories follow a regular pattern and include silver and silver plate, jewellery, porcelain, works of art, pictures, prints, frames, tribal art, books, garden

SW10

BUYER'S PREMIUM: *10%*
SALES: *Most days of the year at 10.30am, 11.00am or 2.00pm.*
VIEWING: *Mon 8.45am-7.00pm, Tue to Fri 8.45am-4.30pm, Sun*

11.00am-4.00pm.
UNDERGROUND: *Fulham Broadway*
BUSES: *11, 22*

furniture and architectural fittings. There are also collectors' sales, which include cameras, scientific and musical instruments, juke boxes, gaming machines, toys and dolls, militaria, textiles, fountain pens and cigarette cards. There is a public car park next to the saleroom.

SW7

BUYER'S PREMIUM: 10%
SALES: *Most weekdays at 10.30am, 12.30pm, 2.00pm or 5.00pm (times vary).*
VIEWING: *Mon 9.00am-7.30pm, Tue to Fri 9.00am-5.00pm, Sat 10.00am-1.00pm.*
UNDERGROUND: *South Kensington*
BUSES: *14, 30, 45, 49, 74, C3*

CHRISTIE'S SOUTH KENSINGTON

85 Old Brompton Road. Tel: (071) 581 7611

2,000-3,000 lots. A variety of auctions is held every week, and there are often two sales a day. Categories include British, Continental and Oriental ceramics, British, Impressionist and Continental paintings, watercolours, Old Masters and prints, printed books, jewellery, silver and plate, carpets, musical instruments and wine. In addition, there are well-attended sales of furniture. The collector's department also holds sales of toys, dolls and teddy bears; models; cameras; scientific instruments; ephemera; railway, motoring and maritime art and literature; and mechanical music.

N1

BUYER'S PREMIUM: 10%
SALES: *Weekly on Mon at 6.30pm.*
VIEWING: *Sat and Sun prior 11.00am-3.00pm and day of sale from 10.00am.*
UNDERGROUND: *Angel*
BUSES: *73, 38*

CRITERION SALEROOMS

53 Essex Road, Islington. Tel: (071) 359 5707

250-350 lots. The auctions held by Criterion Salerooms have increased in popularity since they were founded over three years ago by Mark Dunscombe and Graham Richards. Among the lots are general antiques and decorative items, such as furniture, pictures and ceramics. The goods are set out in a spacious room and prices range from £20 to several thousands. According to Mr Dunscombe, 'prices for antiques are often lower than those of modern equivalents. Buying at auction is a method of obtaining items of quality, which may well be cheaper than most alternatives and which will also have investment value.' The auctioneers have a policy of giving free valuations and use the 'paddle' bidding system.

SW15

BUYER'S PREMIUM:
10% (jewellery 5%)
SALES: *General: fortnightly on Sat at 9.30am. Police Lost Property: monthly on Thu at*

DOWELL LLOYD & CO

118 Putney Bridge Road. Tel: (081) 788 7777

500-1,000 lots. The saleroom covers over 16,000sq ft, and a series of interesting sales is held here. Every other Saturday sees a sale of general household furniture, effects and miscellaneous items, including pictures, carpets, porcelain, domestic and ornamental china, and so on, with many antiques. Once a month, there is a Thursday sale devoted to 'Police Lost Property', which can include almost anything but usually features radios, tools, and always plenty of bicycles. Finally a sale of jewellery is held every Tuesday.

9.30am. Jewellery: weekly on Tue at 9.30am (or Wed, if Mon is a Bank Holiday). **VIEWING:** *General: day prior 9.30am-7.00pm. Police Lost Property: day prior, 9.30am-6.00pm. Jewellery: day prior 9.30am-4.00pm.* **UNDERGROUND:** *Putney Bridge or East Putney* **BUSES:** *14, 22, 74, 220*

FORREST & CO

79/85 Cobbold Road (off Cann Hall Road), Leytonstone. Tel: (081) 534 2931

400-500 lots. The saleroom is close to the grass and trees of Wanstead Flats. Forrest & Co are official auctioneers for various county courts, liquidators, and Customs and Excise, so the sales often include the most amazing mix of goods. There might be food, soft drinks and alcohol, cars and forklift trucks, televisions, stereo recorders and computers, brand new men's, women's, and children's clothing, Pierre Cardin stockings and disposable nappies, full-size snooker tables, garage or office equipment, antique furniture or brand new suites, plus other household furniture and general effects. A truly comprehensive auction.

E11

BUYER'S PREMIUM: *10%* **SALES:** *Fortnightly on Thu at 11.00am.* **VIEWING:** *Day prior 10.00am-5.00pm.* **BRITISH RAIL:** *Forest Gate* **UNDERGROUND:** *Leyton* **BUSES:** *58, 162*

THE GENERAL AUCTION COMPANY

63/64 Garratt Lane, Wandsworth. Tel: (081) 870 3909

1,000-1,500 lots. This auction will not suit those looking for antiques or specialist items, although it does include a great mixture of lots. As the saleroom is small, it is advisable to make full use of the viewing; once an auction is in progress it is very difficult, if not imposssible, to walk around due to the crowds. The proceedings begin in the back room, where 60 or more bicycles are sold off by order of the Metropolitan Police. Some of these may be new. At 12.00 noon there is a general sale of ladders, tools, televisions, stereos, word processors, pictures, jewellery, household equipment, clothing ... the lots are numerous, and many are sold on behalf of liquidators. Even motor vehicles are sold, usually at 2.00pm.

SW18

BUYER'S PREMIUM: *10%* **SALES:** *Weekly on Mon at 11.00am.* **VIEWING:** *Sat prior 10.00am-3.00pm.* **UNDERGROUND:** *East Putney (not near)* **BUSES:** *220, 44*

WC2

BUYER'S PREMIUM: *10%*
SALES: *Ten or twelve a year, usually on Wed, Thu and Fri (or on Fri only) at 2.00pm (no auctions in Jul and Aug).*
VIEWING: *Three or four days prior to sale 10.00am-4.00pm, morning of sale 10.00am-12.00 noon.*
UNDERGROUND: *Charing Cross or Covent Garden.*
BUSES: *1, 1A, 4, 56, 9, 11, 13, 15, 23, 68, 77, 77A, 155, 170*

SW17

BUYER'S PREMIUM: *10%*
SALES: *Fortnightly on Mon at 10.00am.*
VIEWING: *Sat prior 10.00am-4.00pm.*

STANLEY GIBBONS AUCTIONS LTD

399 Strand. Tel: (071) 836 8444

300-2,000 lots. Stanley Gibbons is one of the most famous names in stamps, and has been serving collectors worldwide since 1856. A vast range of specialist auctions is held here, and virtually all the world's top collectors are notified of them. Many of the sales are over two or three days. The comfortable saleroom is situated above 'The World's Largest Stamp Shop' (opposite the Savoy Hotel), which is open six days a week and contains an unrivalled stock of stamps. Staff are always on hand to answer any queries; the auction department is open on weekdays only.

R F GREASBY

211 Longley Road, Tooting Graveney. Tel: (081) 672 2972

1,000-1,100 lots. Many of the lots at these sales are auctioned on behalf of London Transport, or by order of the courts, so the range of goods is enormous. Sometimes the whole contents of a shop or a factory are sold, in which case lots are displayed outside for viewing. Almost anything can be bought — from watches and cameras to cases of alcohol, Sony Walkmans, cars and children's games. Each lot may consist of an assortment of items. One lot recently consisted of a 'bundle of eight umbrellas, two walking sticks, a folding walking seat, three gents walking-length umbrellas, one golf and two garden shades'. As these sales are very crowded it is advisable to make full use of the Saturday viewing.

UNDERGROUND:
Tooting Broadway
BUSES: *44, 280, 127*

HATTON GARDEN AUCTIONS

EC1

70 Hatton Garden. Tel: (071) 242 6452

100 lots. This is a small, friendly lunchtime auction set in the heart of London's diamond and jewellery trading district. The sale is of antique and modern jewellery and silver, and may include domestic and ornamental china. Selling is often over within an hour, so be there on time.

BUYER'S PREMIUM: *10%*
SALES: *Fortnightly on Thu at 1.30pm.*
VIEWING: *Mon to Fri 9.00am-4.00pm.*
UNDERGROUND:
Chancery Lane or Farringdon
BUSES: *22, 501, 28*

HORNSEY AUCTIONS LTD

N8

54/56 High Street, Hornsey. Tel: (081) 341 1156

500-600 lots. The saleroom fronts directly on to the High Street and displays many of its lots in the window. The auctions here are pleasant and good-humoured, and certainly will make anyone new to auction-going feel at ease. Every Wednesday evening there is a general sale, which often becomes so full that the crowd spills out into the street. As the auctioning is fast, you must have a clear idea what you want and how much you can afford to bid.

BUYER'S PREMIUM: *10%*
SALES: *Weekly on Wed at 6.30pm.*
VIEWING: *Tue prior 5.00pm-8.00pm and day of sale from 10.00am.*
UNDERGROUND:
Turnpike Lane (not near)
BRITISH RAIL: *Hornsey*
BUSES: *144A, W2*

LOTS ROAD GALLERIES

SW10

71 Lots Road. Tel: (071) 351 7771

500-600 lots. Lots Road in Chelsea is an excellent place for auction enthusiasts. This lively saleroom is close to Bonham's premises, and a trip to both makes an interesting day out. Lots Road Galleries are under the proprietorship of Roger and Patricia Ross. They are pleasant, busy salerooms, with an enthusiastic and lively auctioneer and helpful staff. Every Monday there are two sales: one of contemporary and

BUYER'S PREMIUM:
12.5%
SALES: *Weekly on Mon at 3.00pm and 6.00pm.*
VIEWING: *Fri prior 10.00am-4.00pm, Sat prior 10.00am-1.00pm and Sun prior 10.00am-4.00pm. Also morning of sale from 10.00am.*

REFRESHMENTS: *Own café.*
PARKING: *None available on the premises.*
STORAGE: *Yes*
TRANSPORTATION: *Yes*
SHIPPING: *Yes*

reproduction furnishings at 3.00pm, the other of antique furniture, carpets, silver, pictures and *objets d'art* at 6.00pm. Harassed parents may leave their children in the crèche downstairs during the Sunday viewing.

SE10

BUYER'S PREMIUM: *10%*
SALES: *Weekly on Thu at 10.00am.*
VIEWING: *Day prior 2.00pm-8.00pm and morning of sale from 9.00am.*
BRITISH RAIL: *Greenwich.*
BUSES: *108B, 177, 180, 188, 199, 286*

MOORE'S AUCTION ROOMS

217/219 Greenwich High Road. Tel: (081) 858 7848
300-400 lots. The saleroom is in the heart of Greenwich, in easy reach of the Royal Observatory. The auctions are well attended and typically include china, glass, furniture and effects, paintings, prints, porcelain, silver, jewellery, books, postcards, stamps, coins and so on. Most of the lots are from the Victorian, Georgian and Regency periods, and there will very seldom be anything dating from after 1940.

W2

BUYER'S PREMIUM: *10%*
SALES: *General: weekly on Mon at 10.00am. Collector's: weekly on Tue at 11.00am.*
VIEWING: *Both: Thu 5.15pm-7.30pm, Fri 9.00am-5.00pm, Sun 2.00pm-5.00pm, day of sale from 9.00am. Collector's: also on Mon prior, 9.00am-5.00pm.*
UNDERGROUND: *Bayswater/Queensway.*
BUSES: *12, 94*

PHILLIPS WEST TWO

10 Salem Road. Tel: (071) 229 9090
500-600 lots. Salem Road is behind Whiteley's shopping precinct in Bayswater. There are two sales each week: a general auction of antique and modern furniture and porcelain on Monday, and a collector's sale on Tuesday, which alternates between pictures and collector's items.

REGENT'S OF FINCHLEY

N3

202 Regent's Park Road, Finchley.
Tel: (081) 343 1605 and 343 3736

400-500 lots. This weekly Sunday afternoon sale in Finchley consists mainly of good-quality antiques. Porcelain, glass, decorative items, furniture, paintings and jewellery of all kinds are on show in the crowded saleroom before the serious business begins. Some of the lots sold recently have included a bottle of vintage champagne, Victorian lantern slides and a collection of historical newspapers. As the 'paddle' bidding system operates, be sure to register on arrival to avoid possible disappointment later.

BUYER'S PREMIUM: *10%*
SALES: *Weekly on Sun at 2.30pm.*
VIEWING: *Fri prior 10.00am-6.00pm and day of sale.*
UNDERGROUND: *Finchley Central*
BUSES: *13, 82, 143, 266, 362*

ROSEBERY FINE ART LTD

SE19

The Old Railway Booking Hall, Crystal Palace Station Road.
Tel: (081) 778 4024

600-800 lots. The saleroom is close to the Crystal Palace National Sports Centre, and is part of the British Rail station. Sales are held fortnightly on a Tuesday, alternating between antique and general sales. Both are well attended.

BUYER'S PREMIUM: *10%*
SALES: *Fortnightly on Tue at 12.00 noon.*
VIEWING: *Sun prior 2.30pm-5.30pm, and Mon prior, 10.00am-8.00pm.*
BRITISH RAIL: *Crystal Palace*
BUSES: *12, 35, 40, 42, 68, 171, 176, 184, P3*

SOUTHGATE AUCTION ROOMS

N14

55 High Street, Southgate. Tel: (081) 886 7888

500-600 lots. This is a weekly sale of general household furniture and effects, with miscellaneous items of all periods from modern to antique. The first 200 lots are usually smaller items of silver and gold, jewellery, watches, brooches and the like. They will usually be followed by beds, lounge suites, tables, electrical goods, linen, paintings, china and so on. This is strictly a cash only sale, and no cheques or credit cards will be accepted. Successful bidders must make at least part payment in cash before leaving the saleroom, and have until 5.30pm on the following day to complete the transaction.

BUYER'S PREMIUM: *10%*
SALES: *Weekly on Mon at 6.30pm.*
VIEWING: *Sat prior 9.00am-12.00 noon and day of sale from 9.00am.*
UNDERGROUND: *Southgate*
BUSES: *121, 298, W6 and W9*

CLWYD

Corwen

FARMERS' MARTS (R G JONES) LTD
See FARMERS' MARTS (R G JONES) LTD,
Dolgellau, Gwynedd

Mold

DODDS PROPERTY WORLD

Victoria Auction Galleries, Chester Street. Tel: (0352) 752552

BUYER'S PREMIUM: *Nil*
SALES: *General: weekly on Wed at 10.30am (except on antique and carpet sale days). Antiques: at irregular intervals on Wed at 5.45pm. Carpets: quarterly on first Wed of Dec, Mar, Jun and Sep at 6.00pm.*
VIEWING: *Day prior 9.30am-1.00pm, 2.00pm-4.30pm. Carpet sales: also 5.30pm-7.30pm.*
REFRESHMENTS: *Refreshments adjacent.*
PARKING: *Own car park.*
STORAGE: *Yes*
TRANSPORTATION: *Yes*
SHIPPING: *Yes*

300-500 lots. Bidders must plan their time at this busy, friendly sale. The main sale begins at 10.30am, and while it is still going on, the sale of outside effects begins at 1.00pm outside. This part of the sale could include cars, trailers, bicycles, building equipment, wheelbarrows and other gardening equipment, chainsaws, timber and so on. It usually goes on for an hour or so. Meanwhile, the main part of the auction begins with electrical goods such as washing machines, dishwashers, spin dryers, cookers and fridges, followed by table items including china (both domestic and ornamental), glass, lamps, books, clocks and so on. The sale finishes with various items of furniture of all grades — some of the pieces may be antiques while others will be almost new. The goods vary in quality, which adds to the interest. Bankruptcy stock is sold without reserves.

Periodically throughout the year there are evening sales of antiques, which replace the normal Wednesday sale and are at no regular intervals.

Special carpet sales are held quarterly on the first Wednesday of December, March, June and September. These offer good bargains in new Axminster and Wilton carpets.

Wrexham

SETH HUGHES & SON

12/15 George's Crescent. Tel: (0978) 265123

BUYER'S PREMIUM: *Nil*
SALES: *Thu at 1.00pm (includes antiques and fine art sale about every three months).*
VIEWING: *Day prior 9.00am-1.00pm, 2.00pm-5.00pm.*
REFRESHMENTS: *None available on the premises.*
PARKING: *Multi-storey car park near by.*
STORAGE: *Yes*
TRANSPORTATION: *Yes*
SHIPPING: *Yes*

250-300 lots. Seth Hughes & Son was established in 1875 and has enjoyed three generations of family involvement. The large showroom-type window in front of the saleroom displays articles to be sold in forthcoming sales. Lots are displayed to their best advantage, cleaned and polished and set out with plenty of room to view, and the proprietors, Mr and Mrs Dan Evans, are on hand to offer advice if needed.

The general sale follows no particular order, and usually contains a wide selection of household furniture and effects, ornaments, bric-à-brac and so on. About every three months an antiques and fine art sale replaces the general sale, with articles such as silver, porcelain, furniture and paintings sold in groups.

DYFED

EVANS BROS

See EVANS BROS, Llanybydder, Dyfed

TERRY THOMAS & CO

St Mary Auction Mart, 2 St Mary Street. Tel: (0267) 236502

500 lots. This sale is held fortnightly in the oldest saleroom in South Wales. It tends to have items of Welsh interest, with Welsh bygones among the lots, which include general household furniture, antiques, craft work, electrical goods, bicycles and so on. The lots are not sold in categories: first a table might be sold, then the box of china underneath it, followed by a painting, a Royal Doulton tea cup, a set of six dessert plates, a pottery vase, an assortment of coins and military badges, a dinner service, a swivel desk chair and a chest of drawers. This helps to keep buyers in the saleroom for the duration of the auction. Periodically the general sale is replaced by a special antiques sale, but selling and viewing times remain the same.

BUYER'S PREMIUM: *Nil*
SALES: *Fortnightly on Wed at 10.30am (includes periodic antiques sales).*
VIEWING: *Mon and Tue prior 9.00am-5.00pm, morning of sale from 9.00am.*
REFRESHMENTS: *Available.*
PARKING: *Town centre car park.*
STORAGE: *Yes*
TRANSPORTATION: *Yes*
SHIPPING: *Yes*

CASTLE AUCTION MART

Unit 4, Station Road. Tel: (0554) 891256

400-500 lots. This is a family-run auction, whose reputation has increased year by year since it was begun by Leslie and Jean Treharne in the mid 1980s. According to Mrs Treharne, 'Local auctions are not only a good way to buy but also an excellent way of making money out of goods cluttering up your home. We're as happy to sell one item for a vendor as a dozen.' The saleroom is centrally located by the railway station, and there is generally a comprehensive range of good and lesser quality furniture and effects. In addition there are often antiques, jewellery, silver, paintings, stamps, coins, cars, vans, boats, caravans and motorbikes. Vehicles are sometimes sold outside, but there are large double doors at the rear of the saleroom to allow the odd single vehicle inside.

BUYER'S PREMIUM: *10%*
SALES: *Weekly on Mon at 10.30am.*
VIEWING: *Day of sale from 9.00am.*
REFRESHMENTS: *Day of sale only.*
PARKING: *Own car park.*
STORAGE: *Yes*
TRANSPORTATION: *Yes*
SHIPPING: *Yes*

G H EVANS & COMPANY

The Auction Sales Centre, Market Place. Tel: (0834) 811151

1,100-1,200 lots. There is a good friendly atmosphere about this sale. Newcomers are greeted with a welcoming nod, and locals seem genuinely pleased to see strangers taking an interest in their auction. The sale is generally full of good bargains, with electrical goods, china, teacups, dinner services,

BUYER'S PREMIUM: *Nil*
SALES: *Fortnightly on second and last Sat of month at 10.30am (general) and 3.30pm (motor vehicles).*
VIEWING: *Day prior 4.00pm-7.00pm, morning of*

sale from 9.00am.
REFRESHMENTS: *Own café.*
PARKING: *Own car park.*
STORAGE: *Yes*
TRANSPORTATION: *Yes*
SHIPPING: *Yes*

teapots, glass, beautiful old-fashioned ornaments (the type that grandmother had above her fireplace), collectables, craft items, and gardening, farming and kitchen bygones, in addition to all sorts of furniture in a wide range of periods.

The sale of motor vehicles and trailers begins outside at 3.30pm. This part of the sale brings in a new set of potential buyers. Once a year, usually in April or May but always on a Saturday at 12.00 noon, there is a special sale of boats, boating equipment and boat paraphernalia. This sale has gained a good reputation over the years, and buyers from all over Wales and England regularly attend.

Lampeter

EVANS BROS

See EVANS BROS, Llanybydder, Dyfed

Llanbadarn Fawr, near Aberystwyth

BUYER'S PREMIUM: *Nil*
SALES: *About every three weeks (approx 18 sales a year) on Wed at 10.00am (includes an antiques sale about every three months, starting at 10.30am).*
VIEWING: *Day prior 4.00pm-6.00pm, day of sale from 9.00am.*
REFRESHMENTS: *Not available on the premises but available near by.*
PARKING: *Own car parking area.*
STORAGE: *Yes*
TRANSPORTATION: *Yes*
SHIPPING: *Yes*

JOHN WATKINS & CO

The Church Hall. Tel: (0970) 612464

400-600 lots. Llanbadarn Fawr is a pleasant old village just inland of Aberystwyth on the A44. The church hall is hired for the three days it takes to prepare a one-day sale. Mrs E A Watkins, who runs the company with her husband from offices at 22 Terrace Road, Aberystwyth, shares the auctioneering with David Evans. The auction will start with perhaps 200-250 lots of 'smalls' which are set out on the table in the front of the hall. These might include whole or part tea and dinner sets, teapots, jugs, plates and dishes of all sorts, silver cutlery, sets of silver spoons and silver-mounted brushes, brass candlesticks and horse brasses, and innumerable miscellaneous items — ornaments, books, photograph albums and so on. The sale also includes good quality furniture and general household effects of all types and values. House clearances sometimes result in television sets, washing machines, dishwashers and the like appearing in the sale.

Every three months or so the general sale is replaced by an antiques sale, which starts at 10.30am and includes 400-600 lots thought to be too good to put into the usual sale.

Llandeilo

BUYER'S PREMIUM: *General: nil. Antiques sales: 10%*
SALES: *General: every third week on Sat at 10.00am. Antiques: at irregular intervals on Tue, times vary.*

JONES & LLEWELYN

The Llandeilo Auction Rooms, 21 New Road. Tel: (0558) 823430

500-600 lots. Jones & Llewelyn started business in this historic little market town more than 40 years ago. Over the years their auctions have become one of the town's attractions, and many visitors put them high up on their list of activities. General Saturday sales are held every three weeks and are conducted on both floors of the old building, starting with 'smalls', such as brass, china, glass, porcelain and pictures. These are followed by period and other furniture. The proceedings are finished off with a sale of electrical goods, kitchenalia and shipping furniture — 1930s and 1940s pieces, which may be particularly good value for money.

Antique and specialist sales of all kinds of goods, from toys to Oriental carpets, are also held from time to time. There are no fixed months for these sales, and they may be during the day or evening. The auctioneers often sell toys, Swansea porcelain and Welsh oak furniture. These auctions attract buyers from all over Wales and England.

EVANS BROS

Mart Offices. Tel: (0570) 480444
Evans Bros hold interesting country auctions in various parts of Wales, selling a wide range of antique and modern furniture, china, glass, pictures, bygones, local craft items and so on. The main sale locations are the Mart Offices in Llanybydder (800-1,000 lots); the Memorial Hall, South Road, Aberaeron (300-400 lots); and Victorian Hall, Bryn Road, Lampeter (up to 600-700 lots).

Llanybydder

VIEWING: *General: day prior 2.00pm-6.00pm, morning of sale. Antiques: Sun and Mon prior 2.00pm-6.00pm, morning of sale.*
REFRESHMENTS: *Own café.*
PARKING: *Own car park.*
STORAGE: *Yes*
TRANSPORTATION: *Yes*
SHIPPING: *Yes*

BUYER'S PREMIUM: *Nil*
SALES: *Llanybydder: monthly on Sat at 10.30am. Aberaeron: monthly on Wed at 11.00am. Lampeter: every eight to ten weeks on Sat at 11.00am.*
VIEWING: *Llanybydder: day prior 9.00am-12.00 noon, 1.00pm-4.30pm. Aberaeron: day prior 3.00pm-6.00pm. All: day of sale from 9.00am.*
REFRESHMENTS: *Llanybydder: van selling snacks. Aberaeron and Lampeter: own cafés.*
PARKING: *Llanybydder: own large car park. Aberaeron and Lampeter: none available on the premises.*
STORAGE: *All: no*
TRANSPORTATION: *All: yes*
SHIPPING: *All: yes*

GWENT

HALIFAX PROPERTY SERVICES LTD (MONTAGUE HARRIS & CO)

The Market Hall. Tel: (0873) 855141
600-700 lots. The Market Hall is something of a landmark in Abergavenny, and its green spire is visible from all parts of town. On Fridays it is the home of a very busy produce market, and it is also the location of the Cornerstone Rennie general sale, which has similar lots. A typical sale will include general household furniture and effects, china, porcelain, motor parts

Abergavenny

BUYER'S PREMIUM: *Nil*
SALES: *Abergavenny: monthly on last Thu of month at 10.30am. Brecon: about eight times a year on Wed at 12.00 noon (includes some antiques sales).*
VIEWING: *Abergavenny: day prior 4.30pm-6.00pm,*

morning of sale. Brecon: day prior 12.00 noon-6.00pm, morning of sale. Both: morning of sale.
REFRESHMENTS: Abergavenny: own café in hall.
PARKING: Abergavenny: at rear of hall. Brecon: hotel car park.
STORAGE: Yes
TRANSPORTATION: Yes
SHIPPING: Yes

and a wide range of miscellaneous items. Vendors can bring in their goods on the previous Wednesday, when the busy preparation begins. Larger items are sold in an annexe known as The Square. Buyers must pay for every purchase in cash, at the completion of each successful bid.

The firm also has an office at the Bulwark Chambers in Brecon, tel: (0874) 3452, which holds eight or so interesting auctions a year at the Wellington Hotel in Brecon. There are no set months to these sales but they always occur on a Wednesday, and include around five general and three antiques sales, with some 300-400 lots in each. Worth enquiring about if you are in the area.

Abergavenny

RENNIE'S

The Market Hall. Tel: (0873) 859331

800-1,000 lots. The Market Hall is in the main street in Abergavenny, and has a distinctive green spire. It is also the home of a Friday produce market and of the Halifax Property Services' general sale. Rennie's sale takes place on the third Thursday of the month (except in January), and includes general household furniture and effects, such as sitting room, dining room and bedroom suites, garden equipment, electrical goods, televisions, china, crockery, bicycles and so on.

BUYER'S PREMIUM: Nil
SALES: Abergavenny: monthly (except Jan) on third Thu of month at 10.30am. Monmouth: several times a year on Thu at 11.00am.
VIEWING: Abergavenny: morning of sale from 9.00am. Monmouth: Tue prior 12.00 noon-4.00pm, morning of sale from 9.00am (closed day prior).
REFRESHMENTS: Abergavenny: café in hall. Monmouth: none available on the premises.
PARKING: Abergavenny: at rear of hall. Monmouth: none available on the premises.
STORAGE: Both: yes
TRANSPORTATION: Both: yes
SHIPPING: Both: yes

The same firm also holds a sale of antiques and fine art several times a year at the Nelson Rooms, Glendower Street, Monmouth. This will usually have some 700-800 lots of furniture, porcelain, pottery, glassware, silver and silver plate, paintings (usually a lot — perhaps as many as 100), clocks, old musical instruments and other good quality articles. The saleroom is on two floors, with the main selling area upstairs. This sale goes on all day and finishes at around 6.00pm.

Monmouth

RENNIE'S
See RENNIE'S, Abergavenny, Gwent

Newport

GRAHAM DANIEL TRINITY AUCTIONS

Trinity Hall, Temple Street. Tel: (0633) 251906

300-400 lots. This sale has the friendly atmosphere of a traditional country auction, even though it is a comparative newcomer, having been in existence for only a few years. Mr Daniel worked in the haulage business in Bristol before arriving in this busy town and setting up the auction with his wife Audrey, who deals with the mound of clerical work.

The sale includes a wide range of household furniture and effects, plus miscellaneous items of all types and values. Lesser

BUYER'S PREMIUM: 10%
SALES: Weekly on Thu at 10.00am.
VIEWING: Daily 9.30am-5.30pm.
REFRESHMENTS: Own café.
PARKING: Car park directly opposite.
STORAGE: Yes

quality items are sold at the start and end of the sale, sandwiching the better goods, but within those categories, lots are sold in the order in which they arrive at the saleroom. A fridge-freezer could follow an Art Nouveau stripped and waxed bookcase and a Victorian pine kitchen table, and be followed in turn by a pine dresser. There is generally a good deal of jewellery, such as gold pendants, Victorian gold diamond set rings, antique brooches and the like. Graham Daniel is official auctioneer to the local constabulary, so expect among other things a great number of bicycles.

The saleroom is open every day of the week for viewing, and members of the public are welcome to pop in, which many do on their way home from work or during a shopping expedition. A friendly and informal atmosphere prevails, which should set at ease those new to auctions.

TRANSPORTATION: *Yes*
SHIPPING: *Yes*

GWYNEDD

MORGAN EVANS & CO LTD

The Anglesey Chattel Auctioneers, The Saleroom, Cattle Market, Gaerwen. Tel: (0248) 421582

400-500 lots. The Cattle Market is on a loop road at the back of the village, about quarter of a mile off the A5 Menai Bridge-Holyhead road. There are three-weekly livestock sales here, and motor auctions on the first and third Thursday of the month. There is also an annual Christmas sale of dressed poultry.

Morgan Evans & Co Ltd's fortnightly general sale is held in Saleroom 2, and includes general household furniture and effects. The firm also holds antique and fine art sales about 17 times a year in Saleroom 1, which is heated, with seating for up to 150 and a good amplification system. This saleroom also has an adjoining licensed bar and small restaurant. Typical lots might include Victorian chests, 'grandmother' clocks, Edwardian jardinières, pine tables, large mirrors, jewellery, paintings and prints, and china, plus collectables — old wirelesses, old toys, militaria, Art Nouveau, Art Deco and the like. There is always a lunch break between 1.00pm and 1.30pm on antiques sale days (not for the general sale).

Anglesey

BUYER'S PREMIUM: *Nil*
SALES: *General: fortnightly on Thu at 10.30am. Antiques: at irregular intervals about 17 times a year on Thu at 10.30am. Motor auctions: first and third Thu of the month at 6.00pm. Dressed poultry: annual on last Wed before Christmas at 11.00am.*
VIEWING: *General: Mon prior 2.00pm-5.00pm. Antiques: Mon prior 9.30am-12.30pm, 2.00pm-6.00pm, morning of sale from 9.00am. Motor auctions: day of sale from 4.00pm. Dressed poultry: morning of sale from 9.00am.*
REFRESHMENTS: *Licensed bar and restaurant.*
PARKING: *Own car park.*
STORAGE: *Yes*
TRANSPORTATION: *Yes*
SHIPPING: *Yes*

FARMERS' MARTS (R G JONES) LTD
See FARMERS' MARTS (R G JONES)LTD, Dolgellau, Gwynedd

Bala

Dolgellau

BUYER'S PREMIUM: *Nil*
SALES: *Dolgellau: monthly on last Thu of the month at 11.00am. Bala and Corwen: on average every two months on Wed at 12.00 noon.*
VIEWING: *Dolgellau: day prior 1.30pm-6.00pm. Bala and Corwen: morning of sale from 9.00am.*
REFRESHMENTS: *All: own cafés.*
PARKING: *All: own car parks.*
STORAGE: *All: by arrangement.*
TRANSPORTATION: *All: yes*
SHIPPING: *All: no*

FARMERS' MARTS (R G JONES) LTD

Smithfield Street. Tel: (0341) 422334

500-600 lots. This is an excellent country sale, offering a wide variety of general household goods and other effects, among them a number of good quality antiques. The sales have local colour and are often attended by old friends. One gentleman I spoke to said that he had been regularly attending the sale for many years, but could not remember the last time he had actually bid for something.

The same company also holds, on average every two months, auctions in the cattle markets at Bala, tel: (0678) 520490 and Corwen, tel: (0490) 412102. They are equally enjoyable to attend.

Llandudno

BUYER'S PREMIUM: *Nil*
SALES: *Weekly on Wed at 10.00am.*
VIEWING: *Day prior 9.00am-1.00pm, 2.00pm-5.30pm.*
REFRESHMENTS: *None available on the premises.*
PARKING: *Car park opposite.*
STORAGE: *No*
TRANSPORTATION: *Yes*
SHIPPING: *Yes*

BALL & BOYD

The Auction Rooms, Back Madoc Street.
Tel: (0492) 877239 and 877230

800-900 lots. The saleroom is centrally located near the Town Hall and opposite one of the largest car parks in Llandudno. The car park is used by the auctioneers for the sale of cars, caravans, trailers, boats and other vehicles. These are sold off during the afternoon when the auctioneer, followed by those who are interested, nips across from the saleroom — an additional touch of interest in an already entertaining and busy sale.

It starts at 10.00am with the goods which are laid out on the tables: bric-à-brac, odd pieces of china, ornaments, lamps, electric fires, gas fires and so on. When these have all gone, the tables themselves are sold. After that there is a lunch break, usually from around 1.00pm to 2.00pm. The sale of furniture starts at 2.00pm and ranges from antique to nearly new, in all sorts of conditions: bedroom, lounge and dining suites, chairs, settees, dressers, pine, mahogany and so on. At 3.00pm, it is time for the sale of vehicles mentioned above, and at the same time, inside, the sale of better quality 'smalls' (small items) begins.

In the meantime, at odd times throughout the day, about 200-250 unnumbered lots are sold. These are called 'A' lots and are all small items — jewellery, silver, mechanical toys and other articles which could be slipped into an unscrupulous pocket if displayed.

This is a family-run business, established for over 36 years. The sale is usually interesting, and there are some good bargains to be had. Add to that the fact that Llandudno is an attractive resort, and you have an excellent day out for the family.

MID GLAMORGAN

PONTYPRIDD SALEROOMS & AUCTION MART

39 Cefn Lane, Glyncoch. Tel: (0443) 403764

400-450 lots. Mr V J Hobbs, the proprietor of this sale, worked for the previous owner of the firm for over 30 years, and 'liked the business so much he bought the company'. The sale includes household furniture and effects, china, glass, pictures, jewellery, bicycles, electrical goods, bygones, craft items and many other goods, mostly of middling value but with some antiques. The lots are attractively displayed — ornaments and crockery, for example, will be neatly set out on one of the dressers or sideboards in the sale. Cheaper items are sold first, followed by jewellery, which is always sold at 12.30pm. At the completion of the jewellery sale and up until 2.00pm, the better quality items will be sold. After those, the sale finishes as it started, with cheaper lots.

Pontypridd

BUYER'S PREMIUM: 10%
SALES: *Fortnightly on Wed at 10.00am.*
VIEWING: *Day prior 2.00pm-7.00pm, morning of sale from 9.00am.*
REFRESHMENTS: *Drinks only.*
PARKING: *Own car park planned.*
STORAGE: *No*
TRANSPORTATION: *Yes*
SHIPPING: *No*

POWYS

HALIFAX PROPERTY SERVICES LTD (MONTAGUE HARRIS & CO)

See HALIFAX PROPERTY SERVICES LTD, Abergavenny, Gwent

Brecon

F H SUNDERLAND & CO

Coliseum House, Wheat Street. Tel: (0874) 622261

300-400 lots. F H Sunderland & Co hold monthly sales of special antiques at Turners Saleroom in Free Street, Brecon. They are well worth attending as they usually offer bargains in all areas of antiques — paintings, china, silver, collectables and so on.

Brecon

BUYER'S PREMIUM: *Nil*
SALES: *Monthly on Thu at 12.00 noon.*
VIEWING: *Day prior 10.00am-5.00pm and morning of sale from 9.00am.*
REFRESHMENTS: *Available.*
PARKING: *Ample near by.*
STORAGE: *Yes*
TRANSPORTATION: *Yes*
SHIPPING: *Yes*

Welshpool

BUYER'S PREMIUM: Nil
SALES: Fortnightly on Fri at 10.00am.
VIEWING: Day prior 1.30pm-5.00pm.
REFRESHMENTS: None available on the premises.
PARKING: Town centre car park.
STORAGE: Yes
TRANSPORTATION: Yes
SHIPPING: Yes

HARRY RAY & CO

The Town Hall. Tel: (0938) 552555

500-600 lots. The Town Hall is in the centre of Welshpool, and with its large clock on top it is difficult to miss. This sale is all a country auction should be: not just a good place to pick up a piece of furniture or garden tool, but also a place where local people meet friends and exchange gossip. The sale is informal, friendly, and offers the possibility of picking up all sorts of goods. It starts with items such as ladders, wheelbarrows, lesser-value furniture and even parts of furniture, gardening tools and equipment, building equipment, perhaps the odd door or window frame or bath suite, and boxes of odd bits. If a lot fails to attract a bidder it is added to the next lot, so one successful bid could find you the proud owner of a box of assorted household items, an old wardrobe, a car tyre and a couple of suitcases full of books.

There are three auctioneers to keep things moving, and the sale soon proceeds to china, ornaments and other better quality small articles. Also in this section is furniture of a wide range of types and values — modern, old or reproduction, pine, chests of drawers, suites for the bedroom, living room and dining room, chairs and so on, with bargains to be had in all departments.

SOUTH GLAMORGAN

Cardiff

BUYER'S PREMIUM: 10%
SALES: On Wed at 11.00am, usually twice monthly.
VIEWING: Mon prior, 9.00am-5.00pm, Tue prior, 9.00am-6.30pm. Antiques also Sat prior, 9.00am-12.00 noon. Morning of sale from 9.00am.
REFRESHMENTS: None available on the premises.
PARKING: Available at Westgate Street public car park near by.
STORAGE: Yes
TRANSPORTATION: Yes
SHIPPING: Yes

PHILLIPS

10 Westgate Street. Tel: (0222) 396453

300-400 lots. This saleroom, which is just down the road from Cardiff castle, holds sales specialising as much as possible in country furniture, particularly Welsh country furniture and other items with Welsh connections, including porcelain. Here there are usually two auctions a month: one of Victorian and later furniture and effects, and one of antiques, at which furniture, silver, ceramics, and paintings are sold among other things. The sale of Victorian and later furniture and effects usually consists of good quality, inexpensive lots.

WEST GLAMORGAN

THOMAS, EDWARDS & ANTHONY MORRIS

The Croft Salerooms, Croft Road. Tel: (0639) 639541

300-400 lots. This is one of those Welsh sales where everyone who enters the saleroom is acknowledged, whether known or not, and where someone can usually tell you about prices fetched in previous sales. Many of the articles are desirable, and many have clearly come from houses where they have been well looked after: the furniture has the deep shine that comes from generations of caring owners, and the ornaments and vases are often old and interesting, if not necessarily 'antique'. Brass items abound, and as a rule fetch good prices: your neighbour in the saleroom may tut-tut the hammer price of a set of brass fire irons, but it is likely to be only a fraction of what it might fetch in a shop.

In contrast to the general sale, the same firm holds catering equipment sales every six months, which are interesting for the private buyer as well as for catering professionals. This latter sale takes place five minutes' walk away from Croft Road, in the cattle market. Periodic sales are also held at the cattle market on behalf of the Sherriff's Office and bailiffs (distrained equipment), and the police (lost property). These sales are also held on a Tuesday.

Neath

BUYER'S PREMIUM: *Nil*
SALES: *General: about every six weeks on Tue at 1.00pm. Catering equipment: every six months on Tue at 11.00am. Distrained/Lost Property: irregular intervals on Tue, usually at 11.00am.*
VIEWING: *General and Distrained/Lost Property: day of sale from 9.00am. Catering equipment: day prior 2.00pm-4.30pm, morning of sale from 9.00am.*
REFRESHMENTS: *Available at the cattle market.*
PARKING: *Available at the Cattle Market.*
STORAGE: *Yes*
TRANSPORTATION: *Yes*
SHIPPING: *Yes*

· SCOTLAND ·

BORDERS

Peebles

LAWRIE & SYMINGTON

Peebles Market, South Parks, Caledonian Road.
Tel: (0721) 20280

700-800 lots. This is a good general sale, held in the market which from July to February is also busy with sheep sales. At times during the auction there will be two sales taking place. Selling starts at 10.30am in one of the sheds, when the bidding for perhaps as many as 500 lots of smaller items gets under way. This sale often carries on past 1.00pm, which is when the general sale of furniture begins. The latter usually has 300 lots or so, set out in two sheds.

BUYER'S PREMIUM: *Nil*
SALES: *Monthly on Wed at 10.30am.*
VIEWING: *Sun prior 12.00 noon-4.00pm, Tue prior 9.00am-4.00pm.*
REFRESHMENTS: *Snacks available on the premises.*
PARKING: *Ample near by.*
STORAGE: *Yes*
TRANSPORTATION: *Yes*
SHIPPING: *Yes*

DUMFRIES & GALLOWAY

Annan

THOMSON, RODDICK & LAURIE

See THOMSON, RODDICK & LAURIE, Dumfries, Dumfries & Galloway

Castle Douglas

GELSTON AUCTION SERVICE

St Andrew Street. Tel: (0556) 3591

300-500 lots. Regular attenders of auctions are surprised by very little. The sight of a full-sized stuffed elephant being put up for sale, a conservatory or even an aeroplane, is taken for granted. What does surprise newcomers to this beautiful little Scottish town is the presence of a Canadian auctioneer. Bert Peacock has been running the auction with his wife for over 10 years, having once owned a similar business in Canada.

This is really a very friendly and light-hearted sale with jokes flowing to and fro between the public and Mr Peacock. Indeed it is suspected that many of the people come solely for an evening's entertainment. The sale contains a wide range of general furniture and household effects, as well as antiques. The saleroom is just by the town's only cinema, so it is easy to find. Another way is to follow the general direction of the crowd from about 5.30pm on Fridays.

BUYER'S PREMIUM: *Nil*
SALES: *Weekly on Fri at 6.00pm.*
VIEWING: *Day of sale from 1.00pm.*
REFRESHMENTS: *None available on the premises.*
PARKING: *Free parking on street.*
STORAGE: *No*
TRANSPORTATION: *Yes*
SHIPPING: *Yes*

JOHN GIBSON & SON

2 Irving Street. Tel: (0387) 53670

300-400 lots. Anyone interested in Robbie Burns will need no introduction to Dumfries. The poet is buried in St Michael's churchyard, and Burns' House, Burns' Street, was his home from 1793 until his death in 1796. It is now a museum.

John Gibson & Son is not quite so old, but has been a well-respected firm since 1820. It is an efficient, family-run business which regularly draws buyers and vendors from all over Dumfries and Galloway. The saleroom, at one time a church, is a popular weekly hunting ground for bargain seekers and browsers, packed as it is with a good selection of modern, antique and reproduction furniture, as well as bric-à-brac, Victoriana, ornaments, china and so on. Any cars or boats, or other large objects, are sold in the garage, which is near the saleroom. There is always a break for lunch between 12.00 noon and 12.30pm. The morning sale contains smaller, cheap household goods such as kettles, pots, pans and small furniture (including dining chairs and coffee tables), while the afternoon session is for the larger items.

Dumfries

BUYER'S PREMIUM: *Nil*
SALES: *Weekly on Thu at 10.30am.*
VIEWING: *Day prior 10.00am-4.00pm.*
REFRESHMENTS: *None available on the premises.*
PARKING: *Public car park in Queensbury Street.*
STORAGE: *Yes*
TRANSPORTATION: *Yes*
SHIPPING: *Yes*

THOMSON, RODDICK & LAURIE

60 Whitesands. Tel: (0387) 55366

400-500 lots. Thomson, Roddick & Laurie, established in 1880, conduct an extensive range of auctions, including specialist collector's sales, in Scotland and in Carlisle, Wigton and Brampton in England. In Dumfries they hold four major catalogued sales a year at Easterbrook Hall and Crichton Royal Hospital, Bankend Road. Included are 18th- and 19th-century furniture, silver, metalware, ceramics, glass, jewellery, pictures, prints, collector's items and good reproduction furniture.

In addition there are two major sales of shotguns, firearms and accessories, usually in July and December. Each of these sales covers two evenings, and also includes militaria and sporting prints (Monday) and fishing rods, reels and tackle (Tuesday).

The same firm holds regular and well-attended monthly sales of general household furniture and effects and various miscellaneous items at 20 Murray Street, Annan, tel: (0461) 202575.

Dumfries

BUYER'S PREMIUM: *10%*
SALES: *Antiques: four times a year on Tue at 10.30am. Shotguns etc.: twice a year, usually in Jul and Dec, on Mon and Tue at 6.00pm. General (Annan): monthly on Tue at 10.30am.*
VIEWING: *Antiques and shotguns etc.: day prior 4.30pm-7.45pm, morning of sale from 9.00am, except fishing tackle: day of sale 4.30pm-5.45pm. General (Annan): day prior 2.00pm-4.00pm, morning of sale from 9.00am.*
REFRESHMENTS: *Own cafés.*
PARKING: *Own car parks.*
STORAGE: *Yes*
TRANSPORTATION: *Yes*
SHIPPING: *Yes*

FIFE

Dunfermline

BUYER'S PREMIUM: 10%
SALES: *Weekly on Tue at
11.00am (including antiques
sale every three months).*
VIEWING: *Sat
8.30am-12.30pm, Mon
8.30am-5.30pm, morning of
sale.*
REFRESHMENTS: *Café on
ground floor.*
PARKING: *Own car park.*
STORAGE: *Yes*
TRANSPORTATION: *Yes*
SHIPPING: *Yes*

DUNFERMLINE AUCTION CO (FIFE) LTD

Loch Street, Townhill. Tel: (0383) 727434

300-500 lots. Dunfermline is most famous for the magnificent abbey church in which Robert the Bruce was buried. The weekly auction is held in a compact first-floor saleroom with a café on the ground floor. Many a happy hour can be passed browsing through the large variety of furniture, household goods, bric-à-brac and collector's items gathered here. The auctioneer's stand is usually surrounded by a large and noisy crowd exchanging banter even when the auctioneer is selling. Some of the crowd come from nearby offices and shops; others make a visit to the auction part of their weekly shopping expedition. For range and variety the auction is difficult to beat. Many of the lots come as part of complete house clearances, and there will usually be ornamental and domestic china, brass, paintings, pictures, silver, jewellery and furniture of all types. A special sale of antiques is held in place of the general sale once every three months.

Ladybank

BUYER'S PREMIUM: 10%
SALES: *Weekly on Thu at
6.00pm.*
VIEWING: *Day prior
4.00pm-9.00pm, day of sale all
day.*
REFRESHMENTS: *Usually
a café van outside.*
PARKING: *On street.*
STORAGE: *Yes*
TRANSPORTATION: *Yes*
SHIPPING: *Yes*

LADYBANK AUCTION MARKET

Kinloch Street. Tel: (0337) 30488

500-600 lots. Ladybank is small and the saleroom is easy to find. It stands in Kinloch Street, which runs parallel to the main street. This is an interesting sale which always includes antiques as well as general household furniture and effects — sitting room, dining room and bedroom suites, tables and chairs, garden equipment, cookers, refrigerators and other electrical equipment, bicycles, crockery, parts of or whole tea and dinner sets, ornaments, silver and paintings. Amongst these there may be watercolours, many of them showing local scenes.

Leven

BUYER'S PREMIUM: 10%
SALES: *Fortnightly on Thu at
11.00am (includes specialist
antique and fine art sale every
two months).*
VIEWING: *General: day
prior 2.00pm-5.00pm.
Antiques and fine art: day prior
10.00am-5.00pm.*

ROBERT DOWIE

Station Road. Tel: (0333) 423438

600-800 lots. Leven is a beautiful, clean Scottish town at the western end of the bay of Largo. It is a favourite resort with Edinburgh folk, particularly for fishing and for golf at the Lundin links. It is a shock in this setting to enter the saleroom and hear the very English accent of Mr Vernon J Prangnell-O'Neill as he conducts the auction, although he too is Scottish. Mr Prangnell-O'Neill used to work for Phillips Fine

Art Auctioneers, and has worked in the auction and antique business all over Europe and North America. He runs a very pleasant and friendly auction of general household furniture and effects. The lots are of particularly high quality, even the electrical goods, and there are beautiful china tea and dinner sets, bedroom and dining room suites and so on. Every second month the sale becomes a specialist antique and fine art sale, including jewellery, silver, glass, 18th-century and Edwardian furniture, Persian rugs and the like.

REFRESHMENTS: *Own tea bar with home baking.*
PARKING: *Free parking on street.*
STORAGE: Yes
TRANSPORTATION: Yes
SHIPPING: Yes

MACGREGOR AUCTIONS

St Andrews

56 Largo Road. Tel: (0334) 72431

500-700 lots. St Andrews is best known for its university, and for golf. The Royal and Ancient Club here is the recognised authority on the game, which has spread throughout the world from Scotland. There is a golf club factory near to MacGregor Auctions. Since Mrs S Edwards took over the firm in 1983, it has enjoyed increasing popularity not only locally, but with buyers from all over Britain and, indeed, abroad. The excellent fortnightly Friday sale includes a wide selection of general household furniture and effects in addition to china, silver, crockery, cutlery, ornaments and the like.

Every three months the Friday sale becomes an antiques and fine art sale, which often includes articles withdrawn from the general sale because of their quality. Due to the amount of work involved in preparing this sale (setting out, listing and preparing the catalogue), the previous fortnightly general sale is often cancelled. Telephone before travelling any distance, to check that an auction is taking place.

BUYER'S PREMIUM: 5%
SALES: *Fortnightly on Fri at 10.30am (includes antiques and fine art sale every three months).*
VIEWING: *Thu prior 9.00am-7.00pm.*
REFRESHMENTS: *None available on the premises.*
PARKING: *Own car park.*
STORAGE: Yes
TRANSPORTATION: Yes
SHIPPING: Yes

MacGregor Auctions

56 Largo Road, St Andrews, Fife   Tel: (0334) 72431

Excellent fortnightly sales on Friday at 10.30 am offer a wide selection of general household furniture and effects, also china, silver, crockery, cutlery and ornaments. Own car park.
Managed by Mrs S Edwards since 1983.

GRAMPIAN

Aberdeen

ABERDEEN & NORTHERN MARTS LTD

Furniture Sale Hall, Cattofield Terrace. Tel: (0224) 482323

300-400 lots. The saleroom is in the Kittybrewster area of the town. The very day after the weekly sale, vendors start to bring in lots for the next week's sale. Items might include lounge, bedroom and dining room suites, dressers, card tables, veneered fold-over tables, overmantle mirrors, occasional tables, plated cutlery, dinner canteens, silver, china and glass, ornaments, paintings, Scottish bygones and local crafts, kitchenalia, books, puzzles, children's toys, gardening tools and equipment, electrical goods of all kinds including televisions, and bicycles.

As in most good Scottish sales, almost anything could come up for auction. The goods will vary greatly in condition and value, and a careful search through the lots will generally reveal plenty of bargains. This is not an auction to frighten the new auction-goer, as the saleroom is full of humour and friendliness.

BUYER'S PREMIUM: *Nil*
SALES: *Weekly on Tue at 12.00 noon.*
VIEWING: *Day of sale from 9.00am.*
REFRESHMENTS: *Own café.*
PARKING: *Own car park.*
STORAGE: *Yes*
TRANSPORTATION: *Yes*
SHIPPING: *Yes*

Aberdeen

JOHN MILNE

9 North Silver Street. Tel: (0224) 639336

400-500 lots. Aberdeen is an ancient cathedral and university city, a popular seaside resort and a port busy with fishing and North Sea oil activity. This auction has been part of the Aberdeen scene for over 125 years, and has been run by the Milne family for the whole of that time. It is presently under the stewardship of Robert Milne. Being one of the largest auctions in North East Scotland, it regularly draws in buyers and vendors from all over the region, and much further afield.

Number 9 North Silver Street is a traditional Aberdeen granite building in the centre of the city. Inside there are two large salerooms, one used for the current week's sale and the other being prepared for the next. There is usually a good mix of antique, modern and reproduction furniture and household effects, in addition to silver, pottery, jewellery, glass, pictures and the like.
The sale starts with these small items, and at 12.00 noon moves on to the sale of furniture, finishing at around 2.00pm depending on the number of lots.

BUYER'S PREMIUM: *10%*
SALES: *Weekly on Wed at 10.00am.*
VIEWING: *Day prior 10.00am-7.00pm.*
REFRESHMENTS: *Wine bar and café in basement.*
PARKING: *Metered parking in street or Golden Square Centre car park.*
STORAGE: *No*
TRANSPORTATION: *Yes*
SHIPPING: *Yes*

CLUNY AUCTION

8/9 Cluny Terrace. Tel: (0542) 33318

400-500 lots. Buckie is an attractive little fishing port with an interesting harbour. The saleroom is just a little way from the main street, past the Thistle Bar. It is a stone and mortar building which Mrs B Ferguson, who runs the auction with her husband, remembers being a saleroom when she was a little girl. It later had several other uses, until Mr and Mrs Ferguson saw the need for a country auction in this part of Scotland and started up in the late 1980s. The sale has increased in popularity each year since. Mrs Ferguson claims to have been surprised at first by the number of young folk setting up home who come to buy. 'But when you consider the quality of the older furniture and compare it with what can be bought new today for the same money, it shows how many young couples have an eye for a good bargain.' The saleroom is L-shaped and the rostrum is surrounded by tables containing interesting lots of smaller items, such as all kinds of china, porcelain, jewellery and so on. Furniture is placed around the room, and some at the back is wheeled forward on trolleys for selling. Three or four times a year the sale becomes a special sale of antiques, but selling and viewing times remain the same.

HIGHLAND

FRASERS AUCTION ROOMS

15 Tulloch Street. Tel: (0349) 63252

300-400 lots. Dingwall is a small town with a beautiful old church and cross. It is a little off the tourist map, and is perhaps best known by outsiders for its proximity to Strathpeffer, just over five miles away at the foot of Ben Wyvis, in some of the finest scenery in the Highlands. Those taking the trouble to find their way to Frasers Auction Rooms are in for a treat, because there is a real flavour of Scotland here. Perhaps as many as two-thirds to three-quarters of the people who attend the sale turn up week after week. Many of them attend not only to buy, but also to meet up with friends, catch up with local gossip and chat over local events. As is the case with most Scottish sales, there is always a surprising and interesting range of articles, including furniture of all types, conditions and values. There will also be interesting local bygones, crockery, jewellery, silver, books and so on.

Buckie

BUYER'S PREMIUM: *Nil*
SALES: *Fortnightly on Thu at 6.15pm (including antiques sale three or four times a year).*
VIEWING: *Day prior 2.00pm-8.00pm, morning of sale from 10.00am.*
REFRESHMENTS: *Own light refreshments.*
PARKING: *Ample space near by.*
STORAGE: *Yes*
TRANSPORTATION: *Yes*
SHIPPING: *Yes*

Dingwall

BUYER'S PREMIUM: *Nil*
SALES: *Weekly on Fri at 4.30pm.*
VIEWING: *Day prior 8.30am-4.30pm, day of sale.*
REFRESHMENTS: *None available on the premises.*
PARKING: *Own car park.*
STORAGE: *No*
TRANSPORTATION: *No*
SHIPPING: *No*

LOTHIAN

Edinburgh

BUYER'S PREMIUM:
10%. Lane Sales: nil.
SALES: *Weekly on Sat (two sales), Tue, Wed (two sales) and Fri at 11.00am.*
VIEWING: *Sat sales: day prior 9.00am-5.00pm. Lane Sales: morning of sale from 9.30am.*
REFRESHMENTS: *Available near by.*
PARKING: *None available on the premises.*
STORAGE: *No*
TRANSPORTATION: *Yes*
SHIPPING: *Yes*

LYON & TURNBULL

51 George Street. Tel: (031) 225 4627

120-150 lots. This must be one of the busiest salerooms in Scotland, with six sales taking place each week, most of the year. The Saturday auction is the main event, comprising modern household furniture, electrical goods, paintings, china and general items. There is also a separate auction of antiques at the same time. If you are in Edinburgh on a Tuesday, Wednesday or Friday, try to attend one of the 'Lane Sales', held in the open air at the rear of the premises. These are very entertaining and there is a wide range of lots, encompassing household furniture, kitchenalia, carpets and so on. Wednesday is a particularly busy day, because in addition to the Lane Sale, an auction of 1920s and 1930s furniture, china and bric-à-brac takes place inside the saleroom. All the sales are a browser's paradise, and should be part of any bargain hunter's trip to Edinburgh.

Edinburgh

BUYER'S PREMIUM: *10%*
SALES: *General: fortnightly on Thu at 11.00am. Specialist: weekly on Fri at 11.00am (sometimes more often). Golfing memorabilia: annually in Jul on a Tue (times and locations vary).*
VIEWING: *General: day prior 9.30am-4.30pm. Specialist: two days prior, 9.30am-4.30pm. Golfing memorabilia: day prior, 9.30am-4.30pm.*
REFRESHMENTS: *None available on the premises.*
PARKING: *None available on the premises.*
STORAGE: *Yes*
TRANSPORTATION: *Yes*
SHIPPING: *Yes*

PHILLIPS SCOTLAND

65 George Street. Tel: (031) 225 2266

100-200 lots. Phillips have two salerooms in Scotland, in which over 140 sales are held every year. In the large Edinburgh saleroom, which is diagonally opposite the Assembly Rooms, there are fortnightly general sales of furniture, pictures, ceramics and so on, with a weekly specialist sale on Friday (occasionally on other days as well). The specialist sales come under headings such as 'Antique Furniture, Clocks, Rugs, Works of Art', 'Oil Paintings', 'Silver', 'Oriental Ceramics and Works of Art', 'Ceramics and Glass', 'Watercolours and Prints', 'Jewellery', 'Books', 'Textiles, Dolls and Costumes', 'Decorative Arts', and 'Arms and Armour'.

An annual specialist sale of golfing memorabilia is arranged by Phillips at either their Edinburgh or Glasgow Salerooms to coincide with the Open Golf Championship.

Edinburgh

BUYER'S PREMIUM: *10%*
SALES: *Fortnightly on Wed at 6.00pm.*
VIEWING: *Mon and Tue*

SCOTTISH HOUSE AUCTIONS

5a Unit, 8c Loaning Road, Restalrigg. Tel: (031) 659 6634

400-450 lots. This busy and popular saleroom is in the suburb of Leith, the port of Edinburgh. A landmark to look out for is the Meadowbank Sports Centre. The fortnightly sale attracts a great deal of attention, all the more so during the summer when the Edinburgh Festival is on. In addition to the usual array of household effects there is often brand new furniture, which makes the sale particularly popular with young people setting up home. A considerable amount of office furniture and equipment is usually available here too, as are older furniture and antiques.

LESLIE & LESLIE

77 Market Street. Tel: (062082) 2241

400-500 lots. Haddington is a well-preserved town about 17 miles from Edinburgh on the A1. Market Street is between the two main streets in the town centre. Here Leslie & Leslie hold large, busy sales at quarterly intervals. Each sale lasts three days — Tuesday, Wednesday and Thursday — and begins at 10.30am each day. Lots include modern and shipping furniture, household effects such as electrical goods, mirrors, china and bric-à-brac. There could be some antiques, but these will probably be in need of attention. The best items are kept for the special antiques sale on the following Thursday. This sale will include paintings, china, silver, brass and so on.

ORKNEY

KIRKWALL AUCTION MART

44 Junction Road. Tel: (0856) 2520

250-300 lots. Kirkwall is the largest town in the Orkneys. It has narrow streets and houses with thick walls and small windows, suited to a stormy climate and perhaps reflecting Norwegian origins. Kirkwall Auction Mart is close to the landmark of St Magnus Cathedral. Like most Scottish sales, especially those in remoter places, this one has a special atmosphere which is, no doubt, due to the local way of life. Everybody is acknowledged on entering the saleroom, whether known or not, with a brief nod of the head by those present. Most of the buyers seem to know each other, and occasionally a bidder will shake his head and shout, 'Oh, let old William have it!' There is no particular order of sale. Lots come up as they have been brought in by vendors, and there is a wide range of furniture, often locally crafted. There will also be jewellery, china, silver and miscellaneous items from a myriad of different backgrounds.

prior 11.00am-8.00pm, morning of sale from 11.00am.
REFRESHMENTS: *None available on the premises.*
PARKING: *Ample parking near by.*
STORAGE: *Yes*
TRANSPORTATION: *Yes*
SHIPPING: *Yes*

Haddington

BUYER'S PREMIUM: *Nil*
SALES: *Quarterly. General: Tue, Wed and Thu at 10.30am. Antiques: following Thu at 1.30pm.*
VIEWING: *General: morning of sale from 8.00am. Antiques: day prior 2.00pm-4.00pm, 7.00pm-9.00pm.*
REFRESHMENTS: *None available on the premises.*
PARKING: *Ample parking near by.*
STORAGE: *Yes*
TRANSPORTATION: *Yes*
SHIPPING: *Yes*

Kirkwall

BUYER'S PREMIUM: *Nil*
SALES: *Monthly on Wed at 10.30am.*
VIEWING: *Day prior 2.00pm-5.00pm, morning of sale.*
REFRESHMENTS: *Own café.*
PARKING: *Car park directly opposite.*
STORAGE: *Yes*
TRANSPORTATION: *Yes*
SHIPPING: *Yes*

Stromness

BUYER'S PREMIUM: *Nil*
SALES: *Monthly on Fri at 10.30am.*
VIEWING: *Day prior 2.00pm-5.00pm.*
REFRESHMENTS: *None available on the premises.*
PARKING: *Own car park.*
STORAGE: *No*
TRANSPORTATION: *Yes*
SHIPPING: *No*

WEST MAINLAND MART LTD

Ferry Road. Tel: (0856) 850288

300-400 lots. Ferry Road is known to some as North End Road, but once you are in Stromness it is difficult to miss the market complex. A livestock market is held on Wednesday in the same saleroom as the monthly Friday sale of general household furniture and effects, and a good deal of activity goes into clearing the place up. As at Kirkwall, the sale generally includes several items of good quality furniture. Smaller items, although not perhaps antiques, are often old and lovingly cared for by generations of owners. Typical items include vases, ornaments, china, silver and photograph frames with original pictures. Good buys are often to be had; like the Kirkwall sale, this one seems to be looked forward to as a social event as much as anything else.

SHETLAND

Lerwick

BUYER'S PREMIUM: *Nil*
SALES: *Dec to Jun, monthly on Wed at 2.00pm.*
VIEWING: *Day prior, 6.00pm-8.00pm.*
REFRESHMENTS: *None available on the premises.*
PARKING: *Own car park.*
STORAGE: *No*
TRANSPORTATION: *Yes*
SHIPPING: *Yes*

SHETLAND MARTS LTD

33 South Road. Tel: (0595) 2369

200-300 lots. Lerwick is a busy, cosmopolitan town and its capacious harbour is often crowded with vessels from many nations. Because the auctioneers are preoccupied with livestock sales during the second half of the year, the general auctions are only held from December through to June.

The sales are attended mostly by locals, perhaps because visitors come to these pleasant islands for reasons other than buying at auction. Some remarkable, rare and interesting pieces turn up at these auctions from time to time, perhaps for this very reason.

STRATHCLYDE

Ayr

BUYER'S PREMIUM: *10%*
SALES: *Weekly on Thu at 10.30am.*
VIEWING: *Day prior 8.00am-5.00pm.*
REFRESHMENTS: *None available on the premises.*

THOMAS R CALLAN

22 Smith Street. Tel: (0292) 267681

700-750 lots. Smith Street is in the centre of Ayr, opposite the railway station and next to Burns Statue Square. Burns was born just two miles way in Alloway, in a small thatched cottage which can be visited. Thomas R Callan's saleroom has been a landmark in Ayr since it was started by the father of the present owner, Mr D Callan, in 1933, and recently a third-generation Callan became involved in the firm. The sale contains a wide and interesting range of goods of all values and in all conditions, including antiques.

Selling starts with small items such as boxes of bric-à-brac, pots and pans, silver, tea and dinner sets, glass, jewellery, ornaments, collectables and the like. There is a break between roughly 1.30pm and 2.00pm, when the sale of furniture begins, and the sale ends at around 4.45pm. Every six weeks or so the general sale becomes a sale of antiques. Sales and viewing times remain the same.

PARKING: Own car park.
STORAGE: Yes
TRANSPORTATION: Yes
SHIPPING: Yes

SANDGATE AUCTIONS

Ayr

58a Sandgate and 42 Fort Street. Tel: (0292) 263263
600-800 lots. The saleroom has two addresses, one for the back, one for the front, but both give access. The building itself is an old church. The main sale area is very large, and the auctioneer, Mr W D Grant, stands in what used to be the pulpit. There are three main sales. Two are held in the saleroom and the other in one of the local hotels.

The weekly Tuesday sale is of general household furniture and effects, and includes china, kitchenalia, electrical goods and the like. On the first Friday of the month there is a sale of what they call 'semi antiques', which usually means items from 1860 to 1960. There are usually around 300-400 lots in this sale, which includes inexpensive jewellery and Victorian bric-à-brac.

Every two or three months, usually on a Friday, there is an antiques and fine art sale, which takes place in a local hotel — not always the same one. There may be as many as 800 lots in this sale.

BUYER'S PREMIUM: 10%
SALES: General: weekly on Tue at 10.00am. Semi antiques: monthly on first Fri of month at 10.00am. Antiques and fine art: every two/three months on Fri at 10.00am.
VIEWING: General: day prior 10.00am-4.30pm. Semi antiques: day prior 10.00am-4.30pm. Antiques and fine art: day prior 10.00am-8.00pm.
REFRESHMENTS: None available on the premises, but available near by.
PARKING: Public car park near by.
STORAGE: No
TRANSPORTATION: Yes
SHIPPING: Yes

BIGGAR AUCTION MARKET

Biggar

South Back Road. Tel: (0899) 20002
600-700 lots. Perhaps the reason why many Scottish auctions are so colourful is that the general furniture and household effects sales often take place in the same buildings as the livestock sales. The lots are set out in the rings and byres which are still used to show and sell livestock. The same auctioneer stands in the box from which he sells cattle, and the buyers have the same determined look as their farming counterparts. Here the small items are sold from within the ring first.

Boxes containing varied miscellaneous items are set out on tables, with the better quality items set apart in their own display. The sale moves to the back for electrical goods such as

BUYER'S PREMIUM: Nil
SALES: Monthly on Mon at 10.30am.
VIEWING: Fri prior 4.00pm-7.00pm and morning of sale.
REFRESHMENTS: Drinks machine.
PARKING: On street (no meters).
STORAGE: Yes
TRANSPORTATION: Yes
SHIPPING: No

vacuum cleaners, and for bicycles, linen and carpets. The sale of larger items of furniture begins at 2.30pm after a break.

Dunoon

BUYER'S PREMIUM: 10%
SALES: Monthly on Sat at 11.00am.
VIEWING: Fri prior 2.00pm-7.00pm.
REFRESHMENTS: Own café.
PARKING: Street parking permitted.
STORAGE: No
TRANSPORTATION: Yes
SHIPPING: No

WILLIAM CUNNINGHAM

Bencorrum. Tel: (0369) 4102

400-500 lots. Dunoon is the western side of the Firth of Clyde. One of the most pleasant ways to make the journey is to take a boat. There are ferries from Gourock to Dunoon, or from Ashton to Hunter's Quay near by. There are plenty of small items: silver spoons and sets of cutlery, or jewellery and china. Dinner and tea services are also popular, and fun items such as a 1920s biscuit barrel or a Victorian novelty teapot will create a lot of interest. Fine items of furniture, longcase clocks, sideboards and pictures can be found, but will always attract keen bidding.

Glasgow

BUYER'S PREMIUM: 10%
SALES: Usually two or three times monthly on Tue, Wed, and Thu at 11.00am (may vary).
VIEWING: Two days prior 10.00am-4.00pm or 7.00pm.
REFRESHMENTS: None available on the premises.
PARKING: Sauchiehall Street car park.
STORAGE: Yes
TRANSPORTATION: Yes
SHIPPING: Yes

CHRISTIE'S SCOTLAND

164/166 Bath Street. Tel: (041) 332 8134

200-600 lots. Do not be intimidated by the famous name. You will not be landed with a multi-million pound Van Gogh painting by an inadvertant twitch of the eye. The prices reached here can be quite modest, and in some of the sales a few lots will sell for under £50. Even if you don't expect to buy, a visit enables you to see valuable paintings and rare antiques that you might otherwise never get close to.

The frequency of sales varies. There are usually two or more specialist sales a month, and categories include pictures, furniture and works of art, carpets, clocks and scientific instruments, silver, jewellery, Wemyss ware, golfing, fishing and football memorabilia, whisky, 20th-century Scottish paintings and much more besides.

Glasgow

BUYER'S PREMIUM: Nil
SALES: Jewellery: weekly on Tue and Thu at 1.30pm.
Furniture, electrical goods or jewellery: weekly on Wed at 1.30pm.
VIEWING: Day of sale 9.00am-12.00 noon.
REFRESHMENTS: None available on the premises.
PARKING: King Street car park.
STORAGE: Yes
TRANSPORTATION: Yes
SHIPPING: No

ARTHUR E COLLINS & SON, LTD

114 Trongate. Tel: (041) 552 0489

100-250 lots. Trongate is a busy thoroughfare which has changed a great deal since the days when Burns, Sir Walter Scott, Adam Smith and other great men walked down it. The old Glasgow Cross, at the junction of Trongate, Saltmarket and Gallowgate, is perhaps the best landmark to look for. The saleroom is comparatively small, and easily filled by the 100 or 120 people who attend most sales.

The weekly Tuesday and Thursday sales contain around 200-250 lots of jewellery, which are unredeemed pawnbroker pledges. The quality varies considerably, and lots will fetch anything from £5 to £1,500. The weekly Wednesday sale is usually of 150-180 lots of antique, modern or reproduction furniture, but will occasionally be given over to electrical goods or jewellery. The items in this sale, as in the Tuesday and Thursday sales, will be unredeemed pawnbroker pledges. Lots are sold at the rate of some 120 an hour, so it is important not to arrive late.

GREAT WESTERN AUCTIONS · Glasgow

29/37 Otago Street, Kelvin Bridge. Tel: (041) 339 3290

600-700 lots. This is one of the most friendly sales I have ever attended. It is run by the rare combination of a mother and daughter team, and since Anita Manning and her daughter Lala took over in January 1989, the sale has enjoyed a growing reputation. Private buyers find the friendly atmosphere helpful, and as an additional aid to buyers Anita Manning has produced an informative leaflet which is freely available round the saleroom. It sets out the background to the auction and gives tips on how to bid.

Each sale contains a wide mix of antique and modern furniture, jewellery, silver, ceramics and so on, and a notable number of paintings, watercolours, drawings and prints. There may be as many as 150 hung round the wall, making Great Western Auctions one of the largest non-specialist sellers of pictures in Scotland, if not the largest. The auction starts briskly with the sale of perhaps 150 or so lots of jewellery, silver, silver plate and so on. The paintings, watercolours, drawings and prints are then sold from the walls, and in the early afternoon the furniture and household items are sold.

BUYER'S PREMIUM: 10%
SALES: *Fortnightly on Sat at 11.00am.*
VIEWING: *Day prior 10.00am-6.30pm, morning of sale from 9.00am.*
REFRESHMENTS: *Own café.*
PARKING: *Kelvin Bridge underground car park.*
STORAGE: *No*
TRANSPORTATION: *Yes*
SHIPPING: *No*

KERR & McALISTER · Glasgow

Queens Park Auction Hall, 140 Niddrie Road. Tel: (041) 423 4271

350-400 lots. Niddrie Road is on the south side of the city in rather a quiet area. Quiet, that is, except for Thursday evenings, when it seems to come to life with people walking with that determined gait so typical of bargain hunters. The 5,000sq ft saleroom allows buyers plenty of space for studying the lots. Buyers are rarely disappointed, as there is always a wide range of lots, covering all periods and dates, from high quality antiques to modern items — an elm and ash-stick Windsor chair, a washing machine, a Wedgwood meat dish or a Caucasian carpet, a television, or a William Henry Earp watercolour. Small items such as pieces of jewellery and silver may be kept in the 'smalls cabinet'. Ask one of the staff to unlock it if you wish to look at something more closely.

BUYER'S PREMIUM: 10%
SALES: *Weekly on Thu at 6.00pm.*
VIEWING: *Wed and Thu 9.30am-4.30pm.*
REFRESHMENTS: *None available on the premises.*
PARKING: *Free parking on street.*
STORAGE: *Yes*
TRANSPORTATION: *Yes*
SHIPPING: *Yes*

Glasgow

BUYER'S PREMIUM: *10%*
SALES: *Weekly on Fri at 10.30am.*
VIEWING: *Day prior 10.00am-4.00pm.*
REFRESHMENTS: *None available on the premises.*
PARKING: *None available on the premises.*
STORAGE: *Yes*
TRANSPORTATION: *Yes*
SHIPPING: *Yes*

ROBT McTEAR & CO (AUCTIONEERS) LTD

Royal Exchange Saleroom, 6 North Court, St Vincent Place.
Tel: (041) 221 4456

400-500 lots. Robt McTear & Co hold a regular weekly sale of antiques and paintings. It is held on Friday mornings, in the Royal Exchange Saleroom, right in the centre of the city just 100 yards or so from busy George Square. Selling starts with around 50 or 60 lots of jewellery. Next to be sold is silver and silver plate, porcelain and china, and paintings. The sale finishes with furniture.

The sale is well attended and friendly. It offers excellent buys in a great variety of areas, and there is usually something to suit all tastes and pockets.

Glasgow

BUYER'S PREMIUM: *10%*
SALES: *General: monthly on Tue at 11.00am. Specialist: about 12 throughout the year.*
VIEWING: *General: Sun prior 2.00pm-5.00pm, Mon prior 8.30am-5.00pm. Specialist: two days prior 9.30am-4.30pm, and Sun prior 2.00pm-5.00pm.*
REFRESHMENTS: *None available on the premises.*
PARKING: *None available on the premises.*
STORAGE: *Yes*
TRANSPORTATION: *Yes*
SHIPPING: *Yes*

PHILLIPS, SCOTLAND

207 Bath Street. Tel: (041) 221 8377

This is one of two Phillips salerooms in Scotland. The Glasgow saleroom has monthly general sales of furniture, pictures, ceramics, silver and jewellery. There are also regular specialist sales under headings like 'Fine Jewellery', 'Pianos and Furniture', 'Books', 'Decorative Arts' 'Stamps', 'Oriental Ceramics', 'European Ceramics' and 'Scottish Contemporary Art'.

Greenock

BUYER'S PREMIUM: *10%*
SALES: *Weekly on Wed at 10.00am.*
VIEWING: *Mon, Tue and Thu 9.00am-4.00pm, Fri 9.00am-1.00pm.*
REFRESHMENTS: *None available on the premises.*
PARKING: *Multi-storey car park 100 yards away.*
STORAGE: *No*
TRANSPORTATION: *Yes*
SHIPPING: *Yes*

D B LORAINE

26 West Stewart Street. Tel: (0475) 23150

300-400 lots. This is an enormous saleroom and it needs to be: very often as many as 500 people will attend. When the doors open at 9.00am there is usually a rush to grab one of the 50 or so seats available. The sale's popularity may be explained by the fact that it is the only one in this corner of Scotland. The nearest alternative is Robert Paterson and Son in Paisley, which is 18 or so miles away. Another reason could be the friendly atmosphere and the efficiency of the auctioneers; the firm has been going since 1921 and all the staff have long records of employment with the company. The sale starts with smaller items such as china, crockery, ornaments, silver and lamps, then moves on to televisions, washing machines, fridges and spin dryers. Furniture and carpets are sold last. There is a good mix of quality and types of goods. Prices are variable, but there are usually good bargains to be had.

L S SMELLIE & SONS LTD

Lower Auchingramon Road. Tel: (0357) 20211

400-500 lots. Hamilton is 11 miles south-east of Glasgow, a little to the west of the M74 motorway at the junction of the A74 road and the road which travels through Strathaven to Ayr and Stranraer. The lack of a street number is explained by the fact that the saleroom takes up half the street and is an unmistakable fine old stone building. There are two regular sales. The weekly Monday sale is of general household furniture and effects, and there is a quarterly sale of antiques and fine art, held on the third Thursday of February, May, August and November. Both attract buyers from all over Scotland and from England, Germany, Ireland and North America. The quarterly sale usually has around 500-800 lots. The Monday sale consists of furniture and carpets, china, glass, silver, silver plate, and also electrical goods such as televisions and washing machines. Furniture is sold between 10.00am and 12.00 noon. Between 1.00pm and 2.00pm there is the sale of 'smalls', such as porcelain, crystal, silver, silver plate, china, ornaments and so on. The residue of the furniture is sold between 2.00pm and 4.00pm.

R C LINDSAY

31 East King Street. Tel: (0436) 72315

400-500 lots. Helensburgh is at the mouth of the Gareloch, four miles off the lovely highway which borders the western shores of Loch Lomond. R C Lindsay is a well-established Scottish auction house which was founded in 1863. Angela Reid, the present auctioneer (one of the few female auctioneers in Britain), runs an interesting sale with a good mix of modern and antique lots. It is popular with dealers and increasingly with private buyers, probably because they never know what to expect: lots have ranged from a 1980s fridge to an 18th-century child's rocking cradle. The auction starts in the back room with the electrical items and household goods, and progresses to the main room, where there are better quality lots.

ROBERT PATERSON & SON

8 Orchard Street. Tel: (041) 889 2435

1,000-1,300 lots. Paisley is known the world over as a centre of

Hamilton

BUYER'S PREMIUM: 10%
SALES: *General: weekly on Mon at 10.00am. Antiques and fine art: quarterly on third Thu of Feb, May, Aug and Nov at 10.00am.*
VIEWING: *General: Fri prior 4.00pm-6.00pm. Antiques and fine art: day prior 4.00pm-6.00pm.*
REFRESHMENTS: *Own café.*
PARKING: *Own car park at rear.*
STORAGE: *No*
TRANSPORTATION: *Yes*
SHIPPING: *Yes*

Helensburgh

BUYER'S PREMIUM: 10%
SALES: *Every three or four weeks on Fri (times vary).*
VIEWING: *Days and times vary; check with the auctioneers.*
REFRESHMENTS: *None available on the premises.*
PARKING: *Railway station car park near by.*
STORAGE: *Yes*
TRANSPORTATION: *Yes*
SHIPPING: *Yes*

Paisley

BUYER'S PREMIUM: 10%
SALES: *Fortnightly on Tue at*

10.30am (alternate general and
catalogued sales).
VIEWING: *Day prior
9.00am-5.00pm.*
REFRESHMENTS: *None
available on the premises.*
PARKING: *Own small car
park.*
STORAGE: *No*
TRANSPORTATION: *No*
SHIPPING: *No*

thread manufacture. It is an interesting blend of the old and new, and its parish church is the restored part of a 12th-century abbey. Robert Paterson & Son's premises are to be found two minutes away from Paisley Cross, in a late Victorian construction built by the great-grandfather of the present auctioneer, Andrew Paterson, whose son Robert has joined the firm. That makes five generations of family involvement — the boast is that this is the oldest family auctioneering firm still selling in Scotland.

A large new saleroom was added at the back of the building in 1976. Here, the general sale begins with silver and jewellery, and then moves on to electro-plate and furniture. Everything stops at 12.30pm for a sale of pictures, books and Paisley shawls. Prices vary from £5 to possibly £30,000. Alternate sale days are devoted to specialist catalogued sales of antiques and paintings.

TAYSIDE

Blairgowrie

BUYER'S PREMIUM: *Nil*
SALES: *Weekly on Mon at
6.00pm.*
VIEWING: *Day of sale from
2.00pm.*
REFRESHMENTS: *None
available on the premises.*
PARKING: *Ample space.*
STORAGE: *Yes*
TRANSPORTATION: *Yes*
SHIPPING: *Yes*

Comrie

BUYER'S PREMIUM: *10%*
SALES: *At four-weekly
intervals, on Tue at 11.00am.*
VIEWING: *Sat prior
10.00am-2.00pm and Mon
prior 9.00am-6.00pm.*
REFRESHMENTS:
Available near by.
PARKING: *Ample near by.*
STORAGE: *Yes*
TRANSPORTATION: *Yes*
SHIPPING: *Yes*

J & J HOWE

30 Reform Street. Tel: (0250) 872361

400-500 lots. J & J Howe is a long-established, traditional Scottish country auctioneering company, with many buyers regularly attending its sales. Some of them come to meet friends, and stay to chat until Mr McNaughton, the auctioneer, turns them out, usually long after the sale has finished. The weekly Monday sale starts with small items such as china, ornaments, silver and jewellery, which are set out on tables round the rostrum, and then moves on to furniture and other large items which are placed around the walls. About every two months the sale is devoted to better quality furniture and effects.

WEST PERTHSHIRE AUCTIONS

Dundas Street. Tel: (0764) 70613

500-600 lots. This auction was recommended by a reader from Birmingham. The saleroom is family run, and situated in an old church in the centre of the attractive village of Comrie. Sales take place at four-weekly intervals and the lots comprise furniture, jewellery, bicycles, garden tools, books, crockery, glass and so on. Smaller items of china and collectables begin the bidding; antiques are sold in the afternoon, from 1.30pm onwards. Even if you do not buy anything (and there are usually good bargains to be had), you will be charmed by this sale, which is full of local colour.

WM NEIL & SON (CRIEFF) LTD

22 Galvelmore Street. Tel: (0764) 3276

600-630 lots. Crieff claims to be the most picturesquely situated hill town of Scotland, and is very popular as a health resort as well as for fishing, mountaineering and golf — the Gleneagles golfing centre with its three courses is only nine miles away.

The immediate impression visitors have at these sales is of the neatness and cleanness of the lots. Everything looks as though it has been washed or polished before being set out. Two spacious salerooms give the prospective buyer plenty of room to study the lots, a luxury not afforded by all salerooms. The auctioneer takes bids as he walks around the hall, stopping to stand on a stool at various points so he can see everyone. He starts the selling with perhaps 100 lots of linen, before moving on to furniture and general household effects, crockery, ornaments, jewellery, pictures, prints and so on. There is usually enough of a mixture of antique and modern items to interest every type of buyer.

Crieff

BUYER'S PREMIUM: *10%*
SALES: *Every three weeks on Wed at 11.00am.*
VIEWING: *Morning of sale from 8.00am.*
REFRESHMENTS: *None available on the premises.*
PARKING: *Town centre car park.*
STORAGE: *Yes*
TRANSPORTATION: *Yes*
SHIPPING: *Yes*

ROBERT CURR & DEWAR

Ward Road. Tel: (0382) 24185

400-500 lots. Robert Curr & Dewar is a family firm started in 1862 by an uncle of the grandfather of the present owner, whose son has entered the firm as well. Ward Road is in the centre of Dundee, a short walk from the Tay Road Bridge, and the single-storey saleroom building is almost opposite the main Post Office.

There are two salerooms, with three furniture storerooms at the back. The sales are good-humoured, well-run affairs. On Fridays there are sales of general household furniture, including modern and reproduction, and other household effects such as televisions, washing machines and other electrical goods, bicycles, china and sundry household items. The monthly Wednesday sale concentrates on antiques, fine art and associated lots.

Dundee

BUYER'S PREMIUM: *Nil*
SALES: *General: weekly on Fri at 12.00 noon. Antiques and fine art: monthly on Wed at 12.00 noon.*
VIEWING: *Day prior 2.00pm-7.00pm, morning of sale.*
REFRESHMENTS: *None available on the premises.*
PARKING: *Multi-storey car park one block away.*
STORAGE: *Yes*
TRANSPORTATION: *Yes*
SHIPPING: *Yes*

B L FENTON & SONS

84 Victoria Road. Tel: (0382) 26227

300-400 lots. Dundee is a delight for the auction-goer — it is only a short walk from this sale to Robert Curr & Dewar's salerooms, or to Marshall & Johnston's.

B L Fenton & Sons' weekly sale is of general household furniture and effects. Roughly every two months the general sale is replaced by a special antiques sale at 6 Forebank Road. Times are the same as for the general sale, but viewing hours

Dundee

BUYER'S PREMIUM: *Nil*
SALES: *Weekly on Thu at 10.00am (includes antiques sale about every two months at 6 Forebank Road).*
VIEWING: *Day prior 1.00pm-4.30pm (may be extended for antiques sale).*
REFRESHMENTS: *None available on the premises.*

PARKING: *None available on the premises.*
STORAGE: *No*
TRANSPORTATION: *Yes*
SHIPPING: *Yes*

may be extended, depending on the number of lots. The system of numbering lots may cause confusion: all items brought in by one vendor are given the same number, but they are not all sold at the same time. This makes it doubly important to note exactly what you want to bid for as well as its number. Failure to do so could mean going home with a set of lined curtains instead of a porcelain jardinière.

Dundee

BUYER'S PREMIUM: *10%*
SALES: *Fortnightly on Wed at 6.30pm.*
VIEWING: *Day prior 2.00pm-7.00pm.*
REFRESHMENTS: *None available on the premises.*
PARKING: *South Tay Street car park.*
STORAGE: *No*
TRANSPORTATION: *Yes*
SHIPPING: *Yes*

MARSHALL & JOHNSTON LTD

7 Blinshall Street. Tel: (0382) 24931

500-1,000 lots. The three Dundee sales described in this book are within 15 minutes' drive of each other. Marshall & Johnston Ltd's auctions have been in existence since 1850. The saleroom is a most attractive old church, with the bulk of the auction taking place on the ground floor. Auctioneer Mr Ian Taylor starts his sale with smaller items such as china, porcelain, brass, glass, jewellery, silver, ornaments, mirrors and pictures, including watercolours, drawings, prints and miniatures. They are usually followed by a good selection of antique and modern furniture.

Forfar

BUYER'S PREMIUM: *Nil*
SALES: *Monthly on Fri and Sat at 6.00pm.*
VIEWING: *Day prior 8.00am-5.00pm, day of sale.*
REFRESHMENTS: *None available on the premises.*
PARKING: *Own small car park.*
STORAGE: *Yes*
TRANSPORTATION: *Yes*
SHIPPING: *Yes*

DOIG'S

Chapel Street. Tel: (0307) 62201

200-300 lots. Four generations of the Doig family have been involved in this auctioneering firm since 1888. Mr James Doig's grandfather began the company by selling goods outside the houses of vendors, setting the lots out in the garden or street. Today part of the sale may be conducted outside in summer when the weather is good, but mostly it takes place under cover in a large, former jute factory in the centre of town. There is something to interest dealers, private buyers and browsers here: a Victorian walnut davenport, an Edwardian salon suite, a mahogany chair and other good quality pieces (some of which may need restoration) may be found alongside various items of silver, pottery, electrical goods and gardening tools, as well as kitchenalia and collectables — perhaps an early Singer sewing machine or a collection of early telephone switchboards and handsets.

Montrose

BUYER'S PREMIUM: *10%*
SALES: *General: fortnightly on Sat at 10.30am. Specialist: monthly on Fri at 7.00pm.*

TAYLORS AUCTION ROOMS

11 Panmure Row. Tel: (0674) 72775

2,000 lots. Situated opposite the Montrose Academy in the centre of Montrose, Taylors is one of the largest regular sales in Tayside and perhaps in Scotland, drawing buyers and vendors from all over the region. To get through the vast number of lots at most of the fortnightly auctions, three separate sales take place. Two start at 10.30am. One is in the Panmure Row saleroom and includes smaller items such as china, glass, porcelain, lamps, ornaments, bric-à-brac, collectables, bygones and so on. At the same time lesser quality furniture is sold directly opposite in the main saleroom, Bow Butts. When both these sales are completed, which is usually in the early afternoon, the auctioning of better quality furniture begins in the Bow Butts saleroom and continues until around 6.00pm. Also at Bow Butts, there are monthly specialist sales on Friday evenings, in categories such as jewellery, paintings, textiles and linen, garden furniture, books and so on.

VIEWING: *General: day prior 2.00pm-5.00pm and 6.00pm-9.00pm, day of sale from 9.00am. Specialist: day prior 2.00pm-5.00pm, 6.00pm-8.00pm.*
REFRESHMENTS: *Snacks available.*
PARKING: *None available on the premises.*
STORAGE: *Yes*
TRANSPORTATION: *Yes*
SHIPPING: *Yes*

LINDSAY BURNS & CO LTD

6 King Street. Tel: (0738) 33888

900-1,000 lots. The auction room is a short walk from the railway station, along Leonard Street. The landmark to look out for is the saleroom building itself: a beautiful Georgian former church, standing out among the terraced houses which surround it. The fortnightly sale is one of many attractions in this attractive and ancient city, and typically will include Victoriana, glass, china, ornaments, jewellery, linen, *objets d'art* and Scottish bygones, as well as modern and antique furniture. One of the reasons why so many private buyers are regulars, and why holidaymakers return so often, is no doubt the presence of Mrs Elspeth Burns, who makes sure that everything runs smoothly. Special antique and fine art auctions are held four times a year in place of the general sale.

Perth

BUYER'S PREMIUM: *10%*
SALES: *Fortnightly on Thu at 10.30am (includes antiques and fine art sale about every three months).*
VIEWING: *General: day prior 9.00am-5.00pm. Antiques: day prior 9.00am-6.00pm.*
REFRESHMENTS: *None available on the premises.*
PARKING: *Own car park.*
STORAGE: *No*
TRANSPORTATION: *Yes*
SHIPPING: *No*

LOVE'S AUCTION ROOMS

52-54 Canal Street. Tel: (0738) 33337

300-500 lots. This excellent saleroom, established by Thomas Love in 1869, enjoys a national reputation today. It is now under the proprietorship of Tom Reid, who has over 20 years' experience of the auction business. Sales take place in a recently refurbished building in the centre of Perth, attracting many local buyers. The weekly sale of Victoriana, household effects and miscellaneous items may include some antiques. However, these are usually kept back for inclusion in the quarterly, catalogued two-day sales of antiques and decorative arts. The latter attract bidders from all over the United Kingdom, and prices can run into thousands. Furniture, pictures, metalware, jewellery, silver, silver plate, ceramics, garden furniture, rugs, carpets and much more besides may appear at these sales.

Perth

BUYER'S PREMIUM: *10%*
SALES: *Victoriana, etc.: weekly on Fri at 10.30am. Quarterly antiques and decorative arts sales: usually in Mar, Jun, Sep and Dec on Tue and Wed at 10.30am.*
VIEWING: *Victoriana, etc.: day prior 9.00am-5.30pm. Quarterly antiques and decorative arts sales: day prior 10.00am-5.00pm.*
REFRESHMENTS: *None available on the premises.*
PARKING: *Multi-storey car park opposite.*
STORAGE: *Yes*
TRANSPORTATION: *Yes*
SHIPPING: *Yes*

CO. DOWN

Belfast

BUYER'S PREMIUM: *10%*
SALES: *Weekly on Wed at 11.00am.*
VIEWING: *Day prior 9.00am-8.00pm, and morning of sale from 9.00am.*
REFRESHMENTS: *Own café.*
PARKING: *Ample near by.*
STORAGE: *Yes*
TRANSPORTATION: *Yes*
SHIPPING: *Yes*

Belfast

BUYER'S PREMIUM: *10%*
SALES: *Weekly on Fri at 11.00am.*
VIEWING: *Day prior 9.00am-7.00pm.*
REFRESHMENTS: *Own café.*
PARKING: *Own car park.*
STORAGE: *Yes*
TRANSPORTATION: *Yes*
SHIPPING: *Yes*

Belfast

BUYER'S PREMIUM: *10%*
SALES: *Weekly on Thu at 10.00am. Special antiques sales: monthly on last Wed of the month at 8.00pm (includes art auctions every quarter).*
VIEWING: *All sales: day prior 9.00am-5.00pm and day of sale from 9.00am.*
REFRESHMENTS: *Own café.*
PARKING: *Multi-storey car park near by.*
STORAGE: *Yes*
TRANSPORTATION: *Yes*
SHIPPING: *Yes*

ANDERSONS AUCTION ROOMS

28 Linenhall Street. Tel: (0232) 321401

800-900 lots. The saleroom is in the centre of Belfast, near the imposing City Hall. Andersons Auction Rooms hold very large and busy sales, which draw people from all over Ireland. There is usually an excellent selection of antiques, as well as other furniture, collectables and miscellaneous items. Jewellery of all types and values can also be found in abundance. Sales start with fridges and electrical goods, followed by better quality lots, including antiques, after a 10-minute break at around 1.00pm.

GIBSON & DODDS

451 Donegall Road. Tel: (0232) 312882

500-700 lots. This excellent general auction includes a wide selection of household goods, fine art and a large quantity of good-quality antiques. Sales take place weekly on Fridays, and once a month a popular special sale of jewellery is included in the proceedings. The saleroom is on the ground floor of an old building, in attractive surroundings. Gibson & Dodds enjoy a good reputation and their sales regularly attract bidders from Southern Ireland, as well as Ulster.

JOHN ROSS & CO

37 Montgomery Street. Tel: (0232) 325448

200-300 lots. An Ulster sale, full of Ulster humour and typical Ulster friendliness. The weekly sales offer a wide selection of general household gooods, bric-à-brac and miscellaneous items, including some antiques. However, most of the antiques are kept back for a special antiques sale that takes place on the last Wednesday of each month. The saleroom has two floors, and during the weekly sales the first floor is used for the better quality lots.

Once a quarter, special art sales are held. They usually include paintings, watercolours, prints and drawings by artists from Ulster and Southern Ireland, known and unknown.

· INDEX ·

· INDEX ·

· INDEX ·